The man who
had to hang
.*LOUIS RIEL*.
by E. B. Osler

*"The witchery of paltry things
obscures what is right and
the whirl of desire transforms
the innocent mind."*

Wisdom 4:12

the man who had to hang

LOUIS RIEL

by E. B. Osler

Longmans Green
& Company, Toronto

by the
same
author

LIGHT IN THE WILDERNESS

CONTENTS

ACKNOWLEDGEMENTS

To my wife and children, to the many friends who during the three years it has taken to write this book have offered me encouragement and (often unsolicited) advice, I say "Thank you."

And to the following people who, possessing knowledge that they were cheerfully willing to share, made my research task easier, I express my gratitude:

Miss Marjorie Morley, Librarian, and Miss Clem Combaz, of the Manitoba Provincial Library

Mr. Hart Bowsfield, Archivist, of the Archives of Manitoba

Miss Ruth Murray, Head of Reference, University of Saskatchewan Library

The late Monseigneur A. d'Eschambault, Chairman of the Historic Sites and Monuments Board of Canada

The Reverend Father Pierre Picton, of the Archdiocese of St. Boniface

The members of the Manitoba Historical Society, whose published papers were so helpful

The members of the St. Boniface Historical Society

The Reverend Father Dubuc, O.M.I., pastor of St. Antoine de Padua, Batoche, Saskatchewan

Mr. Pierre Brunet, Assistant Dominion Archivist of the Public Archives of Canada

The Officer Commanding "Depot" Division RCMP, Regina, Saskatchewan

Dr. W. L. Morton, Professor of History, University of Manitoba

E. B. Osler

Winnipeg
January 5, 1961

Part One

FRAMER OF THE MANITOBA ACT

E. B. Osler

the man who had to hang Louis Riel

I

THE PEOPLE
OF THE PLAINS

IF, on a map of North America, you draw a line up the Ottawa River from Montreal and carry it westward, then draw another line from the mouth of the Nelson River on Hudson Bay and extend it into the heart of the continent in a direction slightly west of south, the two lines, representing the thrust of two great European powers—France and Britain—will intersect where the Assiniboine River empties its muddy waters into the Red River of the North. Here today are the twin cities of Winnipeg and St. Boniface, with a combined English-speaking and French-speaking population of more than 400,000 people; but about them there is still a newness, a rawness, that makes one wonder how long they have been there.

Until the seventeenth century, when the process of penetration began, almost everything about the North American continent was a mystery to men of European origin. Three factors made of this mystery a challenge: the possibility of discovering on its rivers a passage to the fabulous Indies; the possibility of finding furs in its forests; the possibility of winning for Christ the souls of the native population.

This challenge was accepted without hesitation by the French-men who colonized the St. Lawrence Valley. These people were caught up from the start in the business of exploring far into the continent, of trading, of doing missionary work among the ab-origines with whom they came in contact. And it was accepted, too, by the men from Britain who came to live along the shores of Hudson Bay—men who were the servants of a company founded in 1670 to trade in furs and gain profits from the wilderness for its shareholders in London.

With the aborigines who inhabited the interior of the continent at the time, these French and English explorers slowly developed a highly profitable barter. In exchange for trinkets and other goods, Indians were delighted to supply the newcomers with furs. This rather one-sided commerce blossomed steadily and for the most part in peace. To be sure, in areas where English and French competition was keenest, trade goods sometimes included fire-water—with disastrous results for the morality and behaviour of the Indians. And sometimes, to ingratiate themselves with a particular tribe, the Europeans took sides in local Indian wars—thereby creating for themselves deadly enemies as well as friends. But in general, because neither French nor English were interested in acquiring land from the Indians, peace reigned between white and red men for more than two hundred years.

What were the original Indians like? Compared with white men, they were defenceless children. Because they were hunters, they lived nomadic lives, moving about the country in bands and fashioning from materials at hand whatever accommodation they required. They knew nothing of the wheel; they wore clothing made chiefly from animal skins; they ate wild rice and fish, berries and venison and buffalo meat. They acknowledged superior spirits that dominated their lives; but they loved liberty to the point of being completely contemptuous of all arbitrary rule. In fact, they could never be enslaved, because, quite literally, they preferred to die if they could not be free. Each man was his own master; the chiefs could not dictate. Tradition and custom made their social system work.

It is thought that about 180,000 of them inhabited the continent before the coming of the white man. Of this number, a relatively small percentage lived in the northern half of the continent, in the west-central section. There dwelt Indians of several races, or "nations". Along the western fringe of the Pre-Cambrian Shield, where forest and lake give way to the prairies, lived the Ojibways; they were a branch of the mighty Algonquin family. In the central valley of what is now Manitoba lived their cousins, the Crees. Along the parkland slopes of the Duck and Riding Mountains lived the Assiniboines; while on the north-central prairies of what are now the United States roamed the Sioux.

Slowly the continent's geography unfolded itself as Frenchmen from the valley of the St. Lawrence pushed westward in their frail canoes, Englishmen from the bleak flats of Hudson Bay explored westward and to the south. But the Englishmen, after making themselves known by exploration, retired to the coast and had the Indians come to them with their furs, while the French were forced by geography to trade aggressively into the very heart of the mysterious country. By the middle of the eighteenth century Du Lhut, de Noyon, La Vérendrye and others had opened routes deep into the western plains. Before the English conquest, France had established forts at or near what are now Winnipeg (Fort Rouge), Portage-la-Prairie (Fort la Reine), Dauphin (Fort Dauphin) and The Pas (Fort Paskoyac).

After 1763, and the American Revolution that followed it, all of northern North America lay under the British flag. But the area was not moulded as yet into one political unit. There were the Maritime colonies, the colony of Canada, the wilderness of the North-west and the Pacific Coast. In that part of the colony of Canada which lay west of the French-speaking St. Lawrence settlement, English loyalist exiles from the old Atlantic colonies began to build for themselves new homes out of the wilderness, while in Montreal English-speaking merchants began to take control of commerce. From here the old French thrust westward would be maintained—after a change of management.

The Frobishers, the McGillivrays, the McGill brothers, Alexander Henry, Peter Pond, David Thompson, Alexander Mackenzie, Simon McTavish, Simon Fraser—names spread like glistening jewels, now, over the face of North America—formed from the wreckage of the old French fur empire the North West Company to maintain Montreal's trade. Tough Scots, or Yankees, all, they sensed the opportunities that still presented themselves in the interior of the continent, in the experience and stamina of the *voyageurs-Canadiens* waiting to be re-employed.

Northward, westward across mighty Lake Superior, up the Pidgeon River, through the Lake of the Woods system, along the Saskatchewan, the Slave, and the Mackenzie rivers, down the Thompson and the Fraser to tide-water at the Pacific's shore, they probed seeking profit and adventure. Trading forts were re-opened at strategic locations, or sprang up for the first time. French-speaking white men occupied them to engage in the fur trade—and, in the natural course of events, took unto themselves Indian wives. Many of these unions were happy and permanent arrangements; almost all of them were fruitful. Priests from Canada followed once again to look after the spiritual welfare of their flock. Gradually a distinct race of half-breed people emerged, a race of "people of the plains" who called themselves "métis".

The English-speaking loyalists in Upper Canada were still too busy making homes for themselves to care what went on in the West, but the Englishmen from England, who traded from the shores of Hudson Bay, were not. In their eyes, what the Nor'-Westers were doing amounted to robbery; for the Englishmen still possessed a royal charter, issued by King Charles II, which gave them an exclusive right to all the furs that could be found in the area whose waters drained into Hudson Bay. Suddenly

4

they realized that, charter or no charter, if they did not wish to lose their fur trade with the Indians, they must stir themselves at last and move inland.

To assert their rights as they saw them, the men of Hudson Bay now entered the interior of the continent; they built forts and left tough traders recruited from the Orkney Islands in charge. These Orkneymen, as the *Canadiens* had done, took unto themselves Indian wives and raised families of half-Indian, half-white blood. Inevitably, the trading rivalry deteriorated into a state of open conflict, which the British Government in London could not afford to ignore. At its insistence the two companies, who were ruining themselves and the fur trade by their competition, entered into a coalition under the old name of the Hudson's Bay Company.

As a reward, the new Company—with its head office in London, of course—was granted exclusive trading privileges in all British North America west and north of the tiny colony of Canada. By the end of the first quarter of the nineteenth century, more than three million square miles—approximately 25 per cent of North America—had become the private preserve of one concern.

No matter how daring, how eager for profit, men may be, they must have food. In most of the Company's domain raising crops of any kind was an uncertain business at that time; but dried buffalo meat cut into strips, or pounded buffalo meat packed in hide bags, could be preserved and transported anywhere men chose to go. The only food regularly available in quantity must come, therefore, from the buffalo that grazed on the plains to the west and south of the place where the Assiniboine and Red rivers met. Here, then, the new Company built Fort Garry. Here, then, the métis—who had become the buffalo hunters for the fur trade—established headquarters. Here, then, was the heart of the whole commercial venture.

At first buffalo hunting had been done by individuals or small

5

bands of métis as the need for meat arose; but over the years the custom developed of uniting seasonally for the hunt. There would be a spring hunt and a fall hunt, during which the métis —men, women and children—would range out on to the plains to the west and south of Fort Garry. Before setting out they would place themselves under the authority of an elected president and twelve councillors; they would select guides, and one captain for every ten hunters. More often than not they would take along with them a priest as chaplain, for most of them were Catholics in the French tradition. The whole undertaking would be carried out with a semi-military precision, for the sake of both efficiency and self-preservation against surprise attacks from the Sioux.

Gradually this organization for the hunt became the framework of métis society; so that even at home, on their potato-patch farms along the banks of the Red or the Assiniboine, these people came to regard themselves as a corporate group, as a new nation capable of running their own affairs.

For nearly two generations all went well. During the early part of the nineteenth century, Lord Selkirk transported a few impoverished Scottish and Irish crofters to the Red River Valley; but the presence of these settlers did not affect adversely the ancient rhythm of life in the land, for they had been sent to complement, not to displace, the old régime.

The Earl of Selkirk was a Scottish philanthropist possessed of large and noble vision; he was also an important shareholder in the Hudson's Bay Company. When it came to his attention that crofters in his native land were being dispossessed of their Highland farms to make way for sheep, he conceived the idea of offering them a new start along the banks of the Red River in North America. After persuading the Company's directors that there would be practical value in having, in the heart of the fur-trade empire, farmers to furnish provisions for their posts, he arranged that these crofters and their families should be moved.

Accordingly, they were brought to their new homes by way of York Factory on Hudson Bay, and given farms along the Red River's banks. For a number of years they lived under conditions of incredible hardship, but in time they managed to establish themselves securely. With the métis hunters and the retired Company officers who elected to stay in the area, they developed a distinct, though primitive, little community.

With the passage of time the Company's monopoly in the West became unenforceable. Private traders had made steady, though not disastrous, inroads into its business. The Minnesota Territory south of Fort Garry had begun to open up; it had become an easy thing to trade illegally with Americans for prices in excess of the Company's tariff. American traders—American cavalry, too, on occasion—ranged into British domain and did what they pleased unmolested.

In the late 1850's, English-speaking emigrants from Ontario (it was called Canada West until 1867) had begun to appear in the area at last, seeking their fortunes. Many of them chose to farm around Portage-la-Prairie; a few more restless spirits set themselves up as independent business men in the village of Winnipeg. By means of a newspaper, the *Nor'-Wester*, established by a pair of these Canadians, they made no secret of their contempt for both the Company's authority and the way of life of the local people. Some of them went so far as to declare openly that the prairies should be developed as a source of revenue for Ontario alone.

Subjected to all this, the older settlers and the métis became very apprehensive—and well they might; for maintenance of order in the British North-west was rapidly becoming a task beyond the ability of the Hudson's Bay Company to perform.

By the 1860's approximately twelve thousand people lived in the little colony. Though all of them came directly under the control of the Hudson's Bay Company and were tried in Company courts when they broke the law, they were able to exert an indirect influence over their government through a sort of local parliament known as the Council of Assiniboia. To this Council local citizens were appointed by the Company from time to time to advise the Governor. All in all, life, though monotonous at times, seems to have been happy here.

By the mid-eighteen-sixties, important people in Britain began advocating that the area be made a Crown colony, to be governed directly from London. Important people in Canada began advocating that it be made part of the new Dominion of Canada which was about to be created. A few voices in the southern half of the continent began suggesting it should be annexed to the United States. Quite obviously, the world was closing in! But the Company had no intention of relinquishing its charter without compensation. A British sovereign had granted it; it was embodied in the law of the land. While the local prestige of the Company went from bad to worse, the British and Canadian Governments haggled with its directors in London. Finally all parties agreed that, on December 1, 1869, the two-year-old Canadian Government would pay the Hudson's Bay Company £300,000; Queen Victoria would then grant to this Canadian Government the task of administering the land. After two hundred years, the Company's rule would come to an end!

During all these negotiations everyone had forgotten the people at Fort Garry. The Company directors had neglected to inform even the Governor on the spot about the details of the deal, while the British and Canadian Governments had neglected to communicate in any way with the twelve thousand subjects of the Queen who resided at the settlement. Isolated in a wilderness, with the nearest telegraph line five hundred miles away at St. Paul, the community was a prey to the wildest rumours.

When at last they became certain that no plan had been considered to give them representation in the Canadian Parliament, the inhabitants began to mutter that they felt no enthusiasm for becoming a "colony within a colony". In this they were merely expressing a wish for representation, as the American colonists had expressed it a century before, as William Lyon Mackenzie and Louis Joseph Papineau had advocated, with arms, in 1837-38 in Canada. Besides, the English-Canadian immigrants they had seen in their midst filled them with fear. Many of them were bully-boy types—the sort to be found seeking fortunes on every frontier—who made it perfectly clear that they would never have the slightest respect for the feelings of the other inhabitants of the colony.

Gradually the conviction developed that while the Indians were to be given reserves on which to live, while treaties were to be signed guaranteeing their rights forever, the white and métis inhabitants of Fort Garry were to have no guarantees at all. The English-speaking colonists and métis considered sending a petition to the Queen. The French métis talked of organizing themselves, as they were accustomed to do on their buffalo hunts, into a military force for their own protection.

From the outset the French-speaking people in the West had been more afraid of Canada than had the English. This was natural: they had more to fear. Their language and their religion seemed at stake, on top of everything else. To them, English Canadians were typified by Dr. John Christian Schultz, a red-blonde giant of a man, a doctor turned trader who was as opportunistic as a shark and violently anti-Catholic. He had made himself Grand Master of the newly formed Northern Light Masonic Lodge; he had been heard to shout: "It was from Ontario this movement to add Red River to the Dominion commenced—it is to Ontario the territory belongs."

Confronted with this sort of self-seeking jingoism, what all the natives began to want were legal guarantees of their freedom. What the French métis specifically began to yearn for were addi-

9

tional safeguards similar to those enjoyed by the people of Quebec—where even the English-speaking minority had legal assurances that their language and religion would be unmolested. In their eyes Ontario—to which they were to "belong" unless they acted to prevent it—seemed to be governed by the Orange Lodge, whose avowed purpose was to exterminate both the French language and the Catholic Church into which they had all been born!

Presently, nature crystallized the issues. In the early 1860's a period of drought had set in; now, in 1868, came a grasshopper plague to ruin the crops utterly. On top of this, returns from the buffalo hunt were pitifully small. (The buffalo were, in fact, disappearing forever from the prairie scene.) Suddenly, the isolated colony faced the prospect of real starvation.

As a relief measure the Hudson's Bay Company authorized $8,000 worth of credits at its store; the U.S. Government sent $4,000 cash; the Government of Quebec, $3,000. The Ontario Government publicly promised $5,000 but never sent it. The Canadian Government, by this time negotiating for possession of the territory, sent in a road-building gang to begin the Dawson Road to the Lake of the Woods.

The road-builders announced that their project should be looked upon as Canada's contribution to the relief of the colony's ills. Not only would they be improving communications between Canada and Red River, they would be providing employment for at least some of the people made hungry by the famine. But the colonists found it difficult to believe that the road-builders were acting in good faith—their actions, somehow, belied their words. For all their declarations of concern over the lot of the people, they employed very few of them; and those they did employ they paid in chits which were exchangeable for goods only at a store set up at Oak Point, by Dr. Schultz, for the purpose of exploiting them.

Another cause of irritation to the people of Red River was the personality of Charles Mair, the Canadian paymaster of the road-builders. He seemed to delight, from the moment he arrived at Fort Garry, in insulting people and impressing upon them his contempt for everything about the colony.

In this same year of 1868, Dr. Schultz, having been sued and committed to the Colony's jail for non-payment of a private debt, was forcibly liberated by a Canadian mob. Shortly afterwards the *Nor'-Wester* announced in strident tones that "the tenure of land is precisely the same with the new-comer as it is with the Hudson's Bay Company—you hold as much as you occupy." This was nothing more or less than a solemn declaration that all Indian, métis, and other native land claims were subject to challenge.

Emboldened by this declaration, a Canadian named James Stewart began staking claims in a block of land adjacent to Fort Garry that had been since time immemorial reserved for Company use; and Canadian members of the Dawson Road work party began doing the same thing at Ste. Anne des Chênes. (During an investigation in 1874, Colonel Dennis, a surveyor, swore on his oath that Schultz had told him of staking and buying from the Indians, in company with John A. Snow, the road-builders' superintendent, a tract of land near Oak Point. He was perfectly well aware that the métis claimed this land as their own, for he had asked Dennis whether, under the circumstances, the Canadian Government would support him.) Small wonder that the natives thought they could see a land rush developing which would sweep them aside forever!

William McDougall, an Ontario-born politician, was the Minister of Public Works in the Canadian Cabinet at this time. It was through his department that the road-building project was administered. Because of his association with it, McDougall took on, in the eyes of the people of Red River, all the less desirable characteristics of some of his employees. Rightly or wrongly, he became known by reputation in the colony as a "land-grabbing Orangeman" who could not be trusted.

In the summer of 1869 two Canadians, Colonel John Stoughton Dennis and Captain C. A. Boulton, arrived in the colony to begin a survey of its lands. Immediately, panic swept through the settlement; their presence seemed to confirm the connivance of Canada in all that had taken place during the previous year.

In vain did Dennis repudiate publicly the claim-staking activities of his countrymen and assure the local inhabitants that their interests would be safeguarded. In vain did he write to Ottawa, warning that "a considerable degree of irritation exists among the native population, in view of surveys and settlements being made without the Indian title having been extinguished." In vain did he caution that "the uneasy feeling which exists in the half-breeds . . . with regard to what they conceive to be premature action taken by the Government" ought to be dealt with in some way.

McDougall, ensconced behind his shiny desk in Ottawa, chose to ignore these portions of his representative's reports. Being an empire-builder both by inclination and conviction, he pressed on relentlessly with his task. And at Red River the local inhabitants —especially the métis segment of the colony—had reached the point of refusing to believe anything a Canadian might say.

To further aggravate the situation, the Company's Governor could add nothing official to Dennis's soothing words; for his directors in London had neglected to tell him that they had given Canada permission to begin the survey, that the turn-over of territory was about to take place.

In an effort to prove his good faith, Dennis postponed the local survey, removed his men from the environs of Fort Garry, and began instead to run the principal meridian due north from the American border. At the same time he began running a base-line westward to Portage-la-Prairie and another due east to Ste. Anne. Unfortunately, the one to Ste. Anne had to pass through a métis settlement known as St. Vital. As Colonel Dennis wrote, in his formal report of the matter to his superiors: "Captain Webb was stopped in his surveying operations by a party of men . . . on Monday, October 11th, having projected the base-line mentioned easterly from the meridian to within about three miles of the Red River."

At last the old inhabitants of the colony had accepted the challenge of the new. At last they had dared to call halt to the activities of these strangers whom they all feared. The man at the head of the unarmed "party of men" who forced Captain Webb to stop his work was named Louis Riel.

II

THE COMPANY
NO LONGER RULES

FROM beside the woodpile where he stood, Riel let his gaze play lovingly upon the scene around him. The whole world seemed filled with peaceful promise this October morning. To one side, the yellowing poplar leaves, the blood-red oaks; to the other, on the slope towards the river, the black soil of his mother's land, granted to his grandfather Lagimodière as a reward for walking from the Red River settlement to Montreal, bearing a message for Lord Selkirk, in the winter of 1818. Between him and the woods, beside the curving trail from St. Boniface, lay the family home. The house was a plain, square-timbered structure, with a steep-pitched roof, a porch sheltering the door, and a lean-to addition on the northwest side—it reminded him, vaguely, of the *habitant* farm houses he had seen in *la Province de Quebec*.

For all its simplicity, it was a well-built little house. Louis' mother, Julie Riel, often commented on how lucky she was to own it; and yet life was no sinecure for a widow with a growing family, in this hard young land. Her own relatives, the Lagimodières, were a numerous clan, and if the worst ever came to the worst they could be relied upon to support her; yet she did not find it easy to raise her children alone, without her husband's help. Her eldest son, Louis, was grown up now; on his next birthday he would be twenty-five years of age. Sara, her second living child, was twenty-one and a Sister of Charity. But the others—four girls and three boys, ranging in age from nineteen to six—were still her responsibility in a very real sense. Though she loved them all, Louis had always been her pride and joy; and it comforted her immensely to have him home again with her now.

Eleven years ago Bishop Taché had visited the Riel's home. He had said: "Madame, I have great faith in your eldest son," and he had requested permission to send Louis east for a higher education. And when she and her husband had given their permission, Louis had set out, along with Daniel McDougall and Louis Schmidt, for old Quebec. After travelling through the United States, the boys had arrived in the great metropolis of Montreal. Louis had been assigned to the Sulpicians there, McDougall to *le Collège de Nicolet*, Schmidt to St. Hyacinthe. Though McDougall had been sent home after his first year and Schmidt had been forced by ill health to give up his education after his second, Louis had remained at Montreal until almost the end of his course. Then, upset by news of his father's death, he had dropped out and gone to live with his uncle and his paternal aunt, Mr. and Mrs. John Lee.

For some time after that Louis had been restless. Unable to find work that suited him in Montreal, he had moved westward to the fast-growing American town of St. Paul. But last summer, prompted by tales of hardship and famine brought to him by travellers from the North, he had decided to go home.

Now, a year later, he was still glad he had come home. In spite of all the troubles that brewed on every side, it was good to be alive on such a day. And, as to the troubles, who could tell? Sometimes, when one swore that a thunderstorm was in the offing, the weather miraculously cleared. Perhaps, after all, the troubles that he most feared now would work themselves out in the end.

Troubles had been gathering for a long time at Red River.

But accomplishments had been piling up, too. Without even leaving this property, he could see evidence of this. Half a mile away, south-eastward along the trail, lay the tiny school-and-chapel of St. Vital. When he was a boy, it had been necessary to journey all the way to St. Boniface for his primary education; now his young brother Alexandre and little sister Henriette could walk to their classroom in a matter of minutes. It was marvelous to reflect that more than sixty local children were taught in this little establishment, where ten years ago there had been nothing. It was marvelous to reflect, too, that other parish schools had been built in the colony—at St. François Xavier, at Ste. Anne, at Ile-à-la Crosse and at St. Norbert, where his sister Sara was teaching.

A steadier breeze reached the poplar leaves and caressed his freshly shaved cheek. To be alive on such a day! To savour life with every nerve and fibre! To be free! To have such infinities of time and space around one again, in place of the unnerving clamour of life in a crowded city! Those grey seminary walls, those soulless business buildings—he was not made to fit inside them. He was made for the *pays en haut*, where a man had grouse to shoot and horses to ride, and the good Red River flowing forever past his door. How could the kind people he had lived with in Quebec, or the land-grabbing immigrants from Ontario—or the Yankees in St. Paul, for that matter—understand how he felt right now? How could they be expected to know how deeply a métis felt about his own homeland? It was too much to ask, even of God, that they should. But he knew, for he himself was métis. His maternal grandmother had been the first white woman to dwell permanently in this land. His paternal grandmother had been a half-breed girl, descended from a Montagnais chief. This country was in his blood—and it was good blood, too!

He turned back to the family woodpile. These days were at

the end of nature's cycle. Cold weather would be upon them soon—death before the resurrection of spring. It was knowledge of this that made so poignant, so bitter-sweet, this gentle time of peace. At any instant now, with its full force and fury, winter would envelop them from out of the North.

Suddenly, a voice cut through his thoughts. It was a familiar voice, sharpened by urgency, and it came to him from across his mother's field, from the direction of the river. Straightening, he peered to the westward, where the brown waters of the Red River flowed. At the top of the bank, just starting across the freshly turned earth, was his cousin André Nault. "Louis! Louis! Come quickly," he called. "The surveyors are upon my land!"

Without a word Riel laid aside his axe, moved to meet Nault. As he walked, excitement mounted within him. This was what he had been made for—this taking of other people's burdens upon his own broad shoulders! "Our people will need a leader, Louis," his father had told him before he left for the East. "A leader with education—one who can talk to the stone-faced men who run this world and make them understand." Well, for years he had been preparing himself to lead his peoples, and he had that education now. Perhaps the moment to use it had arrived.

They met near the centre of the field. "The surveyors, Louis," Nault explained breathlessly. "There are five of them on my land. They are driving their stakes everywhere. They have no right to do that."

"No. They have no right." Riel's voice was cold, brittle as a January night; but inside he glowed with expectation.

"I tried to stop them. My neighbours have gathered to help. But they paid us no heed. If you would come, Louis? You speak English. They would understand you."

"I will come with you and try," Riel said shortly. Then he followed Nault down to the river bank.

Wordlessly they slid the canoe into the water, clambered in, took up paddles. These surveyors must be stopped! If one allowed them to march across one's land, contemptuously shouldering one aside as if one did not exist, soon one *would not* exist as far as they were concerned. And when the land deal had been approved, when the Canadian Lieutenant-Governor—they said it was to be McDougall, that land-grabbing Minister of Public Works, and he was already on his way—when McDougall and his hand-picked Council installed themselves at Fort Garry, there would be nothing to stop the Canadians from doing what they pleased. Truly, he and his people must establish some rights for themselves *now*, before it was too late.

They reached the opposite bank, beached the canoe, climbed up through the mud onto the level plain. The land was bare ahead on the western side, not treed as it was on the side where Louis lived. Standing on Nault's property, you could see for miles to the west. Southward, there was a bluff of poplars, and to the north the tree-fringed bank of the river as it snaked its way across the five miles of prairie that lay between them and Fort Garry. This was a peaceful sight; yet here beside him now was a handful of Nault's neighbours, and there, half a mile from the house, the little cluster of ill-willed men. The neighbours had gathered in silence, like mourners at a newly prepared grave. Wordlessly, they shuffled after Louis as he started towards the intruders. A feeling of elation mounting within him, he walked straight towards the leader of the gang.

"Good morning gentlemen," he said cordially in English. "There seems to be a misunderstanding here."

The leader of the surveyors frowned. He was a short, fair-haired fellow, lacking both natural grace and perception. One glance at Louis' eyes, at the set of his mouth beneath the heavy moustache, should have been sufficient to convince him that this new-comer must be handled with care. "Misunderstanding?" he countered.

"Yes. You see, this is Mr. Nault's land, sir. He bought it from the Company in the regular way. You have no right to trespass on his property."

The man reddened. He stared at Louis insolently, examining his moccasined feet, his trousers with their brown and white stripes, his flannel shirt, his flaming red sash. "Be off with you —all of you!" he commanded at last. Then he nodded to his men to begin their work again.

A feeling of lightness swept upwards through Louis' brain; his body felt, suddenly, as if it were detached from his being. He was tense with elation, but he knew he must be reasonable.

"This is Mr. Nault's land," he repeated quietly. "You have no right to it, or to be upon it."

The surveyor shrugged. He turned his back to Riel. "Go on with your work," he ordered his men loudly. Nault and the other métis behind Louis muttered, but they did not stir.

Two of the surveyors picked up a chain lying on the ground, and moved away from each other so that the chain became taut between them. Louis felt very much alone; then, suddenly, he knew what he would do. With a speed and grace that surprised him, he moved between the pair holding the surveyor's chain, kicked it hard. One of the men dropped his end; the chain went slack. Louis stepped firmly upon it. "You shall go no further with this farce," he declared.

The leader of the surveyors was very red in the face now. He stood where he was, gaping at Riel, as astounded as a general might be if some private had dared to trip him. While his men waited for an indication of what they should do, the little group of métis, magnetized by the authority of Riel, closed in a circle about them. Louis remained silent, let the tension he had created mount; but he continued to stand on the chain. It seemed to him at this moment that he was the centre of the world.

Presently the leader of the surveyors shrugged. "All right, men.

19

Pack it up. We've better things to do than argue with a gang of half-castes." To Riel, he said ominously: "You'll be hearing about this, my man."

Louis smiled, bowed, stepped off the chain. Part Indian he might be—though not "half-caste" by a long way; but he had taken the measure of this pure-white fellow today. Looking at his cousin, he winked. "I think I will go inside with you, and visit with your wife while I am here." Nault nodded, smiled. "Come on, then. She's always pleased to see you."

The two métis strolled off towards Nault's house; the others, seeing that their point had been won, nonchalantly dispersed. Only the surveyor and his men remained, gathering their equipment, on the field. The flint had been struck, the tinder well and truly set ablaze. For the first time, men from Ontario had been forced to acknowledge that the métis had a claim to this land; and these métis had been shown that they should not bow to the land-grabbing immigrants from the East. Now, when the news spread abroad, everyone at Red River would take heart.

Walking towards his cousin's house—tall, handsome, fair-skinned as any pure-white who spent his time outdoors—Louis seemed cool, deliberate, unruffled. But inside he was on fire. He had answered the call, as he had known he must do. He had proved he could lead his people with success. Bishop Taché, his father, his own inner certainty—all were correct. He was destined to be no ordinary man. From now on, nothing would stop him!

Governor Mactavish looked up from behind his desk as Louis entered the room. Before him he saw a thick-set young man of a little above average height, sturdily built, with a rectangular face and a high, broad forehead beneath a mass of chestnut-coloured hair. The eyes were hazel; the nose prominent, almost Roman; a generous moustache fell over a pair of full, firm lips.

The determined chin revealed a fact that the Governor had already guessed: here was a character whom one should not brush off as a mere parish malcontent seeking his hour of local fame.

"Sit down, Mr. Riel," he said courteously. "I suppose you know why I sent for you?"

"Why did you send for me?" Louis was not being belligerent—merely non-committal, as anyone accused by authority would be.

"Colonel Dennis, the head of the Canadian surveyors, came to see my chief trader this morning. He lodged a complaint against you—something about interfering with the work of his men. Is this true?" The Governor spoke with infinite weariness, as if life itself demanded almost more effort than he could muster.

Looking at him now, Louis saw death beneath his face, the presence of a wasting illness that seemed to be eating up every ounce of spirit with the sinew it consumed. He felt pity for the Governor, and almost said so; but one did not extend sympathy to a proud old man.

"Colonel Dennis's men were trespassing on my cousin's land. I told them to get off," he said evenly. "My friends and I have decided that since you will not protect the people of Red River from such abuse, we have a right to protect ourselves."

"Your friends and you?" the Governor repeated. "I suppose among them you would include Father Ritchot. I hear he has been very active during the last little while from his rectory at St. Norbert."

"Père Ritchot is a good parish priest, Monsieur," Riel answered stiffly. "Unlike some other people here, he concerns himself with the welfare of his flock. He did not tell me to stop the surveyors, if that's what you are trying to say."

"Mr. Riel," Mactavish persisted mildly, "all I hope is that you are not bent on following in your father's footsteps. As you must be aware, he caused the Company much trouble in his time."

Louis flushed, forced himself to control his temper. "My father and his friends broke the Company monopoly. They won for my people the right to trade with whom they pleased. Everyone here has prospered by what he did." Slowly, self-consciously, he stood up. "But I did not come here to discuss what you would call the faults of my father."

Mactavish was too ill to accept the challenge. Instead, he attempted to smile. "Sit down, please. Sit down." Then: "You are quite right. Let history take care of itself, eh? The point is —and you know this as well as I do—the directors of the Company have seen fit to sell, for a certain sum of money and some land reservations, all their right and title to the North-west. They have agreed to sell it to the Dominion of Canada, though the final formalities have not been worked out so far as I know. Colonel Dennis and his party are simply engaged in a survey here, in anticipation of the actual change-over. I'd be much obliged if you'd not cause unnecessary trouble."

"Unnecessary?" Louis' voice rose in spite of his efforts to control himself. "I cause no trouble that is not necessary, I assure you. Because I insist that the rights of my people—who have lived here for a hundred years on their fathers' side and since time immemorial on their mothers'—be safeguarded, how can you say I cause *unnecessary* trouble? Look what has happened to the métis, to the Indians, in the States. Can you guarantee that the same will not happen to us when the Canadians take over here?"

"I can guarantee nothing." There was an infinity of emptiness in the Governor's tone. He did not look up as he said the words. Then, very quietly: "This is a time of change, Mr. Riel. I— I don't know what to make of it myself. I'm not even sure when my authority as Governor is supposed to end." With a slight surge of the old vehemence: "Everything is being arranged in London, and London no longer chooses to keep its trusted servants informed." The Governor's thin lips twisted in bitterness now. "I neither authorized these Canadians to come here with their survey gangs, nor forbade them. The matter is entirely out of my hands."

"Do I understand you to mean that the authority of the Company here is at an end?" Riel asked sharply.

The Governor shrugged, made no reply. Quite apparently, he was a broken man. He was sick and discouraged; it pained him almost as much as did his illness to know that after so many years of service the very foundations of his long career were being destroyed. There was a financial factor behind his bitterness, too: he, like all the officers of the Hudson's Bay Company, had always been entitled to a share of the Company's profits in the area he governed. Now there would be no more profits, neither would there be any work for him to do. While this land which he had cared for during all his adult life was looted mercilessly by men who did not try to understand it, he and others like him would be sent into retirement.

If he judged the signs of his present illness correctly, there was nothing ahead for him but death. Not that he would be sorry to receive it, the way the world was going. All the same, it was painful to see one's life work fall apart like this, to see it trampled down by greedy trespassers who saw no beauty, no purpose, no design, in all one had laboured to achieve. But there was nothing to be done about it now. He and Bishop Taché had gone to Sir John Macdonald at Ottawa, as had the Anglican Bishop Machray, and had warned him how it all would end; but the "great man" had chosen to ignore their advice. His mind had been on other things—like votes, and land to be given to railroad speculators, and a crazy dream of extending his power from sea to sea.

Now, two centuries of Company rule were drawing to an end, an end that would result in chaos, exactly as he had predicted it would. So be it then! He had done what he could; he would rest in peace. And always the pain of that other hurt, that illness burning him from within, kept consuming him night and day, so that he almost didn't care any more.

Looking at the man, Louis knew the interview had come to an end. Standing again, he bowed gravely, made his way to the door. The Company's authority at Red River had ceased. It had melted away. The Governor himself had almost admitted it. Yet neither the Canadian nor the British Parliament had proclaimed any new arrangement by law. While men on the other side of the ocean argued about money, this colony was drifting like a rudderless ship in an angry sea. And all the time the passengers on board—his own métis and the other inhabitants of Assiniboia—were in peril of their lives. Surely, someone must take the helm and set the vessel again on its course.

Everyone knew that a Lieutenant-Governor from Canada was on his way westward now; that he would be William McDougall, the present Minister of Public Works and a French-hating Orangeman; that, to garnish its high-handedness with a trimming of legality, the Canadian Parliament had passed an Act for the Temporary Government of Rupert's Land. But McDougall had not arrived yet; and even if he had, his presence would only make things worse, judging by what people said about him.

When you got right down to it, by what right could this new so-called Governor impose his will? The métis were British subjects, but they were not Canadians, nor ever had been. Surely, then, they could ignore the Canadian legislation from which McDougall received his "powers". Unless he came armed with some definite authority from the Queen—a proclamation signed, sealed, and nailed to Fort Garry's gate for all to see—McDougall would have no more right to rule here than did he, Louis Riel! In fact, he would have less; for Riel could at least count on the support of the majority of the people here.

The métis were not slaves, to be bought and sold with this land! They were free men; they always had been. They must fight back now and establish their rights while they had the chance. As the English had done in England, as the Canadians had done, too, they must secure their freedom from arbitrary authority before it was too late.

Walking across the courtyard towards the south gate, Louis tried to recall the philosophy, the legal training, he had learned in Montreal. No one ruled here now; the colony at Red River was a political vacuum. Did it not follow, then, according to the natural law of nations, that the people might unite in the Queen's name and form a temporary government of their own? A year and a half ago a Canadian named Thomas Spence had proclaimed a "Republic of Manitoba" at Portage-la-Prairie. The British Government had made him dissolve it, giving as their reason that *the Company still ruled*. But the Company did not rule today; Governor Mactavish had as good as said so. Neither did the Canadians rule as yet. Very well, then; now was the time to make sure that they never would rule, except on terms congenial to the people living here!

Louis swung into the saddle and guided his mare across the newly completed floating bridge that spanned the Assiniboine. If he went home and called a meeting of his people, and told them that the Company's rule has come to an end, might they not agree to create an organization around which the whole colony could rally?

He was at the water's edge now, the historic heart of the North-west, where the muddy Assiniboine flows into the Red River of the North. On the other side of the Assiniboine, above the towering bank, sprawled the Company's stone Fort Garry. Across from him on the east side of the Red lay St. Boniface Cathedral. An hour's ride to the south lay his mother's farm. It was a pity Bishop Taché had gone to Rome; Louis would have welcomed a chance to discuss his thoughts with him before riding home. But the Bishop had always shown faith in him in the past; no doubt he would approve of anything he might do now. As for the other inhabitants here, the Scots and Irish and retired Company people who lived to the north along the Red, he judged that they would not oppose him. But they were unorganized; only if the métis gave them a lead would they act to protect themselves.

No one among the twelve thousand people at Red River would oppose him, except the few hundred hotheads of the "Canadian" party, who had come here only to cause trouble in the first place. Their leader was Schultz, who published the bombastic *Nor'-Wester*—and distributed it in Ontario, crying for Canadian annexation and pretending that his paper represented the point of view of the people here. What a joke *that* claim would be—if it weren't for the mischief it caused among Canadians in the East! Hadn't more than eight hundred natives of Assiniboia joined together and got out a petition protesting against the paper's tone?

He thought of Mair, who wrote sarcastically amusing letters home about the women of Red River—and saw to it that a Toronto paper published them. (Or he had done so, until he was horse-whipped publicly by Mrs. Bannatyne for his pains.) He thought of Snow, the road-builder, who had been fined for feeding liquor to the Indians; of Dennis, with his arrogant, all-pervasive survey gangs. Once Riel had organized the resistance of the native people here, he could deal with these characters handily, for under their bluster they were not really strong enough to impose their will. Father Ritchot had always said that; and he himself had proved it on André Nault's land.

And from now on, because of the admitted powerlessness of the Company, he would have the law of nations behind him to justify his deeds.

III

IN DEFENCE OF
THEIR OWN LIBERTY

O N October 16, 1869, leaders of the métis people met in Father Ritchot's rectory at St. Norbert. After much discussion and soul-searching, they decided to organize the "nation" to deal with this crisis in the manner in which it would be organized for a buffalo hunt. As for the priest, his point of view can be summed up quite simply: he believed that unless some definite guarantees were forthcoming from the Canadian Government, his flock would be swept away by a tide of Protestant, Anglo-Saxon immigration from the East. Thus, he concurred in everything Riel had done so far.

The first thing they agreed to was the formation of *Le Comité National des Métis de la Rivière Rouge*, and to act henceforth only in its name. By means of this committee—which they hoped would ultimately include all the "natives" in Assiniboia—they thought they would impress on the outside world that it was not merely a few malcontents, but the organized majority at Red River, who demanded concessions. When they offered Louis the presidency, he declined it on grounds of youth and inexperience (he accepted, however, the post of Secretary when it was proferred to him); so they elected John Bruce, an older man with no particular merits or defects, as President *pro tem*.

Four days later the métis leaders met again, this time in John Bruce's home. According to every current rumour, Lieutenant-

Governor McDougall could be expected at the border any day now. As they saw it, if he crossed into the colony before the people had reached agreement as to their demands, the Canadian representative would, in effect, have taken possession. After that it would be exceedingly difficult to negotiate a bargain. But so long as Canadian authority remained non-existent the people had a right to establish the terms under which they would accept it. So they decided that McDougall must be prevented at all costs from entering Assiniboia.

Accordingly, it was resolved that a small party of armed men, under Janvier Ritchot, should be despatched to the border point at Pembina. At the same time a larger party, led by Ambroise Lépine, should take up a position near St. Norbert, where the road from the south could be most easily closed. If and when McDougall appeared at either place, he was to be turned back, by order of *Le Comité*. Meanwhile Riel and John Bruce would begin the slow task of organizing support for themselves throughout the colony.

On the 25th, both Riel and Bruce were summoned before the Council of Assiniboia. This body functioned entirely separately from the Company's fur-trading organization in the North-west. Its members were appointed at the suggestion of the local Governor (who was himself appointed by the Board of Directors in London) or on the application of any of the inhabitants. According to Hudson's Bay Company regulations of June 26, 1841, their jurisdiction was restricted to an area "in all directions fifty miles from the forks of the Red and Assiniboine". Though final authority remained with Company headquarters, all legislative and judicial functions within the community rested in the local Councillors' hands.

On this particular day, because Governor Mactavish's illness had confined him to his bed, Judge John Black was in the chair. The other Councillors present were: the Anglican Bishop of

Rupert's Land; the local chief trader, Dr. Cowan; Dr. Bird; Messrs. Dease, Sutherland, MacBeth, Fraser, and Bannatyne. An official record exists of the proceedings:

The Minutes of the last meeting having been read and approved, Mr. Black proceeded to say that at the last meeting, as the Council was aware, an Address had been prepared for the purpose of being presented to the Honourable William McDougall on his arrival in the settlement; an event which was expected to take place at some very early date. That the Council, while preparing the Address, were impressed with the conviction that the feelings of welcome and loyalty therein expressed were concurred in by the settlement generally, or at least were so far shared by the great majority of people as to preclude all idea of open demonstration of dissent. He was very much concerned now to say that, unhappily, such was not the case and that a large party among the French population appeared to be animated by a very different spirit. . . . According to information lately received . . . they [the French] had organized themselves into armed bodies for the purpose of intercepting Governor McDougall on the road . . . with the openly avowed intention of preventing his entry into the settlement.

This was a serious business, the consequences of which might be exceedingly grave. It was hoped that "by calm reason and advice", the French "might be induced to abandon their dangerous schemes". In pursuit of this objective, Mr. Black and the other Councillors began to question Mr. Riel and Dr. Bruce "as to the motives and intentions of the party they represented".

The style used to record these proceedings is elegant, confident, dull; yet the meeting itself must have verged on the tumultuous. "In the course of a long and somewhat irregular discussion," the minutes disclose dryly, "Mr. Riel said . . . that his party was perfectly satisfied with the present Government and wanted no other; that they objected to any government coming from Canada without their being consulted in the matter; that they would never admit any governor . . . unless delegates were previously sent with whom they might negotiate as to terms and conditions under which they would acknowledge him; . . . that they intend to send him [McDougall] back; that they consider they are acting . . . for the good of the whole settlement . . . [and] in defence of their own liberty."

And that, it appears, was that. For no matter how earnestly they entreated him, "Mr. Riel . . . refused to adopt the views of the Council and persisted in expressing his determination to oppose Mr. McDougall's entrance into the settlement."

Louis had well judged the temper of the times. It would be impossible to rally sufficient opposition against him to force him to back down. The local Company officials were powerless and almost indifferent as to what he did; the English-speaking natives of the lower settlement were reluctant to become embroiled; those among his own people who disagreed with his policy could be shouted down. Given time, and with no interference from outside, he could swing them all around to his point of view.

On the way home from their appearance before the Council, Riel and John Bruce called at St. Boniface Cathedral. The old church, with its "turrets twain", the church known to *voyageurs* and buffalo hunters all over the continent, had been destroyed by fire while Louis was in the East. Now a new one stood in its place. There was a rawness to it still; its uncompleted steeple rose only to the level of the roof's crown. But already it was a symbol of permanence, stability, self-control, in the métis' lives.

The pair had intended to call on Abbé Lestanc, who was in charge while Bishop Taché was away in Rome. When advised about the formation of *Le Comité National* a week ago, the priest had assured Riel that he would not oppose it. As far as he was concerned, if the métis were being treated like dogs by the Canadians they were entitled to defend themselves. But this did not mean that they had the right to attack, he had added quickly, or to impose their will on the rest of the colony by force of arms. In short, so long as their activities were defensive, the Church would not stand in their way. Good enough! Now, after their session with the Council, it would be common courtesy to bring the Abbé up to date on all that had happened.

Near the steps of the Bishop's residence they met a man—a young man, bold-looking, with rubicund complexion. He carried a stack of books under one arm. "If you're looking for Father Lestanc, he's not at home," he told them easily in English.

Louis' face showed disappointment.

"Can I give him a message for you? I'll be seeing him in the morning."

Louis shook his head. "It's not important. I'll catch him some other time."

Obviously, the young man was in a conversational mood. He had noticed them coming from the Fort, he said. Had Mactavish got wind of what they were up to?

When Riel assured him that the Governor knew all about the activities of *Le Comité National*, the young man grinned and told him it wouldn't be long now before he found himself clapped into jail.

Louis laughed. It was just like O'Donoghue to come out with a remark like that! Would the man never get it into his head that Red River wasn't Ireland, that Mactavish didn't conduct himself like an English land agent there? O'Donoghue's heart was in the right place. His only trouble was that he itched to stage a revolution.

They bade the young man good-bye and turned their horses'

heads towards the south. As they rode along, Louis still thought of O'Donoghue and the ideas he represented. Suppose it really was too much to hope that Britain would play fair with the métis? As quickly as the doubt came to his mind he dismissed it. William O'Donoghue was a good enough mathematics teacher (he had taught school at St. Boniface ever since Bishop Taché had brought him to the colony from the States); but when it came to politics or philosophy, well—Louis would trust his own judgment, thank you.

O'Donoghue was an Irish-American; he, too, had been ear-marked for the priesthood, but had failed; he was younger than Riel. Though he was a fine fellow and delightful company for an evening, he could be tiresome at times, for his whole background had made him inflexibly resentful of the British Crown. It seemed that he saw in this métis agitation an extension of the age-old struggle in Ireland. Why, only the other day, he had got up at a meeting and made a speech on the subject. Before all those half-literate people he had insisted that only by shaking themselves free from Perfidious Albion could they ensure that justice would be done. (As if even John Bruce, here, knew who or what "Perfidious Albion" stood for!) Then he had shouted that the métis should rise in arms and call upon the States to annex them.

At this point Riel had interrupted to say such talk was non-sense; and strangely enough O'Donoghue had seemed not to mind. Even when Louis had asked him why anyone would want to join the States, he had simply shrugged and smiled. But it was a good question, and all that audience knew it. Why *would* any of them want to join the States? Hadn't the métis in Minnesota Territory suffered just as much at the hands of the Americans as the ones at Red River were suffering now?

"All right," Riel had ended as soon as this point was made clear, "if we keep the British Crown out of this and get on with

RIEL
and some
of his
COUNCILLORS,
1869-70

—

Standing at right,
facing inward:
Thomas Spence

BACK ROW: Le Roc, Pierre DeLorme, Thomas Bunn, Xavier Page, Baptiste
Beauchemin, Baptiste Tereaux
MIDDLE ROW: Pierre Poitras, John Bruce, Louis Riel, W. B. O'Donoghue,
François Dauphinais
FRONT ROW: Bob O'Lane, Paul Proulx

RIEL'S COUNCILLORS IN 1885

1. *Johnny Sansregret.*

2. *Pierre Parenteau (a famous buffalo hunter).*

3. *Pierre Gariepy.*

4. *Philip Garnot, secretary.*

5. *Albert Monkman.*

6. *Pierre Vandal.*

7. *Baptiste Vandal.*

8. *Toussaint Lucier (reputed to be the strongest man in the North-west).*

9. *Maxime Dubois.*

10. *Jimus Short.*

11. *— Tourond.*

12. *Emanuel Champagne.*

Gabriel Dumont,
Métis military leader

Louis' Mother, Julie Riel,
and his only son, Jean

the job of organizing ourselves, we'll all be better off. What we want is justice, not a change of sovereignty. And Mr. O'Donoghue, here, would be well to bear that in mind!"

And now O'Donoghue was feigning surprise at the fact that Riel was not in jail. Louis shrugged. Let the man cherish his fancies if they amused him—just so long as he didn't try to turn *Le Comité National* into an Irish revolutionary movement. If he were to succeed in *that*, he might truly upset the applecart. There were plenty of people already who were only too ready to cry treason whenever a poor métis objected to being kicked in the face.

Well, no matter what O'Donoghue might think, Riel had won his point. Today he had ascertained quite clearly that the Council was not prepared to oppose him seriously. The next step would be to swing them to his side. After that, with the whole colony solidly behind him, he would show O'Donoghue how easy it was to get justice without fighting, if you had patience and you really tried.

Out on the plain to the south of the colony of Assiniboia, William McDougall led his tiny *entourage* towards Fort Garry. Laden down with baggage and a sense of his own importance, he was advancing like a Roman procurator of old, bent on bringing law and order to an area that needed to be tamed. When he reached his domain he would be the first Canadian ruler the West had ever known.

Because there was as yet no railroad through British territory from Canada to the West, he had been forced to travel through the United States, as a private citizen, as far as St. Paul. To do so had been a humiliation, to be sure, for it demanded a sort of compromise with destiny that rankled his imperial nature; but the alternative to using the American route would have meant a tedious expedition through the lake-and-bush wilderness of the

Canadian shield, and he was much too busy a man to consider that. And now his journey was almost done. In a few more days he would be at Fort Garry, where, with his staff of Canadian advisors, he would take up the reins of government.

As the Minister of Public Works in the Dominion's first Cabinet, and as one of the chief Canadian representatives at the London conferences that had decided the fate of the North-west, he had been rewarded with (or, as some people whispered, banished to) his present office. From the start the Prime Minister had been apprehensive of his tendency towards arrogance. Having supplied him with a royal commission which read, in part: "We do hereby constitute and appoint you *on, from,* and *after* the day to be named by *Us* . . .", John A. Macdonald had taken pains to remind McDougall that he would be entering the colony only as a private citizen. In addition, he had cautioned him, both verbally and in writing, to do nothing more for the present than observe local conditions and make ready the machinery of his administration. As the territory would not become a part of Canada until the anticipated transfer of December 1st had actually taken place, he would have no legal rights as Governor until then.

But McDougall was not disposed to stick to either the letter or the spirit of his commission. He saw himself as the Great White Father representing the Queen; he saw the people of Red River as mere savages, to be ruled with a heavy hand. Under the circumstances caution, legal niceties and common sense could be thrown to the wind. It never occurred to him that the natives might already be civilized, that his legitimate task might be—as Macdonald had visualized it—merely to integrate Red River smoothly into the Canadian whole.

But the people of Red River *were* civilized. By any definition of the term this was true. In spite of the Company's rapidly weakening position, they conducted themselves in accordance with an agreed-upon code of government still, of law and order, of social behaviour. They had proved over and over again that among them the common good took precedence over the good of the individual. There existed almost none of that anarchic individualism that is popularly associated with the early days in the West. Until Canadians began to arrive on the scene, serious crime was so rare as to be almost unknown. With the exception of the Indian population at the fringes of the colony, and probably a few Jews, they were Christians all. While certainly the majority were uncultured, still, by any yardstick, they were as civilized as the people of Ontario and Quebec—and more civilized than the inhabitants of many newly formed settlements in the lawless American West.

This error in McDougall's outlook was a common one. Most of the Canadian, and a few of the British, politicians dealing with the impending transfer shared it with him. Indeed, it survives to this day in the folk-memories of our nation. In actual fact, while it must be acknowledged that the Hudson's Bay Company was incapable by this time of continuing to provide adequate government for the territory, the people of Red River were worthy of something better than the government-by-decree that McDougall planned to give them in its place.

For—at least at first—it would be government-by-decree. In his own mind McDougall was sure that the people deserved nothing better. He knew he could expect some resistance to his plans, but he was prepared to deal with it firmly as it arose. Though the party travelling with him was small, he had under his control a shipment of rifles and ammunition for three hundred men. He planned to distribute these arms among the Ontario-born Canadians in the settlement as soon as he was safely at Fort Garry, thereby creating overnight a constabulary to enforce his will. The "natives" would soon find out that he was a man to be reckoned with; they would soon come to realize the futility of further talk about rights. There might remain in the settlement an undertone of grumbling, to be sure, but no opposition of a serious nature would arise.

Nine years before, a discerning English traveller named Lord Southesk had written some thoughtful comments about the métis of the North-west. He had said:

> Too many at home have formed a false idea of the half-breeds, imagining them to be a race little removed from barbarians in habits and appearance. . . . They build and farm like other people, they go to Church and to courts of law, they recognize no chiefs (except when they elect a leader for their great hunting expeditions) and in all respects they are like civilized men, not more uneducated, immoral, or disorderly, than many communities in the Old World.

Too bad McDougall had not read and digested such a sound observation. And yet, if he had, would he have conducted himself more discreetly? It is doubtful that he would, for, though he came west as a representative of the whole Canadian Cabinet, actually he looked at the problems confronting him from a regional point of view. As far as he was concerned, what was good for the people of Ontario was good for all of Canada—including the natives of Red River whom he was about to rule.

Being an economic determinist, an imperialist, a hasty convert to the new doctrine of the survival of the fittest, quite honestly he saw the West as nothing more than an empty vessel that must be filled. The few thousand inhabitants already there were to him like mere ants at the bottom of the pitcher. By pouring men from Ontario over them until they were swamped, he would accomplish two admirable things: he would staunch a wasteful flow of emigration to the United States from British soil by deflecting it westward; he would create another English-speaking territory in the Dominion to overbalance the French-speaking pressure of Quebec that had been built into Confederation with the signing of the British North America Act. If the existing westerners got drowned in the process, what would it matter in the end? The whole operation would be good (Ontario) politics. He and George Brown, the editor of Toronto's *Globe*, had been preaching the logic of the scheme for years.

And now the stage was set for his little play within a play. He himself had written it; the choicest parts were his. Being Lieutenant-Governor, he would order up the curtain as soon as he arrived.

On October 30th he reached Pembina, a tiny village containing eight or ten buildings. As he drew up to the customs-house on the American side of the border, he was surrounded by a party of armed men. Their leader handed him a note, addressed to him in French. It had been written at St. Norbert nine days before.

Monsieur: Le Comité National des Métis de la Rivière Rouge intime à Mon. W. McDougall l'ordre de ne pas entrer sur le Territoire du Nord-Ouest sans une permission spéciale de ce Comité.

Par Ordre du Président, John Bruce

It was signed, as Secretary, by Louis Riel.

He must not enter the Territory, *his* Territory, without permission! Whose permission? Incredible! And yet—as he glanced again at the determined faces on every side, at the tiny *entourage* of his own followers—it dawned on him that perhaps this order should not be treated lightly. And he *had* been warned by Macdonald not to cause any trouble. Perhaps, after all, prudence would be in order today instead of valour. With all the dignity he could muster, he turned aside.

"We will camp here for the time being," he announced brusquely to his staff, "until I have had an opportunity to ascertain what Governor Mactavish thinks of this treasonable behaviour."

During the days immediately following Riel's meeting with the Council of Assiniboia, conditions in the colony remained relatively quiet. In the lower settlement the English-speaking people reacted much as Louis had predicted they would. After several meetings, they announced that the Dominion "should assume the responsibility of establishing among us what it, and it alone, has decided upon". As far as they were concerned, they would receive the incoming Governor "with respect, but there is no enthusiasm". In the upper settlement, among the French métis, there was an insignificant flurry of opposition to *Le Comité National*. On the 27th about eighty men, led by Messrs. Dease and Goulet, attended a meeting at which they begged their countrymen to disarm; but—thanks to Father Ritchot, who came out strongly in favour of *Le Comité's* stand—their efforts collapsed. In fact, in the end "some twenty . . . of Mr. Dease's party [came over] to their side".

Indeed, the prevailing currents of opinion were setting everywhere in the colony in the direction Louis had predicted they would set. After the collapse of the protest meeting led by Dease and Goulet, the Council of Assiniboia had decided to advise McDougall *not* to enter the North-west at this time. Even before reaching this decision, they had refused to consider a request from a delegation of Canadians who demanded that all English-speaking people be called to arms against the métis; in fact, they had asked them bluntly if they were trying to start a civil war. All this meant that the Canadians in the colony were becoming isolated, while everyone else was beginning to think of the settlement as a political unit capable of deciding matters for itself. If a little more time were given for this trend to develop, all would be well at Red River again.

At home Louis was treated differently than he had ever been treated before. It was as though the sense of mission he had guarded within himself for so long had suddenly become a family possession. He, the eldest son, always his mother's favourite, was looked upon now, in a thousand little ways, almost as if he had publicly declared himself to have a vocation. In the eyes of his family he had become a human being dedicated to an almost superhuman cause.

On the 18th his beloved sister Sara had written from the convent at St. Norbert: "This morning two communions were offered, and tomorrow three intentions will be tendered, to bring grace and Heaven's blessings to our dear Louis." And she had told her mother, with all the authority and enthusiasm of a happy twenty-one-year-old nun, to "ask Heaven to bless his efforts, and to give him the health, the talents, the graces, the intelligence necessary to finish successfully what he has commenced". Further, she had instructed Eulalie and Joseph (aged sixteen and thirteen respectively), and even little Alexandre, to offer their prayers often for "dear Louis". So now the whole family was storming Heaven with prayers on his behalf—and he knew he *must* succeed!

On October 22nd, the day Louis became twenty-five years old, they had all gathered in the kitchen and recited the Rosary. As they meditated on the five joyful mysteries of St. Mary's life, they had asked the Blessed Virgin to pray that Louis, like herself, might somehow be a servant of God. Perhaps it had been as a result of these prayers that he felt so happy now, so confident that the course on which he had embarked was the right one.

November 1st is All Saints' Day, a holy day of obligation in the Catholic Church, the day set aside to honour every unknown human being who during the long course of centuries has taken up Christ's Cross and followed Him. As Louis listened to the priest reading from the Gospel according to St. Matthew at Mass that morning in the chapel of St. Vital, he must have thought it singularly appropriate:

> Blessed are the poor in spirit: for theirs is the kingdom of heaven. Blessed are the meek: for they shall possess the land. . . . Blessed are they that hunger and thirst after justice: for they shall have their fill. . . . Blessed are they that suffer persecution for justice' sake. . .

The words must have thrilled him, comforted him beyond measure, for it was as if the lesson they contained had been set down with great forethought, hundreds of years ago, for the consolation of his beloved métis today. Could it be that Christ wanted to assure him that God the Father was on his side? If the words were true (and he did not doubt it) then his people were blessed indeed: for *they* were poor, *they* were meek, *they* were hungry, often. They thirsted desperately for justice. Weren't they suffering persecution at this very moment while others enriched themselves at their expense? Surely, if the Canadians could be persuaded to listen to this Gospel they would abandon their present conduct and go home!

But they could not be persuaded to listen. In fact they themselves were bent on preaching a quite different gospel of their own. On the very day that word reached Riel of yet another triumph for his cause, word also came of a development that might be disastrous if allowed to go unchecked. McDougall had been stopped at the border by forces of *Le Comité National*; wisely, he had decided to remain where he was for the time being. But Colonel Dennis, the surveyor, had begun a recruiting campaign at the northern end of the colony, calling upon the English-speaking settlers to take up arms against the French. Though it was true that most of the settlers were adopting an attitude of "wait and see", the potentialities of this appeal were dangerous in the extreme.

Dennis's argument was that the métis, being more numerous than the rest, were trying to take advantage of the situation to force their racial and religious views on everyone else, that only when the Canadians gained control of Fort Garry would the English settlers be safe. It was an emotional appeal; it could not fail to have some attractive aspects in the eyes of English-speaking Presbyterians. Even if local history proved beyond a doubt that the two races could live side by side in peace, there would always be a few restless souls quite willing to forget the fact.

And all Dennis needed was a few. If he could in some way make it appear that he had the support of the English settlers, then, if one of them was involved in some skirmish and was shot, a little oratory would bring every English Protestant in the country to his side. Disaster would follow, surely—perhaps civil war; and the Indians, taking advantage of this, would rise and massacre every man, woman and child they could lay their hands on.

What was the matter with Dennis, anyhow? Riel asked himself. This was the 19th century; political affairs should not be decided by force of arms! If the Canadian party could only be kept isolated from the rest, justice would yet be achieved without fighting. But if the English settlers were to join up with the Colonel, the Canadians would seize Fort Garry, and—in the name of *all* the people—they would invite McDougall in. Once he had proclaimed himself Governor, the time would have passed for peaceful resistance. And the métis would be driven off their land to the poplar-treed fringes of their plains.

Whoever possessed Fort Garry controlled the country. For the good of everyone, McDougall must be prevented from controlling the country. Therefore, the métis soldiers must seize Fort Garry before Dennis had a chance to do so. They must do this legally, on the ground that *Le Comité National* comprised the only group sufficiently well organized to protect the settlement. They must be scrupulously legal; they must give Mactavish an undertaking, in the name of the people, that they would compensate the Company for any losses sustained. They must expropriate the Fort and the goods inside it in an orderly, civilized way.

On the following day, after drifting into Fort Garry by ones and twos from St. Norbert and their homes along the Red, armed métis under the command of André Nault quietly took possession of the Company's headquarters. No one fired a shot in opposition. When Riel appeared before Governor Mactavish to explain the reasons for his action, the Governor seemed only mildly excited by the whole affair. "I must protest against what you have done, Mr. Riel," he said wearily. But he added: "I must admit, however, that it is a logical move. Had you not made it, someone else would have, no doubt."

And so, without so much as an argument, *Le Comité National* took under its "protective" wings the seat of government of the colony of Assiniboia.

IV

I DO NOT TRUST McDOUGALL

THIS Company fortress that Riel now undertook to "protect" was actually a very fine piece of property, far and away the finest in the British North-west. Behind its stone walls more than a dozen buildings, most of them two storeys high, housed the men and provided shelter for the trade goods without which the Company's business could not have been carried on. All the buildings—the Governor's residence, the flour mill, the fur and pemmican stores, the powder magazine, the officers' and clerks' quarters—nestled within a rectangle measuring three hundred feet by six hundred. Gates in the north-west and south-east walls gave access to the village of Winnipeg and the Assiniboine River.

Immediately to the north, close enough to be dominated by the Fort still, were the blacksmith's and carpenter's shops, also the combined jail and court-house. To the south were the steamboat landing and a large warehouse. Off towards the east, in the triangle of land formed by the union of the rivers, lay the grist mill and the flat area on which ox-cart brigades assembled each year before setting out for the West.

Three-quarters of a mile northward across the bare plain, where the Portage trail and the main road to the Lower Fort met, was the village of Winnipeg. It was tiny still, but emitting already unmistakable sparks of vitality. Here the independent traders—Bannatyne, McKenny, Larsen, Higgins, Fonseca, Begg, and others—focused their hopes for the future. Here the tinsmith Ashdown plied his trade and dreamed of becoming a hardware merchant. Here George Emmerling, who had come north on spec with one barrel of whisky and two of apples, ran a tolerably comfortable hotel; and Onis Marchamp, having started with a tiny bar in one small rented room, ran a first-class saloon.

Here in Winnipeg, the Hudson's Bay Company, the Catholic Church, and the Anglican Church had all recently found it advisable to open "branches". The Company now ran a local store under the management of Mr. Moncrief, while the Churches supported missions named St. Mary's and Holy Trinity, under the guidance of Oblate Father McCarthy and Archdeacon McLean, respectively. Here, too, Schultz and his fellow-Canadians eyed the main chance and cocked their snooks at Riel and the Company and all that the old order stood for.

As soon as he had installed his men in Fort Garry, Riel commandeered, as an office for himself and a council chamber for his Committee, the large house facing the river that had at one time been the Governor's residence. (The new residence at the north-west end of the Fort was where Mactavish now lived.) Then he established his own sleeping-quarters at the home of his cousin, Henry Coutu, who was a butcher in Winnipeg. By this action he hoped to suggest that Governor Mactavish was still to be respected in the colony, that métis soldiers were merely guarding the Fort on behalf of the people as a whole.

Next morning he turned his attention to administrative problems. The executive of *Le Comité National* was short of educated men; he must do what he could to correct this situation. First he sent for O'Donoghue, the Irish-American teacher at St. Boniface College. He told him that to win their fight for justice the local people must prove their worthiness to control their own affairs. They must be scrupulous in everything they did; their financial relations with the Company and with everyone else must be beyond reproach. In order to achieve this condition, *Le Comité* would need a competent treasurer. Would O'Donoghue—forgetting any notions he might have about turning the present state of affairs into a revolutionary movement—be willing to act in this capacity?

The Irishman said that he would. For almost half an hour Riel explained what he conceived to be the new treasurer's responsibilities. Then he dismissed O'Donoghue and called in his old friend Louis Schmidt.

This was the man with whom Riel had gone east to school. Still slight of build and small-boned, he was healthy now, as he had not been during his days at St. Hyacinthe. Happily for the affairs of the moment, Schmidt had just arrived back at Red River after a summer of freighting between the forks and the railhead at St. Cloud. He would be just the man to look after the paper work involved in the running of *Le Comité National*.

Louis Schmidt was pure métis. He was born in the same year as Louis Riel, at Lake Athabasca in the far North-west; both his mother and his father had been born in the North-west. While he was yet an infant, his mother took him several hundred miles to Lac-la-Ronge so that Father Thibault could baptize him in the proper clerical manner. From then until he was eight, he lived almost as a savage; then Father Faraud opened a mission near his home and insisted that he receive an education.

Shortly after this the family moved to Red River, because his mother, fearing she had cancer, sought medical attention there. Up the Athabasca River they came, across the twelve-mile Portage-la-Loche to Ile-à-la-Crosse, through the northern river system to Cumberland House and on to Le Pas. When they shot the Grand Rapids, where the Saskatchewan empties itself into Lake Winnipeg, young Schmidt was so thrilled by the experience that he begged to shoot them again. When he got to Red

River, he was equally thrilled by his first sight and taste of bread.

At St. Hyacinthe he was a good student. During his first year there he placed third in his class—just behind another young student named Adolphe Chapleau. But the eastern climate did not agree with him, and those in authority decided to send him home. Back at Red River he worked for a while for Father Lestanc, copying the Cree grammar and dictionary of Father Lacombe. Then, when he heard that the American General Sibley had asked Father André to lead a mission to the Sioux, Schmidt volunteered to go along with the priest as his secretary.

After that adventure he became a sort of man-of-all-trades for Bishop Taché—convoying supplies, preparing résumés of news and of outstanding articles that had appeared in Canadian and European periodicals for circulation among the outpost missions, and teaching at St. Boniface College. One winter he was engaged by the American Government to open a new mail route between Abercrombie on the Red River and Helena, Montana—and, caught in a blizzard, froze his left foot so badly that part of it had to be amputated. It was with the money paid to him for this assignment that he bought oxen and carts and set himself up as a freighter.

He was, then, an old friend of Louis Riel; he was also, by experience, eminently suited to lend a hand. Now, when the métis chief asked him to become his secretary, Louis Schmidt consented to do so.

Within an hour, acting on Riel's instructions, he despatched a note to Lépine at St. Norbert, ordering him to send an armed party to Pembina, where McDougall had taken up residence, inside British territory, in the Hudson's Bay Company fort. The aspiring Lieutenant-Governor must be allowed no opportunity to claim that he had established a government within the colony; he must be escorted back into the United States, and told to stay there.

46

With the help of O'Donoghue and Schmidt, Louis spent most of the next few days making a business-like appraisal of the Company's stores. Every item was systematically accounted for. Among other things, they discovered more than three hundred old "Brown Bess" muskets, with ample ammunition, in the magazine. After commandeering what he thought he would require for the use of his guards, he gave Mactavish a receipt in the name of *Le Comité*; the rest of the fort's contents he left under Company control.

When this task was finished Riel turned his attention to the guards. By now more than four hundred armed métis had gathered at Fort Garry. To make sure they did not become dangerously restless, it was imperative that they should be subjected to rigid rules of behaviour. From his own experience, Riel knew that most of them were unsuited by temperament and custom to long periods of disciplined inactivity. They must be organized into small squads that could be frequently alternated on duty, and schedules must be drawn up that allowed most of them to be home on leave most of the time.

While Louis was attending to these matters, the colony remained quiet. Apparently, the majority of the people at Red River accepted without protest his move to "protect" the Fort. *Eh bien!* Perhaps the time had come to call upon them outright for support. Towards the end of October John Bruce had written M. Provencher, a French-speaking member of McDougall's staff, to tell him that *Le Comité* would be more than willing to negotiate with the Canadian Government. In his reply, Provencher had asked how much popular support the métis "insurgents" enjoyed. To answer this question convincingly, Riel now resolved to invite all the inhabitants of Red River to send delegates to a meeting. Accordingly, on November 6th, he sat down with Louis Schmidt and composed the following proclamation:

The President and Representatives of the French-speaking population of Rupert's Land in Council—the invaders of our rights being now expelled—already aware of your sympathy, do extend the hand of friendship to you, our friendly fellow-inhabitants, and in doing so invite you to send twelve representatives, in order to found one body with the above Council of the French-speaking population, now consisting of twelve members, to consider the present political state of the country, and to adopt such measures as may be deemed best for the future welfare of the same.

A meeting of the above Council will be held in the Court House at Fort Garry, on Tuesday November 16, at which the representatives will attend.

By order of the President,
Louis Riel, Secretary

Winnipeg, November 6th, 1869

It was a master-stroke of diplomacy. At once it gave the lie to Dennis's propaganda; for it offered the English-speaking minority equality with the French métis. At the same time it laid the groundwork for concerted political action. The two métis took it over to the office of the *Nor'-Wester* to have it set up in type, so that it could be distributed throughout the colony.

But their scheme was not to be executed without a hitch. The paper—founded in 1859 by a pair of Canadians named Buckingham and Coldwell, owned for three years by the bombastic Dr. Schultz, and currently the property of Dr. Walter Bown, an ex-dentist from St. Paul—stood for everything to which the métis were opposed. The present proprietor had no intention of co-operating in any way with Riel. He told him so. Thereupon Louis called in some guards, seized the building, and locked its owner in a back room. Then he sent for James Ross, a native who had for a short period in the sixties himself operated the paper, and prevailed upon him to set up the proclamation in type. By the following morning copies had been printed and distributed to every corner of the settlement.

During the next few days Riel and his principal adherents visited all the English-speaking parishes. Everywhere they went they found themselves actively opposed by members of the "Canadian" party. They found, also, many of the English-speaking natives quite openly expressing resentment over the high-handed manner displayed by *Le Comité National* in seizing Fort Garry. Nevertheless, because these same natives agreed that a peaceful solution to the present crisis must be found, Riel was able to persuade them to send delegates to the meeting he had proposed.

On November 7th McDougall, in anguished exile at Pembina, wrote Governor Mactavish. This was the third letter he had penned to the Hudson's Bay Company's representative since his arrival at the border. On the 2nd he had announced that he would remain where he was for the time being, at the same time advising the Governor to publish a proclamation against the "insurgents". On the 4th he had informed Mactavish of his ejection from British soil and asked him for advice. In this third letter he protested strongly against the Company's lack of opposition to the seizure of Fort Garry, and announced that he would stay where he was until official word of the transfer had reached him.

On the 9th Mactavish replied: "Measures . . . of a positively coercive nature have not been resorted to, for the simple reason that we have had no reliable force to insure their safety and success. . . . [But] we have been insistent in our efforts to impress upon the leaders . . . a just sense of the illegality and danger of the course upon which they have entered." He ended his communication with this laconic statement: "To the Council and myself it appears that your early return to Canada is . . . advisable."

McDougall possessed no authority in the colony; by now the people knew it. No doubt the Council had asked itself what could be accomplished by pretending that he had. When the Canadian party petitioned Mactavish to proclaim McDougall's rule, or, failing that, to take control of things himself again, he refused even to give them a reply. (Though they appealed to him to use his "authority" now, hadn't they been the very ones who refused to obey him in the past? On what grounds, then, could he expect them to obey him now?) Probably Mactavish's attitude can best be summed up in this manner: he knew himself to be without real power, yet he felt a strong responsibility still for the welfare of the colony. Surely, so long as Riel commanded the support of the majority of the people, no good could come of opposing him.

On the morning of November 16th, twenty-four elected delegates—twelve English-speaking, twelve French—met in the court-house outside Fort Garry's walls. Anxiously, Mactavish waited to see what would come of their deliberations. As far as he was concerned, if they could agree on a course of action the crisis would be eased immeasurably. But this was the one thing that Riel's Convention of Twenty-four could not do.

Among any group gathered to consider questions of a political nature, it is always easier to agree on what they are *against* than on what they are *for*. So it was among the delegates assembled now. They were inexperienced in the art of politics; they did not know that game of give and take.

During the first two days of the convention, almost their entire time was spent in haggling over the list of rights they wished to present to Canada for consideration. Confronted with this dissension, this inability to get things done, and subject as he was to pressure from McDougall and the Canadians in the colony, Mactavish began to fear that chaos would result. Lying in his sick-bed, he came to the conclusion he had erred in not opposing Riel more firmly. Suddenly, without warning, he acted to reverse his previous position.

Impetuously, he drew up a proclamation addressed to "all whom it concerns". Riel's action in preventing people moving on the public highway was illegal, he said; the seizure of "goods and merchandise of various descriptions" was unlawful; interfering with the public mails was illegal, too; the actions of certain persons in billeting themselves in Fort Garry and in forcing McDougall to vacate the Hudson's Bay Company post at Pembina were to be condemned; no one had any right to "resist arrangements for the transfer of the government of this country . . . made under the sanction of the Imperial Parliament". He ended by appealing to the citizens to ratify and proclaim this, his public note of protest, then to "disperse themselves and peaceably to depart to their habitations".

Riel was coldly angered by this act, for he concluded that the Governor had tricked him deliberately. Without a moment's reflection he ordered Mactavish put under house arrest. Then he claimed the floor of the convention. He had put an end to the Company's interference; he would put an end to this wrangling, too. He wished now to introduce his own list of rights.

He spoke moderately enough. But the English-speaking members were suspicious, now, because of his high-handed treatment of the Governor. They refused to agree formally to anything Riel proposed. Though they admitted that they could find nothing wrong in principle with the list of rights he had drawn up, they refused even to consider methods whereby these could be presented to the Canadian authorities. They began to whisper among themselves that perhaps Dennis's ideas about the need for Canadian protection had some merit for them after all.

Immediately after this episode the convention was adjourned for two days, so that the court-house could be used for a criminal trial. Then, on November 22nd, when it had reconvened, Thomas Bunn arose to offer a proposal. They should recommend to the Council of Assiniboia that McDougall be allowed in; then they should negotiate with him for the acceptance of their list of rights. This was a backward step and foolishness as well. Hearing it, Riel lost his temper, publicly, for the first time. "Mr. Bunn is suspicious of the men I keep under arms here," he thundered at the top of his voice. "Is he unaware that the Council of Assiniboia is without power and that McDougall has at his disposal three hundred rifles?" Without waiting for a reply, without attempting to prepare the ground in any way, he went on to propose that they ignore McDougall, form a provisional government, and begin negotiating directly with the Canadian Government in Ottawa.

Perhaps it was a logical suggestion; certainly it was one that had been in Riel's mind for some time; but the English-speaking delegates refused even to consider it. They reminded Louis that, legally, the Company's rule was still in effect and that they were not empowered to override its authority. After much argument it was agreed that the convention should adjourn once again, this time until December 1st, so that delegates could go home and discuss this new proposal with their constituents. And that, for the time being, was that.

The following interlude was almost like that which precedes a general election today. The key issue was whether or not the Company's rule had decayed to the point of extinction. All over the colony meetings were held to discuss the question. While the Canadians—in constant, clandestine communication with McDougall at Pembina—busied themselves trying to influence the people against the formation of a provisional government, Riel and his men did the reverse. Feeling as between the Canadian and the French-métis proposals became very hot indeed.

Mention has already been made of the rifles and ammunition included in McDougall's baggage. These were not actually with him at Pembina now. At the first hint of trouble they had been

deposited in the Hudson's Bay Company storehouse at George-
town, Minnesota; but the métis did not know this fact. In order
to make sure the arms would not reach the Canadians in the
colony, Riel insisted that all inbound shipments be inspected by
his men. Now, on November 24th or thereabouts, right in the
heat of the "election" interlude, several carts under the control
of Dr. Schultz were seen passing Fort Garry's walls. They were
bound from the south towards the village of Winnipeg.

With a party of four armed men, Riel rode out to stop them
—"merely as a matter of form", according to a Canadian eyewitness who later reported the incident to Colonel Dennis. He
then accompanied Dr. Schultz to the latter's storehouse. The
account, which is here somewhat condensed, proceeds:

> On entering the store Riel said: "Are these all your goods?"
> "No. Government property." Riel then said: "By the bye, that
> reminds me—I may as well take an inventory of them in case
> any party should remove any portion, and it would be laid
> to us." Riel put two [of his men] in charge, and went off in-
> tending to return. While he was away the doctor hired the
> guard to assist in carrying the cases into the house. They left
> their arms in the store. While they were so employed, the
> doctor locked up the store. Riel returned some couple of
> hours afterwards. He demanded entrance to the store, after
> soundly rating his men. The doctor refused, and told them
> he would have to use force. The doctor put his back to the
> door, and refused entrance unless Riel promised not to remove
> anything. Which Riel did. Riel, all at once, came to the con-
> clusion that it was rather late to take the inventory.

This may not be an accurate account of the incident; but in
any event, it is an amusing one. Be this as it may, after satisfy-
ing himself that the shipment contained nothing more dangerous

than government pork intended for the road gang working on the Dawson Trail, Riel and his guards returned to Fort Garry. That was the end of the matter as far as they were concerned. It is more than likely that Riel himself forgot about this incident, for shortly afterwards something happened in Winnipeg that momentarily eased all tension and gave promise of an end to the present anxieties.

A small group of English-speaking natives had by now definitely decided that they saw justice in the French-métis stand; but they were convinced that the present drift towards armed conflict must be reversed. The leader of this group was Alexander G. B. Bannatyne, an independent trader of some substance in the colony and a member of the Council of Assiniboia. At this time he was forty years of age and related by marriage to Hudson's Bay Company Governor Mactavish. (Both men had married daughters of Andrew McDermot, who was perhaps the most prominent non-Company man in the West.) He was respected universally for his fairness and common sense. Now, under his chairmanship, a meeting of the electors of Winnipeg was called for November 26th. Both Riel and Schultz were invited to attend. Because the villagers insisted on it, an atmosphere of reasonableness prevaded the gathering from the very start.

The situation was, in fact, extremely fluid. At this time Major Wallace, one of the surveyors now employed by McDougall as a spy, reported that many people thought the United States to be the natural outlet for the settlement. According to him, the natives of Red River swore they would never submit to the injustice of a council from Canada being appointed to rule them. If McDougall had come alone, his informants had told him, he would have been allowed to air his views—and perhaps been thrown out later, if the people did not approve of these views. The crux of the matter was that they wanted control of their own affairs. And in this regard, they asked why the people of

Red River should be treated any differently than the people of British Columbia, Newfoundland, or Prince Edward Island. Major Wallace himself discounted all these arguments; in his opinion, the whole thing was nothing more or less than a Republican-Fenian movement. If McDougall wanted a recommendation from him, the French should be forced by threats of Canadian troops to disarm.

At this meeting, after the métis chief had outlined his ideas, he was applauded widely. When another man countered with a bombastic "loyalist" speech, Dr. Schultz himself arose to admonish him. It seemed for a while that positive progress towards peace would be made. But the hope was still-born. Everyone present agreed that English and French should unite with the members of the Canadian party under a new, strong executive council acting in the name of the Hudson's Bay Company; everyone agreed that such a council would be more acceptable as a stopgap than a provisional government; yet no one could decide who had the right to vote for this resolution. And on this note of indecision, the meeting bogged down. Riel and his métis returned to Fort Garry; Schultz and his friends went back to his house in the village. There was nothing further that either of them could do until the Winnipeg group had solved the problem of voting authority among themselves.

By this time winter had firmly set in. All across the prairie nature's growth had ceased for the year. The arid time-for-waiting season stretched ahead like a wide, white river-bed, with nothing to bridge it but faith in the future and provisions put away during the warm summer months. For this the métis at Fort Garry were well prepared; they could feed a small army indefinitely, for all the Company's stores were under their control. Suddenly, it occurred to some of the Canadians that they could do the same. If the supply of pork in Dr. Schultz's house was moved from under Riel's nose to the Lower Fort, they would be in as strong a position as the métis to sit out the winter. Hastily they began to mobilize at the north end of the settlement.

Now Colonel Dennis, their leader, was at this moment in Pembina with McDougall. A few of the cooler characters among the Canadian party prevailed upon their comrades to make no move without their leader's consent. Then they despatched Mr. Newcombe, one of their members, to the border for advice.

McDougall, it appeared, had other plans. Shortly afterwards, he reported to Ottawa:

> I thought it very undesirable to allow a "fight" to take place about Government property, until some collision had occurred which would excite the feelings of the English and Scotch half-breeds against the insurgents. Moreover, the Hudson's Bay Company officers were still the nominal rulers; and as their Sheriff [McKinney] was notoriously in the interests of the rebels, it appeared to me better that none of my agents should provoke a collision before December 1st.
>
> I do not regard the possession of these government stores by Riel as of much consequence. . . . If the measures I have taken to organize an armed force to seize Riel should prove successful, the provisions will soon be again in our possession.

Concerning McDougall's "measures . . . to organize an armed force", more will be said later. Suffice it to mention here that, at the very moment Riel and his men were waiting in Fort Garry to see what would result from the constructive proposals to which they had subscribed, about 250 young hotheads were fomenting trouble quite openly in the northern end of the colony. Riel could not know their ardour would be checked by official decree. When he learned of their activity, he assumed that they were preparing to advance against Fort Garry. To him it seemed clear that Schultz had been play-acting at the meeting in Winnipeg, in order to gain time while his associates gathered recruits for the Canadian cause. Instantly, he doubled his guard and announced that he had withdrawn his offer to compromise.

From now on the métis leader would make sure that he was deceived no more. From now on he would insist that an independent provisional government be set up in the name of the French and English settlers alone—a government that would control the colony until terms could be negotiated successfully with the Government of Canada. Ringed all around with such mountains of suspicion and bad faith, Bannatyne's efforts towards unification were smothered almost at birth.

Like most winter mornings on the Prairies, December 1st dawned cold and clear. This was the day on which Riel's Convention of Twenty-four was to come together again. As the delegates from the parishes reassembled in Fort Garry's courthouse, nothing indicated that a bomb was about to explode in their midst. Although they had discussed with their constituents the question of the Company's authority to govern, there was no unanimity in the directives they had received. They were divided still in their private opinions; they did not know yet what final steps they should take to promote the welfare of the colony. And they were wary, once again, because of Riel's recent changes of mind. As Louis moved to his place among them he could feel both their general goodwill and their wariness, almost as if they were conflicting physical things.

No sooner had the meeting been called to order than a young man rushed in. His name was Robert Tait; he was a delegate to the convention; he demanded to be heard on a subject of the utmost importance. In his hand he held a copy of a proclamation issued in the Queen's name. It was agreed by everyone that he must be heard.

"Victoria, by the Grace of God, of the United Kingdom, of

Great Britain and Ireland, Defender of the Faith . . . to all whom it may concern, greeting: Whereas"—and "whereas" and "whereas"! As Tait read on, it became abundantly apparent that the transfer of the North-west to Canada had in fact taken place, that the despotic rule of McDougall had actually begun. Whether anyone liked it or not, the Hudson's Bay Company's claim to authority was finally extinguished. Whether anyone liked it or not, the colony had become a part of Canada now! And they had all better take note that

> we have seen fit by our Royal Letters Patent . . . to appoint the Honourable William McDougall of the City of Ottawa in the Province of Ontario in Our Dominion of Canada . . . to be at Our pleasure the Lieutenant-Governor of the North West Territories . . . and we do hereby authorize and empower and require and command him in due manner to do and execute in all things . . . according to the several provisions and instructions granted or appointed him by virtue of Our said Commission. . . . Of all which Our loving subjects . . . are hereby required to take notice and govern themselves accordingly.

When Tait's voice at last grew silent, pandemonium for a short time gained the upper hand. Then the more level-headed among the delegates began to organize their thoughts. How had Tait gained possession of this document? they asked. How long had he had it in his hands?

Colonel Dennis had handed it to him just now, as he came towards the court-house. He had told him to bring it to the convention. The colonel himself had ridden on northwards, towards the parish of St. Andrews, with another copy. He said he had ridden all night, that he had come right through from Pembina without a stop. When someone asked how the proclamation could have been dated December 1st, as Dennis must have left early yesterday morning, someone else brushed the objection aside by stating that McDougall could easily have given him a copy in advance. And so the discussion continued, jeopardizing whatever chances there were for constructive debate.

At first Riel felt shattered by the news brought by Tait. But as he recovered his equilibrium, he began to wonder if, perhaps, the whole thing was a fraud. He had been tricked by the Canadians before. Perhaps their representative would be dishonest enough to forge an official document now. But he doubted it. In any event there was no use wasting time in speculating over something that could not at the moment be proved. The important thing was to salvage what could be salvaged of the convention. As soon as he felt it possible to do so, he demanded and secured the floor.

On his feet, he reminded his audience of the purpose for which they had assembled today: they were here to consider whether the Colony of Assiniboia was without effective government. If this proclamation was genuine, such consideration was no longer necessary. Nevertheless, the validity of the list of rights to which they had all subscribed remained unaltered. In a reasonable voice and in a quiet manner he moved that this list of rights should be sent to McDougall, with a demand that he forward it to the Canadian Parliament forthwith.

Someone seconded the motion; it was debated and then passed. The delegates all agreed that the people of Red River had grievances which were worthy of consideration by the Canadian Cabinet. Then one of the English-speaking delegates proposed that they send a deputation, instead of a single messenger, with the list of rights to McDougall at Pembina. This deputation would serve a double purpose: not only would it deliver the convention's resolution, it could act as a welcoming body; it could escort the Lieutenant-Governor into the colony when he had agreed to their demands.

Instantly, Riel was on his feet again. No one was going to escort McDougall to Red River, he thundered. No one was going to ask him to agree to anything! More quietly, he reminded his audience that the resolution they had just passed required McDougall to submit their list of rights to the Parliament of Canada.

Someone protested that McDougall was their Governor now. Riel countered, somewhat lamely, that perhaps he was and perhaps he was not. (Though he had no serious conviction as yet that the proclamation was not genuine, it would serve his purpose to pretend for the moment that he had.) Turning to Louis Schmidt, who was recording the proceedings, he told him to make a note of what he was about to say. Then, with all the acting skill he could command, he delivered his parting shot.

"I do not trust McDougall," he said slowly. "I do not like the arbitrary tone that runs through this 'proclamation' that he claims has been issued by our Queen. We are not slaves to be bought and sold! We are a free people who have a right to negotiate terms of union with the free people of Canada." He shrugged. "You think I am wrong. *Eh bien*! Go, return quietly to your farms. Stay there in the arms of your women. Give this example to your children. But watch what we do. We will labour and obtain a guarantee of our rights and yours. We have come finally to the parting of the ways."

V

GOVERNMENT
EX NECESSITATE

RIEL dismissed the delegates to his convention on December 1st. A full week passed before he made another decisive move—a week in which it came slowly to be believed that McDougall's proclamation was a forgery. The rumour to this effect had started with members of the Canadian party themselves; they had been heard to boast that the whole thing was a ruse designed to undermine the métis position. It soon became so wide-spread that responsible men like Alexander Bannatyne and the Anglican Bishop, Machray, were known to have said it might be true.

Governor Mactavish refused to deliver an opinion. Coughing out his life's energy in his room in Fort Garry, he stated over and over again that he had heard nothing definite from his directors in London; until he did, he would not know what had or had not happened.

Riel believed now that he would have to abandon his plans if the people became convinced that the proclamation was genuine; he hoped still that he would be called upon to implement them if they discovered conclusively that it was false. For a whole week he watched and waited in Fort Garry. During that time he told himself that whether or not he went down to defeat, this much he had actually achieved—he had drawn the people together so that, before the proclamation, they were almost ready to agree to the establishment of a provisional government in the

Queen's name. To remind them of what they had accomplished together, he caused to be printed and circulated about the colony the list of rights to which their delegates had formally assented.

It was as well that he did this, for divisive forces were busily at work. Along with the proclamation he brought to Fort Garry, Colonel Dennis had come armed with a commission signed by McDougall. This commission gave him the right to arm and drill men, including Indians, and lead them against the French métis. As "conservator of the peace", he now rode about the colony fomenting war.

A contemporary once said that Dennis was "descended of martial ancestors, confident in his skill as a commander". And it certainly seems that at this time he was itching for a fight. In 1866, in Ontario, his military reputation had been seriously deflated when a Fenian "army" from the United States had captured Fort Erie largely because Dennis had led his men into a trap. Perhaps he hoped now that by achieving a victory over the French métis he would re-establish himself as a military man.

Whatever the motives behind his activity, as a recruiting officer he was not an overwhelming success. The English-speaking settlers harboured grave doubts concerning the authenticity of the proclamation; they thoroughly approved of the moderation and common sense displayed by Riel's list of rights. As a result, very few of them answered Dennis's call to arms. They might be unwilling to join the French métis against the Canadians, but they were just as unwilling to join the Canadians against the French métis.

The members of the Canadian party and the Indians were not so aloof; they flocked to the side of Dennis and his appointed deputies—Dr. Schultz in Winnipeg and Captain Boulton at Portage-la-Prairie. Their actions alarmed all sensible people. Only seven years before, 650 men, women and children had been massacred by the Sioux in Minnesota Territory to the south.

Sane colonists remembered this and asked themselves if *any* cause, particularly the Canadian one, was worth risking a repetition of such a tragedy.

The tiniest spark might now kindle an all-consuming blaze. Lower Fort Garry, twenty miles down-stream from the village of Winnipeg, was in the Canadians' hands. At St. Peters, below the lower Fort, the Swampy Crees were flocking eagerly to arms. At Portage-la-Prairie, to the west, the Sioux were working themselves into an ominous state of excitement. And on the southern fringe of Winnipeg an undisciplined garrison of Canadian toughs had gathered in Schultz's house to guard their supply of Canadian pork.

Three-quarters of a mile from these toughs, at the Forks of the Red and the Assiniboine, Riel was soberly conscious of the responsibility that rested on him now. He himself was in no danger of being overwhelmed, for Indians and the members of the Canadian party could do him no harm so long as he held Fort Garry; but the rest of the colony might suffer devastation from the forces at work in their midst. He must watch events carefully; he must move, if necessary, before it became too late. Unobtrusively he gathered all his best men about him. As soon as he had learned definitely whether the proclamation was genuine or not, he would act.

Ambroise Lépine was one of the best of the métis hunters. According to Louis Schmidt, who left memoirs of the times, he "was the exact opposite to Riel. He was cool, positive; though his presence was not arresting he was gallant. He possessed a military bearing and great muscular strength. He was born to command, and became quite naturally the military commander of the métis soldiers." It made sense that Riel should recall him now from his duties on the Pembina Trail and appoint him the military chief at Fort Garry. When, on December 7th, Lépine arrived, he brought with him André Nault, who had news of the greatest importance: before coming north he had ascertained beyond doubt that McDougall's proclamation was a fraud!

According to Nault, no official word had arrived from Ottawa concerning the expected transfer. Becoming tired of waiting for it, McDougall had taken matters into his own hands and composed the proclamation. After signing it on behalf of the Queen, he had stepped across the border with six men and two dogs and read aloud his forgery for the benefit of whom it might concern. Himself convinced of its validity, Dennis had then brought it on to Red River.

This had been the private action of an overwrought man; neither the Queen nor the Canadian Government had known a thing about it. There was no shadow of authority behind the whole foolhardy move. McDougall's performance would have been amusing had not its results caused disaster to the unifying trends at work in the colony at the time. But as it was, the people were divided, no one had authority to lead them—and they were threatened by an Indian war.

Riel alone possessed the necessary force to act. A politician's course would have been to reconvene the Convention of Twenty-four. But was there time for such a move? Reluctantly, he concluded that there was not. Until the Canadians were disarmed, until the Indians had been calmed and dispersed, democratic processes would not be possible. For the sake of life and limb the French métis, who alone were equipped to do so, must assume authority and move to preserve the peace. Only after that could the people be invited to chart out a future course of action.

When he had decided what he would do, Riel summoned Lépine to his side and told him to take twenty men and a cart into Winnipeg and seize all the fire-arms and ammunition he found there for sale. To make sure that people understood that this action was an official act of confiscation, not theft, he had better give receipts for all the arms he gathered in. Quite

PHOTO TAKEN AT REGINA IN 1885

BACK ROW: *Constable Black, NWMP; Rev. Louis Cochin, O.M.I.; Captain Deane, NWMP; Rev. Alexis André, O.M.I.; Beverley Robertson*

FRONT ROW: *Horse Child, youngest of Big Bear's sons; Big Bear, A. D. Stewart, Pound-maker*

Prison de Regina. 15th November 1885.

Bien chère Maman,

J'ai reçu votre lettre avec votre sainte bénédiction. Hier matin, le Bon Père André a attaché votre lettre au dessus de l'autel: et il a dit la sainte Messe pour moi, en action de grâce et en l'honneur de Marie Immaculée en me tenant pour ainsi dire lui même à l'ombre de votre bénédiction. Ce matin, le Bon Père a pris la lettre de votre bénédiction; il me l'a mise sur la tête, au moment de la messe et comme célébrant, il donne la bénédiction; et c'est ainsi qu'unissant sa bénédiction à la vôtre, il a répandu sur moi les grâces de la messe et l'abondance des biens spirituels et temporels que vous implorez en ma faveur, en faveur de ma chère épouse, de mes chers petits enfants, de mes frères et sœurs bien-aimés, de mes beaux frères et belles sœurs chéris, de mes neveux et de mes nièces

---

Letter from Riel to his Mother,
the day before his execution

sensibly, Lépine asked in whose name he should sign the receipts.

"You can sign them in the name of the Provisional Government of Rupert's Land," Riel replied quietly, "the new government that I am about to proclaim."

When Schmidt, who was also present, protested the legality of such an act, Riel assured him that it was perfectly legal. McDougall's pretentions had been unmasked; the Company had shown its inability to carry on. In fact it had abandoned the people to a "foreign" power! If someone did not take hold of affairs soon, there would be a civil war. Under the circumstances the people had a right to establish a provisional government, so long as they did so in the Queen's name. The whole question had nothing to do with allegiance—he had pointed that out before.

Riel was on sounder ground than he realized. On November 26th Sir John A. Macdonald had cabled London, saying "Canada cannot accept North-west until peaceful possession can be given." The following day he had written McDougall: "An assumption of government by you, of course, puts an end to that of the Hudson's Bay Company's authorities. . . . There would then be, if you were not admitted into the country, no legal government existing, and anarchy must follow. In such a case . . . it is quite open by the law of nations for the inhabitants to form a government *ex necessitate* for the protection of life and property." And he had warned McDougall to remain where he was at the border until further notice. But, even as his instructions travelled westward, the impetuous representative of Canada had illegally assumed the government of the Northwest Territories and had thus, unconsciously, set up the conditions his Prime Minister feared.

On the following day (December 8th), by means of a notice signed "John Bruce, President" and "Louis Riel, Secretary", the Provisional Government was proclaimed. Throughout the colony the event was accepted quietly, though without enthusiasm. In the village of Winnipeg the only sign of outright opposition was provided by the party of toughs who had barricaded themselves inside Schultz's house.

Of these there were almost fifty. In addition to the men there were three women, for two of the men had brought their wives with them when they came to "protect" the Canadian supplies, and Mrs. Schultz was already in the house. Dennis, at the Lower Fort, was enough of a soldier to know that they had barricaded themselves inside a trap. While engaged in his recruiting campaign, he had despatched a message ordering them to abandon the position and retire northward; but his order had been ignored.

For the following three days guards of the Provisional Government kept the Canadians under constant surveillance. In the métis leader's eyes it would make no sense to attack them when they were bottled up already in the building and could do no harm. But few of Riel's men shared this point of view. The season was almost mid-December now; the weather was bitterly cold; and it was they, not Riel, who were required to mount guard outside this enemy stronghold. Why not put an end to their discomfort by storming Schultz's house and locking the trouble-makers securely in jail? Their restlessness was infectious; it spread, as these things will do at such times, to the more than four hundred idle métis presently billeted in the fort.

Alexander Bannatyne was still playing the role of peacemaker. Now he carried a message from Riel to Schultz. The presence of armed Canadians so near Fort Garry was a menace to the Provisional Government. They must disband, surrender their arms and supplies and proceed immediately to their homes. The messenger was greeted with loud jeers. "Tell Riel to try and make us!" the Canadians shouted. In due course Bannatyne reported that his mission had failed.

Faced with the restlessness of his men and this insolent challenge, Louis felt that he must act. Having announced publicly that he would maintain the peace, for the sake of law and order it was up to him to do so. While the villagers of Winnipeg looked on, he took a hundred men and three cannon from Fort Garry and quickly surrounded the Canadians. Everyone must surrender his arms within fifteen minutes, he announced, or suffer the consequences. Looking down the mouths of the silent cannon, the defenders realized at last that their position was untenable. From an open window of his home Schultz called down that they would capitulate.

Within the appointed time the men and women surrendered. As soon as they had done so Lépine gathered up their fire-arms and ordered these removed to the fort.

"Take the prisoners with you," Riel told him. "Lodge them for the night in the clerks' quarters. I will interview them personally in the morning."

Schultz stepped forward. "My wife is sick, Riel," he said quietly. "And what about the other ladies? Where will you quarter them?"

Riel had not thought of that; but it was a good question. They must suffer no discomfort on his account. "Mrs. Schultz and the other ladies will be provided with accommodation in a Company official's house," he replied courteously. "We will see to that. You yourself may stay with them." Then he turned to the women and bowed. "I am sorry to inconvenience you, ladies. Will you be so good as to go along with Monsieur Lépine? Have no fear; I myself will follow shortly."

As the little band of prisoners started for Fort Garry between two files of guards, Louis turned to face the rest of his men. His red toque, his long blue *capote*, the pistol tucked neatly beneath the wide *assomption* belt at his waist, made him look every inch a warrior. "Now! We will go inside and confiscate the enemy's supplies," he announced with precision. "This will be done in an orderly fashion. Anyone caught looting will be severely dealt with."

In the warehouse behind Schultz's place they found the barrels of pickled pork that the captured men had been guarding so ostentatiously. Riel ordered them removed at once to Fort Garry. They found something else, too. During the fifteen minutes given them to surrender, the Canadian garrison had turned the place into a booby trap calculated to obliterate the entire métis force that had flushed them out. Hastily dousing their fires, they had stuffed gunpowder up every chimney, up every stove-pipe, in Schultz's house. If one of the métis had struck a light to stave off the gathering darkness, all of them would have been blown to kingdom-come!

As he comprehended the enormity of this, Riel almost lost control of himself. Schultz and all men like him should be swept from the surface of the earth! But his own common sense took over just in time. The immediate danger had been side-stepped; the Canadians were locked safely in jail now; nothing would be accomplished by taking punitive action against them. Quietly, he gave the order to retire.

After his experience with treachery at Schultz's house, Louis adopted a new, uncompromising attitude towards the members of the Canadian party at Red River. The colony needed peace, but these people had shown clearly that they were out for blood; they had demonstrated beyond a doubt that they would stop at nothing to gain their objectives. They had lifted the whole question of confederation with Canada out of the area of rights, and set it down again in the jungle of survival. From now on Riel would take no unnecessary risks with them or with anyone else. The sale of liquor would be forbidden in the taverns during the Christmas season; the streets of Winnipeg would be patrolled by métis guards; the prisoners in Fort Garry would remain locked up until they had sworn on the Bible not to bear arms against the Provisional Government again.

Confronted with Riel's proclamation, with the capture of Schultz and his men, with the new stiff attitude of the métis and the continued indifference of the majority of the English-speaking settlers, Colonel Dennis gave up hope for a victory with arms. On December 9th he wrote McDougall: "It is a matter of sincere regret to me . . . that, as a body, the English-speaking portion of the Red River Settlement . . . cannot be counted on in any measures of an aggressive character . . . to put down the French party. . . . [They] would do anything, many of them, rather than offend the French; now, as they say, they see from the 'list of rights' that the French ask nothing very unreasonable." On the same day, persuaded by Anglican Bishop Machray, he disbanded what remained of his "force". Disguised as a squaw, he slipped across the border to rejoin McDougall at Pembina.

The following day was Sunday, the one day of the week on which the Company's flag usually flew from its pole in Fort Garry. After Mass at St. Boniface Cathedral, Louis announced that there would be a celebration. Instead of the Company's flag, a new flag would be raised. This was an original creation; the métis council had conceived it. Against a white background, the lilies of France and the shamrocks of Ireland had been arranged around a buffalo of the plains. From now on it would stand for the authority of the new Government in the Colony of Assiniboia.

He invited those present to cross the river with him and take part in the official ceremony. As an inducement, he added that for this one occasion the ban against intoxicating liquor would be lifted, so that they all could drink a toast to their flag. After the banner had been raised and the spirits rationed out, Louis made a speech stressing the loyalty of his Government to the

Queen. Then he dismissed the crowd and went back to his governmental tasks.

Later that day he suppressed the *Nor'-Wester*.

On December 13th he received a message from McDougall requesting him to come to Pembina for a conference. This was the first evidence of good sense that the aspiring Lieutenant-Governor had shown since he arrived in the North-west; but the game was too far advanced for Louis to co-operate now. Recalling his experience with the forged proclamation, his brush with treacherous death at Schultz's house, he decided to ignore the invitation. Instead, he remained in Fort Garry. Faced with utter failure across the border and rising antagonism from the Americans in his midst—humiliated, frustrated, cheated of his glorious dreams—McDougall struck camp and began the long journey home.

Now the Provisional Government reigned supreme—and the Canadian Cabinet must acknowledge this fact, or face the risk that the Americans would do so first. Two months and a few days after stopping the surveyors at St. Vital, Riel had achieved success beyond his wildest dreams. Without shedding a drop of blood, he had arrested a drifting situation before it became too late; deftly, he had turned a flood of disastrous events to the advantage of his people. By his actions he had placed the inhabitants of the North-west in a position from which they could sooner or later force the Canadian Government to negotiate with them over the terms under which they would be willing to enter Confederation. He had demonstrated emphatically to officialdom in Ottawa and London that *all* the people of Red River were human beings, and not mere statistics to be moved from one column of paper to another at will.

But there was one thing remaining to be done before it would be prudent to negotiate with anyone: Riel's Government must be broadened at the earliest possible moment. So far it by no means represented the people as a whole, though it governed in their name. All success had been achieved by the actions of the French métis alone. In order to stop up this last chink in his armour through which a wedge might be driven by the politicians in Ottawa, Louis now turned again to the business of bringing the English settlers to his side.

In the days of *Le Comité National* they had almost joined forces with his French métis. If McDougall's proclamation had not been thrown into their midst to confuse them, their delegates might well have agreed to do so on December 1st. But could they be persuaded to work with him now? Could they be coaxed into taking up the question again at the point where they had abandoned it? After thinking about it at some length, Louis became confident that they could. The process might take time, but that did not matter, for there was no Canadian force to oppose him in the colony now.

It was a time for confidence, to be sure. The season of Advent was well advanced; Christmas was drawing near. Soon, Christ the Redeemer of all men would be celebrating His birthday among His brethren once again. Louis, who had studied at a church college and knew the liturgical year as well as he knew the secular calendar, was very conscious of the note of expectancy that echoes through all the Church's prayers at this time. During Advent mankind was appealing to God for a Saviour, for a personal model from which permanent inspiration could be drawn, for a leader who would break the chains of slavery that bound them to material cares. On Christmas Day mankind would receive one, in the person of the Divine Babe, and even the strife-filled prairie around Fort Garry would become a place of peace and warmth and wonder for a little while; for the coming of Jesus was both a historical fact and an ever recurring miracle in the hearts of all Christian men.

"Rejoice in the Lord always; again I say, rejoice." This had been the message of the opening prayers at Mass the previous Sunday. Taken from St. Paul's Epistle to the Philippians, the words had been written more than eighteen hundred years ago in a corner of the Mediterranean world that Louis would never see; but they possessed the ring of truth in them still. Men *did* have something to rejoice about; they could find peace and liberty and purpose in everything they did if they were willing to acknowledge and take into their hearts the Prince of Peace whose birthday they recalled at Christmas time. If ever there was a season in which they could draw together and hope for better things, it was *now*!

For a week, for ten days, a sort of restless peace existed in Assiniboia. On December 17th Riel went to Oak Point to arrange for the protection of Canadian Government supplies there. On the 22nd, after requesting Governor Mactavish in vain for a loan, he commandeered over £1,000 of Company money, giving a Provisional Government receipt in return. Two days later, he seized more goods from the Company's stores and used them to pay his soldiers' wages.

In spite of these activities, all remained quiet at Red River. Most people were willing by now to acknowledge that Riel and his men were performing a difficult task well, that they were keeping better order and administering the colony more efficiently than had Governor Mactavish during the past six months. Yet the English settlers still refused to close ranks with the French métis. They still insisted that before committing themselves they must know what the attitude of the Canadian Government would be to such an act. In spite of all that Louis said and did to reassure them, it seemed that their hesitancy would require yet more time to be overcome.

On Christmas Eve word came to Riel that a distinguished visitor from Canada had arrived at St. Norbert. His name was

Father Thibault. He was well known and well liked at Red River. At one time he had been Grand Vicar of the Diocese of St. Boniface and the parish priest of St. François-Xavier; before that he had been a missionary in the North. He came west now as a Canadian emissary.

Almost three weeks before, he had received his instructions from the Honourable Joseph Howe, Secretary of State in the Canadian Government. These instructions had begun, rather grandly: "Referring to your kind consent to undertake the delicate task of representing the views and policy of the Government to the people of the Hudson's Bay Territory. . ." And they had gone on to tell him to proceed to the West, and explain to the natives there the seriousness of what they were doing. He was to assure them that Canada had no intention of treating them any differently than British subjects had a right to expect to be treated. In short, he was to return to the region he knew and loved so well and carry out there a "mission of peace and conciliation".

When he heard this news Riel did not know what to do. It went against his instinctive judgement to allow more Canadians into the colony—the ones already there had caused enough trouble during the last little while. But the priest was well esteemed by all the métis and he did not dare to keep him out.

Years later Louis Schmidt described the episode as follows:

Christmas of 1869 was greeted at Red River in a military fashion, with a salvo of eighteen cannons from the walls of Fort Garry. Midnight Mass was celebrated as usual at St. Boniface Cathedral, but one noticed few men present. Next morning Father Thibault arrived from St. Norbert. Riel was suspicious of the old missionary's influence. Not daring to prevent him entering the Territory, he nevertheless confiscated his papers and held him a virtual prisoner in the Episcopal Palace.

The priest disclosed that he had not come alone; he had been accompanied as far as the border by Colonel Charles de Salaberry, a prominent French-Canadian layman, the son of the officer who had repelled American invaders at Chateauguay, in 1813. He had spent some time, years ago, in the West. The colonel had remained at Pembina and would not enter the colony until assured that he would be welcome. This caution resulted from the advice of McDougall, whom they had met on the trail and from whom they had received grave warnings about the ferocity of the métis.

On the next evening Riel and several members of *Le Comité National* gathered in Fort Garry's council chamber before a roaring fire to discuss the coming of the emissaries and other matters. Lépine was there, to report on the formation of *Le Conseil Militaire*, a sort of military committee which he headed and which included the captains of the different armed brigades. O'Donoghue was there, too, and Louis Schmidt; and Father Ritchot, the parish priest of St. Norbert, who had been appointed chaplain to the métis guards.

Suddenly, while they talked, the door opened and there before them was a squat fellow, swollen into the shape of a Christmas pudding by the amount of clothing that he wore. Obviously, the man had journeyed for some distance through the bitter night; his fiery nose, his glowing cheeks, his black moustache flecked with white and frozen quite stiff by the cold, amply revealed this fact. As he removed his toque they recognized him; he was a French-Canadian immigrant who lived and did odd jobs in St. Norbert.

"*Bon soir*, Théophile Biste," Louis said in a tone of voice that revealed both courtesy and curiosity. "What brings you out on such a night?"

"*Bon soir*, Louis", the *Canadien* replied. "I come from St. Norbert at the request of your sister Sara, in the convent there.

I have with me a gentleman whom she desires that you should see."

"And where is this gentleman, pray?" Louis asked.

Biste pointed over his shoulder with a stiff, square thumb. "In a cariole, out in the courtyard. Your sentries are keeping their eyes on him."

"Go and get him, by all means. Bring him in here to the fire."

Presently the stranger was ushered into the room. As he stood beside the door Riel advanced to meet him, hand extended, while the others watched. He was about the same height as the métis chief and solidly built, as was Riel. His flowing hair, his mutton-chop whiskers, were tinged with grey; the skin of his face lacked the tautness of youth; permanent pouches lurked beneath the intelligent eyes. Obviously, he was well into middle age; just as obviously, he was a man of some importance in the outside world.

"My name is Dr. Tupper," the stranger said in English, though his accent was not of the British Isles.

"And I am Louis Riel. Anyone whom my sister sends to me is welcome, Dr. Tupper. But tell me—what brings you here at such a season?"

Tupper smiled. It was a warm smile and genuine. "*You* do, Mr. Riel." Then: "Before I explain further, perhaps I might avail myself of your fire?"

Louis stepped aside. "Forgive me for not suggesting it. Please do."

Without a word the stranger moved to the fire-place; for a long, silent moment he stood gazing into the flames while its heat soaked through his clothing. Then he turned to warm his back. Facing the room, he cleared his throat and began: "As I was saying, I came to see *you*, Mr. Riel. Before leaving Pembina I was told that Father Ritchot would be able to arrange a meeting; that is why I stopped at St. Norbert to look him up."

The priest in the corner stirred. He was middle-aged, bearded; his eyes gleamed alertly behind steel-rimmed spectacles. "I am Father Ritchot," he said.

Tupper bowed. "While I was looking for you, Father, I went to the nunnery by mistake. There I met Sister Riel. She was kind enough to arrange that I should be brought on here."

Riel knew well who Dr. Tupper was. Already his initial charm had been replaced by wariness. "First a high-ranking priest, then a scion of the Quebec aristocracy, and now a famous Member of Parliament!" he quipped. "Why all this sudden attention, Dr. Tupper?"

"I cannot speak for your other visitors, Mr. Riel, but I come about a purely family matter, I can assure you. You see, I have a daughter Emma, about whom my wife and I are very anxious. Last July she married Captain D. R. Cameron, of the Royal Artillery. Later during the summer he was ordered west with Mr. McDougall. Naturally, my daughter accompanied him. At Pembina your men refused Mr. McDougall entrance to the North-west—there is no need to discuss the merits or demerits of that occurrence now—but, foolishly, Captain Cameron, with my daughter and all their baggage, tried to come through to Fort Garry. They were turned back at St. Norbert."

"It was my Adjutant-General, M. Lépine, who turned them back. He reported the matter to me," Riel stated quietly. Then he turned to Ambroise and explained in French what the visitor had said. Lépine nodded and smiled: he remembered this Captain Cameron, with his wagon-load of furniture and household goods, with his pretty little wife sitting up their beside him. He remembered, too, how the officer had coloured when told he could go no further; how he had pointed at the barrier erected across the trail and shouted with all the authority he could command: "Take down that blasted fence!" He remembered how pleased with himself he had felt when he confiscated the whole outfit and sent Captain and Mrs. Cameron back towards the border where they belonged.

"Though they suffered no harm to their persons," Tupper went on, "all their belongings were seized. They are young people, Mr. Riel, and by no means wealthy. I have come all the way from Halifax to ask you to give them back their chattels."

Louis did not reply immediately. Perhaps he was trying to decide whether this was another Canadian trap. Then, making up his mind that it was not, he said: "*Le Comité National des Métis* is an organization of civilized men, Dr. Tupper. Anything they confiscate they keep stored out of harm's way. If you will return with the man who brought you here and remain in his house overnight, I promise that all your daughter's things shall be delivered up to you."

"You are very kind," Tupper acknowledged. Then, quite casually: "While I am here, would it be possible for me to go into Winnipeg to see how the townspeople are faring? There is a great deal of interest in the East, you know, and—"

"No!" Riel cut firmly into the middle of the doctor's sentence. "We have been tricked by Canadians before, Dr. Tupper. We do not intend to be tricked again."

Tupper showed no emotion. He shrugged. "No matter—it was merely a thought. I dare say you have good reasons for taking such a stand. I withdraw my request, Mr. Riel, and accept your kind proposal."

VI

THE THIRD EMISSARY

ALL next day Dr. Tupper waited at St. Norbert for his daughter's possessions to be brought to him. At about four o'clock in the afternoon two sleds arrived at the door of Théophile Biste's home. Into them had been piled all the trunks and crates and boxes in which the Camerons' belongings were packed. Riel had been as good as his word; not an article had been stolen. Immediately afterwards Father Ritchot arrived and invited the doctor to spend the night at his rectory.

As they drove towards the little house beside the church, with the two sleds full of chattels behind them, Tupper opened the conversation. "I hope, Father Ritchot, you do not suppose I was foolish enough to come all the way out here for these trifles."

The priest shrugged, but made no comment.

"My object was to see you."

Again the priest shrugged. "*Oui?*"

Tupper turned to him—as one practical man to another. "You do not speak English very well, do you Father?"

"I have almost no English," the priest confessed.

"And I have almost no French. Certainly not enough to discuss with you the things I want to discuss. Because of this, I propose that we should go to the nunnery and get one of the young ladies I met last night to interpret for us."

Without a word Father Ritchot turned his cariole towards the

78

convent. Sister Macdougall would interpret for them. Her father had come to the colony from Sault Ste. Marie; her mother had been an Indian, converted to Christianity by the *Canadien* missionaries; she herself was fluent in both English and French. A few minutes later Dr. Tupper and the priest were discussing the situation at Red River.

Dr. Tupper was blunt; he told the priest that it was impossible for the "rebels" to succeed in holding the country against Canada, but that if they avoided shedding any blood they would obtain everything they could desire by negotiation. He added that the leaders who accomplished this result would be entitled to great consideration.

Father Ritchot was equally blunt. Canada could never conquer the métis, he said. In a country as large as this, they could retire indefinitely and sustain themselves by hunting. As a last resort they could join the United States.

Tupper shook his head. "I do not believe the United States would welcome them, for it would mean hostilities with England. As you know, they have just recently finished a terrible civil war. Peace is on shaky foundations still. Washington would not risk a move that might give the South excuses to break away from their Union again."

For almost two hours they continued their discussion. Father Ritchot told Tupper exactly what were the grievances and the aspirations of the métis; Tupper told the priest what he hoped Confederation would mean, ultimately, to the North-west. And he disclosed to him one cardinal fact that no one outside the Canadian Cabinet knew at this time—the fact that, though the Hudson's Bay Company had attempted to turn their territory over to the Canadian Government on December 1st, as arranged, the Government had refused to accept it until law and order was restored within the area.

Afterwards, the men retired to Father Ritchot's rectory, where they ate and slept that night. In the morning, Dr. Tupper departed for Pembina. This was the first candid discussion that had been held between first-class exponents of the métis and the Canadian causes. Had it taken place six months earlier, in all probability the trouble at Red River would never have occurred.

As a result of what Tupper had said, Father Ritchot persuaded Riel to allow Vicar-General Thibault his full freedom in the colony and to send to Pembina for the other emissary, Colonel de Salaberry. Had it not been for the arrival of a *third* official from Ottawa at this point, all might have gone well. But from the moment this third emissary set foot in the Colony of Assiniboia, the situation began to deteriorate again.

Donald A. Smith, the bearded, cold-eyed district manager at Montreal of the Hudson's Bay Company, was the third emissary sent to Riel by the Canadian Government. Born at Forres, Morayshire, Scotland, in 1820, he had come to North America in 1838 and signed on with the Company at £20 a year. His uncle, Jack Stuart, a North West Company partner, had accompanied Simon Fraser when he explored to the mouth of the river now bearing his name; and Stuart had subsequently become a chief factor in the reorganized Hudson's Bay Company.

After serving for three years as an apprentice clerk at Lachine, Smith had been sent to Tadoussac, on the lower St. Lawrence. In 1848, he had been moved to the coast of Labrador, where he spent the next twenty years. At this bleak post he had educated himself by reading deeply in the arts, the sciences, and philosophy. There, also, he had married a charming métisse named Isabella Hardisty. She was the daughter of his superior officer, Chief Trader Hardisty. Previous to this union she had been given, according to the custom of the country, to a fur trader named Grant; but the "marriage" had not been a success.

In 1853, Smith had succeeded his father-in-law to the command of the district. Then, in 1864, he had returned to Britain on leave. While there he had made a point of meeting the Governor and Committee of the Company. One of the results of this contact was his promotion, in June of 1869, to his present post. To sum up, Smith knew what life on the fringes of civilization was all about.

During his service he had managed to find out what life in the cities was all about, too. Through his cousin, George Stephen, he had been introduced to all the Bank of Montreal people and to important men in the shipping world; over a period of years he had been able to establish himself, in his own right, in the financial circles of Montreal. This he had done by persuading the men under his jurisdiction that he personally, rather than the Company's "Officers' and Servants' Account," should act as their banker. With their savings, which he invested in industrial stocks and mortgages, he slowly came to represent in his own right a sizeable block of stock in the Bank of Montreal. As the bank prospered, the value of this holding increased considerably. By 1869 he was well on the way to becoming a very rich man.

In a few more years Smith would be recognized as a national figure, but at this time he was still relatively unknown. On November 24th he had forwarded to the Honourable Joseph Howe, Secretary of State at Ottawa, a copy of the report sent east by Mactavish in October, after Riel's brush with the surveyors. In his covering letter he had concluded: "I beg . . . on behalf of the Company, to offer the assurance that their Governor, Factors, and Officers generally will use their influence and best efforts to restore and maintain order throughout the Territories." Subsequently, after having accepted an invitation to the capital, he had suggested to the Prime Minister that he be sent out as Acting Lieutenant-Governor, with troops, to secure the area for the new Dominion.

Sir John Macdonald was far too wise a politician to act on this proposal. He had made up his mind already not to send a new governor to the Territory for the time being. Imperial troops he might despatch later, when summer came, but only to impress the Americans with Britain's continuing interest in the Dominion—*not* to fight Riel. But, said Macdonald, Father Thibault and Colonel de Salaberry had left for Red River already, to find out what must be done to appease the natives there. If Smith thought it worth while to follow them, he could be provided with credentials, too.

Smith thought it worth while. What Sir John did not know, what no one knew at the time, was that Smith, in addition to being a district manager of the Hudson's Bay Company, was well on the way to becoming its biggest shareholder. In 1863 the Company had been purchased and reorganized by a group of speculators in London. By means of a dubious promotional campaign these speculators had boosted the price of its shares to unsound heights; then they had unloaded on innocent buyers most of their holdings. In the process they had made great profits. With the announcement of the terms under which the Company's charter would be relinquished, the price of the stock had begun to fall again; recent news from Red River had been grave enough to turn this decline into a rout.

What the new shareholders failed to realize was that they would be getting far more than £300,000 from the deal. Under the terms of the transfer the Company would retain one-twentieth of the arable land in the West. Over the long term this land could not fail to become immensely valuable. Though it could be argued that, as a paid executive, he should have spoken out, nowhere is there any evidence that Smith advised his shareholders to retain their stock. In fact, there is a very strong suspicion that it was at about this time that he began buying Company stock for his own account, at the abnormally low prices then prevailing. All that was necessary to experience a capital gain was to ensure that the original deal with Canada became a fact.

On December 10th, Joseph Howe sent the Government's letter of instruction to Smith at Montreal:

I have the honour to inform you that His Excellency the Governor General has been pleased to appoint you Special Commissioner to enquire into and report upon the causes and extent of the armed obstruction offered at Red River. . . . Also, . . . the causes of discontent. . . . Also, to explain . . . the principles on which the Government of Canada intends to govern the country. . . . And also to take such steps, in concert with Mr. McDougall and Governor Mactavish, as may seem most proper for effecting the peaceful transfer of the country and government from the Hudson's Bay authorities to the Government of the Dominion.

Though the formal commission confirming these instructions was not signed until another week had passed—and was not forwarded to him until January 25, 1870—Donald A. Smith set out immediately for Fort Garry.

In truth, the situation required urgent attention, at least from Canada's point of view. More than a month had slipped by since Sir John had cabled London refusing to accept the Territory until peaceful possession could be guaranteed. More than three weeks had passed since the Company's directors had insisted that their responsibility had come to an end. At any moment now the outside world might begin to ask who was, in fact, responsible for the "British" North-west. Canada must be ready to reply that *she* was—or run the risk of losing the lot. And if she were to lose her stake in the West, the dream of an empire stretching from sea to sea would fade under the torrid glare of American "manifest destiny"; and the central provinces, along with the Maritimes, would wither away and die.

When considered alongside such high matters of policy, the aspirations of a few thousand people on the banks of the Red River of the North seemed very unimportant indeed.

When this third emissary appeared at Fort Garry, he took care not to emphasize the fact that he had been commissioned by the Canadian Government; because he was a Company official, it seemed quite natural for him to take up residence in the Fort. After assuring Riel that he would do nothing to upset his Provisional Government, "legal or illegal, as it might be", he was granted freedom to communicate with people in the settlement. Whereupon he began systematically to undermine the *status quo* at Red River.

A few of the prisoners captured at Schultz's house were harmless English-speaking colonists who had been attracted by the Canadians' recruiting drive. Their families and friends, quite naturally, were anxious to see them freed; yet because, so far, the hotheads among them had succeeded in keeping any of the prisoners from taking Riel's oath, they all remained in jail. Right away Smith saw where he could turn their stubbornness to his own advantage. Using the anxieties of their families as a lever, he talked among the English-speaking people against Riel. At the same time, hinting that he had full powers from the Canadian Government to straighten matters out, he placed more than £500 in bribes in the hands of a few uncommitted métis. As a result of all this activity, he managed to rekindle suspicion against the French among the members of the lower colony and to reopen temporarily the old split within the métis ranks. In a few days the situation became once again extremely fluid.

On January 8th Riel announced that John Bruce had resigned as President, "due to ill health", and that he himself had succeeded him. On the following day the prisoners in Fort Garry attempted to escape. All but two were immediately recaptured. One of the pair who remained at large was a young lad named Thomas Scott. By this time several of Riel's councillors had seceded, and Louis had begun to realize what the new Commissioner was up to. Confronting him, he made Smith admit that he was, in fact, an emissary of the Canadian Government, that he had come to bargain with the colonists. Riel then asked to see his credentials. Smith said he had left them at Pembina for safekeeping. Thereupon, Riel ordered that they be brought to him so that the powers set forth in them might be revealed.

When Smith sent Richard Hardisty, his brother-in-law, to fetch them, Riel attempted to intercept him at St. Norbert; for he desired to see for himself whether or not the claims made by Smith were true. In this he was unsuccessful, and word spread through the colony that Smith had openly defied Riel.

The situation could be allowed to drift no further. Whether Smith liked it or not, Riel commanded the only effective power in the colony. If he was undermined, who or what would take his place? For the sake of peace, a meeting of all the people must be called at which the terms of Smith's commission might be openly revealed. Then the people could decide for themselves what the next step should be.

On January 19, 1870, crowds gathered from far and near at Fort Garry. Because there was no building at Red River large enough to hold them all, they gathered on the snow in the flat southern courtyard inside Fort Garry's walls. The métis, the Scots, the English, the Canadians, assembled to hear Smith speak. Bundled to the ears against the bitter cold, flailing their mitted hands across their chests, dancing on one foot and then the other to keep their toes from freezing, they waited for the meeting to get under way.

Thomas Bunn, an English métis, was elected chairman. Judge Black, of the Company's court, was elected secretary. At the suggestion of Colonel de Salaberry, Riel himself was chosen to come up on the platform and interpret proceedings to the métis.

Standing there in the brilliant sunlight by the store, the wily Scot beside him and his own guards at his left, Louis was confident that all would go well. This sea of expectant faces tilted upwards like tame fish at feeding time, these hundreds of people before him, were neighbours; he knew most of them as friends. Smith could do him no damage now that he had been forced to state his case publicly. But the man would bear watching, all the same.

"Gentlemen," Donald A. began in a voice as cold and clear as the January air he breathed, "I will read to you first the terms of the commission issued to me by the Honourable Joseph Howe, Secretary of State for Her Majesty's Government in the Dominion of Canada. Though it is a long document, I think it important that I do so; for it establishes definitely the reasons why I am here." Dramatically, he held up the paper for all to see. Then, while Riel translated his words into French, Smith lowered his head as if studying his text.

The Canadian emissary began by reading his letter of instruction from Howe. He followed this with a personal letter to him from the Governor-General, Sir John Young. Then he asked Father Thibault to let him read from despatches that he (the priest) had brought west, from the Government of Canada to Governor Mactavish and Bishop Machray, and explained as his reason for desiring to do so that they revealed quite clearly the Queen's attitude towards her Red River subjects. Riel and O'Donoghue had confiscated these despatches. They protested now that the people had assembled to consider the contents of Smith's commission only. But they were shouted down and the question of whether or not the request should be granted was put to a vote. Whereupon the meeting decided unanimously that the letters in question should be produced.

While these documents were being found, Smith read a copy of a telegram, dated November 26th, from the British Colonial Office to the Governor-General. In it, both the people of Red River and the Canadian Government were held to be blameworthy for the "troubles" now taking place. Among other things, it said: "The Queen does not distrust Her subjects' loyalty in those settlements", and attributed their opposition to "misrepresentation or misunderstanding". Further: "If they have any wish to express or complaints to make, they will address themselves to the Governor of the Dominion of Canada." It seemed clear from these words that the forwarding of a "Bill of Rights" would be looked upon with favour from on high.

So far, all had progressed satisfactorily; everyone had shown marked respect for constitutional procedure. But the meeting had been going on for five hours and it was growing dark. When someone proposed that they adjourn until noon tomorrow, the suggestion was accepted by the assembled throng.

Next day, when the meeting had reassembled, Smith read more letters to the people. He ended by disclosing the terms under which McDougall had been sent west in the fall. (The man had been authorized to engage in preliminary arrangements only, with Mactavish, for the organization of the government of the Territories.)

Now was the time for Riel to assume the ascendancy again. When he had finished translating this last document, he caught the chairman's eye. "This is all very interesting, very informative, Mr. Bunn," he said. "But I fail to see what can be accomplished by continuing with it. And besides, it is very cold out here. From all we have heard it appears perfectly obvious that the Government of Canada will be prepared to grant us a liberal constitution as soon as they know our wants and requirements. Would it not be sensible, Mr. Chairman, to refer the whole matter to a convention of the people for consideration?"

Everyone was ready to go home now. They all cheered when the suggestion was put to them. "This convention might be composed of forty members," A. G. B. Bannatyne shouted from his place in the forefront of the throng; "perhaps twenty men elected from the English-speaking parishes and twenty from the French. If they were empowered to state the case of Red River to Mr. Smith, he could then decide what should be done."

The people cheered again, and presently the matter was carried by a vote. There followed a flurry of emotional speeches about the solidarity and friendship of the little colony. Then everyone set off for home.

The mass meeting outside Fort Garry had occupied the 19th and 20th of January. On the 25th the Convention of Forty would assemble and get down to business. Meanwhile, on the night of the 23rd, in a blinding blizzard, John Schultz escaped from jail by lowering himself from a window on a rope made out of strips he had cut from a buffalo hide. Immediately he made his way to Kildonan, then north to St. Peters, spreading among the people fabricated tales of métis atrocities. Almost concurrently, rumours began to circulate that the Canadians at Portage-la-Prairie were about to attack Fort Garry. The remaining prisoners in the Fort began an organized campaign of misbehaviour; the métis guards became tense.

But the fear of attack proved in a few days to be groundless. From January 25th to February 10th the Convention sat at Fort Garry. When Riel suggested that Smith be asked to pass judgment, in a general way, on the list of rights already drawn up by the convention of last November, one of the delegates countered that a new list should be composed. By resolution of the delegates, Thomas Bunn, James Ross, Dr. Bird, Louis

Riel, Louis Schmidt, and Charles Nolin were assigned the task. Two days later this committee reported back with their new list of rights. After considering the document article by article, the convention then invited Smith to appear before them. When asked if he could guarantee these rights, the Scotsman explained that, no matter what he himself thought of them, it was Parliament that must make the final decision. Then he ended his remarks by inviting them to send an informal delegation to Ottawa to confer with the Government there.

During most of this time all went smoothly, but when Riel proposed that the Territory join Canada as a province, Smith and many of the delegates opposed him, on the ground that full provincial status involved too much expense and responsibility. Seeking some way to protect the inhabitants' voting power from an influx of land-grabbing immigrants, Riel then proposed that only the land within a radius of approximately sixty miles from Fort Garry should be subject to local control. One of the English-speaking delegates countered that "local control" really meant métis control, for the métis were the most numerous faction in that area.

Instantly, Louis was on his feet. "I hold the position of President," he announced haughtily. "I do so without pretensions. Whenever the interests of the country call for me to resign, if I see that the voice of the people is there, I will obey it."

But the damage had been done. When the matter was put to a vote the majority of the delegates cast their ballots against the idea of demanding provincial status.

Immediately, Riel was on his feet again, this time to introduce in a spirit of revenge a motion aimed directly at the Company. "I propose," he began stubbornly, "that all bargains with the Hudson's Bay Company, for the transfer of this country, shall be carried on only with the people of this country."

Perhaps he had meant merely to make it clear in Smith's

presence that the future of the people at Red River was more important than any monetary claim the Company might advance; but if this was so he had gone too far in his manner of expression. His words inferred that the British Government had no right to decide on what should be done with land over which it held sovereign powers. Again his wishes were defeated, by a vote of twenty-two to seventeen.

Riel was a high-strung, hot-blooded person. For several months now he had been subjected to much self-imposed pressure; his powers of restraint had become dangerously overtaxed. These two small reverses seemed proof to him of the Company's subtle influence, in the form of Donald A. Smith, at work among his people—influence that placed opportunity for monetary gain ahead of the general welfare. He could contain himself no longer.

"The devil take it!" he cried. "We *must* win. The vote may go as it likes, but the measure which has now been defeated must be carried." And he began bitterly to castigate, first, several of his métis followers who had cast ballots against him, then Governor Mactavish of the Company, confined by illness to his bed. Without pausing he switched his verbal attack to bear on Dr. Cowan, whom he accused of disloyalty towards the Provisional Government—and on Bannatyne, whom he accused of entering the fort without a pass! For a moment it was almost as if a madman shouted in that room; then the anger spent itself and Louis, humbly apologetic, sat down. After an instant of embarrassed silence, the convention returned to a consideration of business.

By the next day the convention's job was done. The list of rights they approved was moderate enough. It reflected the desire of the people for continued possession of what was theirs, for protection against greedy new-comers, for exemption from heavy taxation, and for an adequate political status within the framework of Canada.

These men must have forgiven Riel his outburst. Now, when he proposed his last step—the formation of a new, broad-based provisional government that could send delegates to Ottawa with all the authority of the people behind them—they calmly referred the matter to a committee for study. And when this committe brought in a favourable report—and Governor Mactavish sent word from his sick-bed to "form a government, for God's sake"—the motion was carried unanimously, with three delegates abstaining.

On February 9th a truly representative government was finally achieved. The following slate of officers was elected:

Louis Riel	President
T. Bunn	Secretary of State
Louis Schmidt	Assistant Secretary of State
W. O'Donoghue	Treasurer
A. Lépine	Adjutant-General
A. Bannatyne	Postmaster
James Ross	Judge
H. McKenney	Sheriff
Dr. Bird	Coroner
J. Sutherland	Customs
R. Goulet	Customs

In addition, an advisory board composed of twenty-four members was to be elected by the people to assist the Government.

On the following day, after a night of fireworks and rejoicing at the settlement, the new Government selected, and the convention as a whole approved, three delegates to negotiate with Ottawa. These were Father N. J. Ritchot, Pastor of St. Norbert; Judge John Black of the Hudson's Bay Company's court; and Alfred H. Scott, a Winnipeg store clerk who, though born in England, had until recently resided in the United States.

Everyone at Red River was overjoyed. It seemed that the difficulties of the past were finished with, that nothing now stood in the way of a peaceful settlement of the problems outstanding with Canada. After announcing to the convention that Dr. Schultz's property must be confiscated and the doctor exiled under pain of death, as an example of the Government's power, Riel released sixteen of the prisoners. (These men had at last signed an oath that they would not take up arms again; as soon as others did the same they, too, would be granted their freedom.) Then, after setting up machinery for the election of the advisory board, the convention adjourned.

VII

ANARCHY OR
COURT MARTIAL

DURING all this time Dr. Schultz had been stirring up opposition to Riel in the lower part of the settlement. Thomas Scott, who had escaped earlier with Charles Mair, had been doing the same at Portage-la-Prairie. Scott had been captured on the night of December 6th, while trying to break into the fort. He had come west from Ontario during the previous year and had found employment on the construction of the Dawson Road. He was a rough sort, one of those who considered that they could do whatever they pleased in this "wild" land. Among other things, he had instigated a strike against his employer and led it in such a violent manner that he had ended up in the Company's jail charged with assault. Even Donald A. Smith felt compelled, in his official report to the Canadian Government, to describe him as "a rash, thoughtless man whom none cared to have anything to do with".

Now rumours began to reach Louis again that he could expect an attack. This time, as a precautionary measure, he took up permanent residence in the fort and recalled to arms the majority of his métis guards. Soon there were six hundred restless men inside Fort Garry waiting for whatever trouble might arise.

C. A. Boulton, the ex-surveyor, now a major, lived at Portage-la-Prairie. He was by nature a man of moderation; by now he understood the significance of all that had taken place. When he discovered that Scott planned to join Schultz and march

93

against Riel, he tried to dissuade him. What troubles there had been were quieting down nicely now. Why try to stir them up again? But Scott and his followers were angry, unimaginative men. They were determined to release the prisoners and have Riel's scalp as well. Foreseeing disaster to his friends under Scott's leadership, Boulton reasoned that, if he went with them, he might keep them from courting it. With a heavy heart he agreed to join the volunteers.

On February 12th he and some sixty men left Portage and marched towards Fort Garry. The weather was bitterly cold. On the way they met their delegate to the convention, Kenneth McKenzie, who was returning home. This man told them that all was peaceful now and the prisoners were being released. Once again Boulton advised Scott and the others to abandon the expedition. Once again he was overruled. On the 15th the party arrived at the settlement. Passing under the eyes of the métis guards at Fort Garry, they proceeded into the village of Winnipeg. After looking for Riel, whom they had hoped to surprise at his cousin's home, they moved on to Kildonan, where they found Schultz waiting for them as planned, with several hundred men and a small cannon. The combined force billeted itself in a semi-military fashion in the local school-house and in the Presbyterian Church nearby.

Many of the local settlers were appalled by the vision of armed conflict they saw materializing before them. From the outset these people had refused to bear arms against their métis neighbours. Now, with conditions so vastly improved, it seemed to them utter folly for the Canadians to adopt belligerent airs again. Accordingly, as evening fell, a great many settlers, led by their clergy, came among the encamped war party to plead with its members to disperse. But the Canadians remained adamant. They had assembled to rescue their fellow-countrymen, they argued; they would accomplish what they had set out to do. It mattered not to them that Riel's Government was truly representative at last; and when someone reminded them that sixteen of the prisoners had already been freed, they refused to discuss the point or concede that it altered in any way the merits of their stand.

In Fort Garry, though his restless guards were itching for a battle, Riel watched all this and waited. Paramout in his mind was the old dread that, if the local population began fighting among themselves, almost certainly the Indians would rise and massacre them all. It was for this reason that he had held his men within the fort when the Portage party passed by so provocatively earlier in the day. But his métis guards were not temperamentally suited to inaction; if this deadlock continued, it would become increasingly difficult to hold them in check. Yesterday it had seemed to Louis that his dreams were coming true. Now it appeared that all the gains he had made might blow up in his face. Because of the foolishness of a handful of Canadians, they were drifting towards civil war again. What could he do to reverse the trend?

As he pondered these problems, a guard came to him and announced that a Miss Victoria McVicar had presented herself at the gate and wished to see him. He thought for a moment, then nodded. "*Ah, oui*! She is the pretty cousin from Fort William who is staying with the Bernard Rosses. Show her in, by all means." Presently she entered and stood before him. She was small and looked intelligent and sensitive. The métis guard hovered by the door, eyeing her suspiciously; it was not like his chief to receive women in his rooms—he was as celibate as a priest, this one. Reading the man's thoughts, Louis bade him curtly to leave and close the door behind him.

Turning to face his visitor, he bowed deeply. "You show commendable courage, Madamoiselle, coming here alone like this. I am indeed honoured by your presence."

She acknowledged his courtesy, then came quickly to the point. "I am here to ask you to release the remaining prisoners," she said gravely.

"There is nothing I would rather do, believe me, than to grant your request. But it is impossible, I am afraid."

"Nothing is impossible, Mr. Riel."

"Perhaps not—at least in theory," he agreed with a smile. "But how can I release the prisoners? They themselves admit they would go straight away to swell the ranks of my enemies. Unless someone can persuade them to be sensible, they must remain where they are."

"I have talked to Major Boulton, Mr. Riel. He and his men only want the prisoners released. If you do as I ask there will be no attack from them."

Louis moved to the window behind him, stood there for a moment gazing down at the dirty courtyard below. "I have no desire to keep these men in custody," he said slowly. "But—even if what you tell me is true, even if Boulton can be trusted—how can I release them when I *know* they will bear arms against me? It is too much to ask. My men would never forgive me." He turned to her. "I have already released sixteen men. The others I would have freed, too, if they had sworn to behave themselves. But they refuse to swear, so they must remain where they are."

Miss McVicar gave him the suggestion of a curtsy. "I will tell Major Boulton what you have told me." Then, without further comment, she took her leave. After ordering the guard in the passageway to escort her to the gate, Louis returned to his desk, sat down, and addressed himself to the pile of paper work that awaited his attention there. He dismissed the charming visitor from his mind.

Within an hour Victoria McVicar was back. She had met Mr. Bannatyne in the village of Winnipeg; she had told him of her visit to Riel. His canny merchant's mind had immediately perceived that her interview opened up new possibilities for the solution of the present difficulties. Together, they had started once again for Fort Garry.

Now, with the trader, she stood before the President. As she stated that her companion had some thoughts to present on the subject of the prisoners, she seemed shyer, more hesitant, than before. Then, gracefully, she retired to a corner of the room.

"This young lady has told me of your attitude towards the prisoners, Mr. Riel," the trader began. "I must say it strikes me as a reasonable one. If they would co-operate, you would release them. Is that what you told her an hour ago?"

"That is what I told her," the métis chief agreed cautiously.

"And if you released them, the Canadians would have no further excuse to cause trouble," Bannatyne mused. Then he cleared his throat, scratched his chin with one hand. "I have often observed," he went on dryly, "that when a group such as this are determined on an agreed course of action it is almost impossible to change their minds—so long as they remain a group. But sometimes wonders can be worked by talking to each man by himself."

"So?" Louis asked quietly. He respected this man, but he knew he must be wary of his agile mind.

"So, with your permission, I propose to interview each prisoner singly. They all know me as a reasonable man. I may be able to persuade them, one by one, to sign the oath they refuse to sign as a group. It's worth a try, is it not?"

Riel agreed that it was. In no time at all a room had been set aside for Bannatyne in which he began to interview the prisoners one by one. What he said to each is not known; but before dawn he had persuaded every one of them that resistance to Riel must cease, that for the sake of the common good each must sign the oath demanded of him. For his part, Louis kept his word. As soon as a man had signed the oath he was released.

97

All during the night former prisoners departed, free men, through the gates of the fort. By the time Miss McVicar and Bannatyne had finished their work, it seemed that all cause for friction in the settlement had been removed at last.

But the métis soldiers watched all this with suspicion, for they could not believe that these men, who had proved to be such troublesome prisoners, would sincerely honour their pledge. To them it appeared as if, for the sake of a pretty woman's smile, their chief had placed their cause in jeopardy again. They did not express these thoughts to Riel, but they talked among themselves as restless soldiers are wont to do.

All through the morning of the 16th Louis waited in vain for word that the Canadian war party had dispersed—as soon as they did, he would send home all but the hard core of his métis guards—yet no word reached him from Kildonan. Tension began to mount within the fort. Rumours began to circulate among the guards that the Canadians planned to desecrate their churches, and violate their wives and daughters. No one knew where the rumours came from; no one bothered to find out if they were true. They were on every man's tongue, and in the mind of every métis rose resentment against their leader for releasing the prisoners because a woman had asked him to.

Into this supercharged atmosphere Thomas Norquay arrived with an insolent letter from the rebels demanding that the fort be surrendered, the prisoners released, and an amnesty declared for Dr. Schultz. The letter ended with a deliberate lie, for it declared that several of the English-speaking parishes refused to recognize the authority of Riel. Reading it, Louis flew into a rage, threatened to clap Norquay in jail. Tension among the guards mounted higher—so high, in fact, that it seemed prudent to give them some sort of duty to perform. With a great show of importance, Louis ordered them to go out and seize arms and ammunition that he knew still lay in Bannatyne's store. At the same time he gave this note to Norquay, to be delivered to the Canadians gathered at Kildonan:

Fellow Countrymen:
Mr. Norquay came this morning with a message and even he has been delayed. He will reach you in time enough to tell you that for my part I understand that war, horrible civil war, is the destruction of this country. And Schultz will laugh at us all if after all he escapes. We are ready to meet any party. But peace, our British rights, we want before all. Gentlemen, the prisoners are out; all, they have sworn to keep peace. We have taken the responsibility of our past acts. Mr. William Mactavish has asked you for the sake of God to form and complete the Provisional Government. Your representatives have joined us on that ground. Who will now come and destroy the Red River Settlement?

I am your humble, poor, fair and
confident public servant,

Riel

Early on the morning of the 17th John Sutherland, the Collector of Customs in the Provisional Government, arrived at the Fort. He had not heard of the events of the previous day, and with obvious sincerity, began to plead with Louis to release the prisoners so that feeling in the settlement might be quieted. When he was informed that they had in fact been free men for the past twenty-four hours, he was overjoyed. Mounting his horse, he rode home, on the east side of the Red River, to proclaim the news. New hope caught fire in Riel's mind. Perhaps his actions would be justified after all, and there would be no necessity to fight. When he told his followers this, it became obvious that they did not share his opinion. But, as they knew Mr. Sutherland and trusted him, they agreed to adopt an attitude of wait and see.

During all this time the Canadian party had remained billeted in Kildonan's church and school. Schultz still urged them to attack Fort Garry and overthrow Riel; Bishop Machray and other clergymen still pleaded earnestly that they go home. There were five hundred armed métis in the Fort, the Bishop told them. How could sane men ever hope to carry the place?

In the church this party held captive a young métis half-wit named Parisien, whom they had taken as a spy the previous day while engaged in a reconnaissance into the village of Winnipeg. Now it happened that Mr. Sutherland's house lay directly across the river from the Canadians' camp. At just about the time that Sutherland arrived home, this poor half-wit managed to escape. Seizing a gun, he bolted across the river's ice with the obvious intention of hiding in some woods on the other side. Spotting him, the Canadians gave chase.

Sutherland had not observed this commotion. At his own back door, he dismounted and told his son Hugh to cross the river's ice with his news about the prisoners. Taking the reins, Hugh climbed into the saddle to do his father's bidding. He had proceeded perhaps half-way across the river before he became aware of the disturbance towards which he was riding.

Parisien, in an agony of fear, had lost what little wit he normally possessed. When he saw Sutherland in front of him he mistook him for one of his pursuers, raised his gun and fired. The young bearer of good news fell, mortally wounded with a bullet in his head. Parisien and his pursuers swept past and a moment later Parisien, hit by a hatchet, slumped to his knees. The angry pack closed in around him, beat him mercilessly, there on the ice. It was as if all the fury these bully-boys felt against everyone at Red River must be released against this half-wit métis youth. Then Major Boulton and Dr. Black, the Presbyterian minister, caught up with them and brought them to their senses. Ashamed of themselves, bewildered by their own bestiality, they carried the dying boys into the church. **Dr.** Schultz, remembering for once to be a physician and not a rabble-rouser, did what he could for them; but to no avail. In a little while young Sutherland died; after lingering for two pain-racked weeks, Parisien followed him.

Everyone in Kildonan was shocked by what had taken place. It was not difficult now for Boulton, armed with the message that Riel had sent him earlier, to persuade the Canadians to disperse. His silent, penitent men were transformed by the tragedy they had caused. Many of them had wives and children whom they loved; all but the most fanatical among them could appreciate the enormity of what they had done. The prisoners had been free for twenty-four hours. What possible justification could there be for this sudden shedding of blood? For the first time they had glimpsed the utter finality of death and, glimpsing it, had begun to appreciate that political action was the only honourable instrument for them to use. No longer were they irresponsible brawlers, as they had been when they advanced from Portage-la-Prairie to do battle with Riel. Like a class of chastened schoolboys they gathered together at Boulton's call and prepared for the shamed homeward trek.

But the Canadians' change of heart had come too late. Blood had flowed at Red River at last; and because of it the whole complexion of the trouble had grown dark indeed.

When he heard the news of Sutherland's death, Riel acted at once. As President of the Provisional Government, two possible decisions were open to him: he could ignore the whole series of events that had culminated in this tragedy, or he could take note of them and attempt to apprehend those who were responsible. He chose the latter course. Had he not done so, it is probable that his métis guards would have taken the law into their own hands.

Sweeping out from Fort Garry at the head of their mounted soldiers, Lépine and O'Donoghue surrounded the Portage contingent as it trudged along on its journey home. Because Boulton had the good sense to order his men to throw their weapons into the snow, the manoeuvre was completed without loss of life. Quickly the Canadians were placed under lock and key in the Company's jail. (Some of the men recently released under oath were among them.) Then, without delay, a court martial was convened and four of the Canadians were sentenced to death for taking up arms against the Government and for causing the death of a resident.

A shiver of apprehension travelled from one end of the colony to the other with this news. Mr. and Mrs. Sutherland, parents of one of the dead boys, journeyed to Fort Garry and begged Riel as President to show clemency towards the condemned men. After hearing their plea, he pardoned three. Later they returned with Miss McVicar and Mrs. John Black (their married daughter, the minister's wife) and tried to prevail upon him to pardon the fourth man, too.

Major Boulton was this fourth man. As Riel saw it, he had led the Portage party and was responsible, therefore, for the deaths that had occurred. At first he was adamant in his refusal to consider their request. But when he had cooled down they were able to prove to him that Boulton had, in fact, used all his resources to keep the Canadians in line; whereupon he agreed that the man should not be shot for having failed. Without making a public announcement of this decision, he then promised that the major's life would be spared.

Soon after the delegation had departed, Donald A. Smith came to see Riel—also to beg for Boulton's life. Instead of telling him that the man had already been pardoned, Louis seized the opportunity to drive home a bargain with the hard-headed Scot. In this way he showed political acumen of a calibre of which even Sir John A. Macdonald might well have been proud.

It will be recalled that the Provisional Government had agreed, though Riel had protested about it, to the terms of the transfer that the Hudson's Bay Company desired. Now, if all remained tranquil, Smith's company could expect to receive £300,000 and a grant of one-twentieth of the arable land in the North-west; but if trouble blew up again at Red River, the Canadian Government might continue to refuse to take over the territory. In this case the Americans might still be able to arrange things so that they were "invited" in—as they had done in California and New Mexico—and then Smith might get nothing for his pains. Thus, Riel reasoned, Donald Smith must be as interested in preserving the peace as was he. And if this were so, then he would be willing to co-operate with the existing Government. Smith acknowledged that Louis' reasoning was sound.

Riel then suggested that, as a man of influence, Smith could do much good in the colony if he chose to. If he would promise to go among the people, encouraging confidence in the Provisional Government instead of mistrust, Boulton's life would be spared. Without a moment's hesitation the man of business accepted Louis' terms. Only then was it announced publicly that Major Boulton's life would be spared.

Two weeks passed and it appeared as if all was going well. The most troublesome of the Canadians remained safely in jail. Donald Smith still circulated about the settlement, using his influence on behalf of the Provisional Government as he had promised to do. On the 21st John Schultz slipped out of the colony and made his way eastward to Canada. In a few days' time the delegation from Red River would leave for Ottawa to make known to Sir John their just demands.

Reviewing these facts, Riel had solid reasons to be thankful for the way things were proceeding. The difficult days were behind him now. At the head of his people, and in an orderly way, he had achieved a bargaining status with Canada. Everyone—or nearly everyone—at Red River agreed that it had been worth doing.

But in Fort Garry's jail, almost alone among the prisoners remaining there, Thomas Scott still tried repeatedly to keep the pot boiling. Young, disorderly, insubordinate, he made it a point to insult his métis guards at every opportunity. Perhaps he could not help himself. It was a matter of faith with him that Catholic, French-speaking people were inferior to Ontario Protestants; that half-breeds were more inferior still. Thus, half-breed French-Canadian Catholics—children of the plains—were quite definitely the lowest of the low.

All his life he had been taught this doctrine. He believed it implicitly, for he had grown up in Ontario at a time when, unhappily, all social life, all political activity, all religious interest, revolved around the bitter feud between English-speaking Protestants and French-speaking Catholics. Now, at Red River, where he had come to conquer half a continent in the name of Orange Ontario, he found himself languishing in a crude jail surrounded by métis guards. To him the situation, quite understandably, was intolerable.

On March 1st, two weeks after he had been jailed for the second time, he thought he saw an opportunity to make his escape. Painstakingly he had worked at the door of the cell; now it was ready to be forced. Turning to his cell-mates, he challenged them to follow him. They would rush from their cell, overwhelm the guards, take over the fort! A few Canadians could overpower every métis at Red River. He was as sure of it still as he was of the law of gravity. Barely a handful of men responded to his call. They were wary of Scott now. It was he who had got them into their present trouble. Hadn't it been his idea to march in from Portage? Without further argument Scott put his weight to the door, burst it open and rushed out, calling to the others to come on. Very few followed him.

As soon as they realized what was happening, the guards acted quickly. With comparative ease they stopped the jail-break and restored order once again. But Scott would not quiet down. His blood was up; he could not understand that he had lost. Sneering, taunting, fighting back like one possessed, he goaded the métis until they completely lost their tempers. Roughly, they dragged him out to the courtyard, began to beat him as savagely as he himself had beaten the half-witted Parisien. Then one of the members of the Provisional Government, hearing the uproar, intervened and ordered the guards to stop. Discipline was restored; Scott was returned to jail; the incident was reported to Riel.

Immediately, Riel sent for the trouble maker. The guards who brought him stood by, sullenly determined that he should be punished. The sensitive métis leader could feel their malevolence in the air. He must speak mildly, to cool them off.

With dignity, as befitted his position, he began: "You have caused a disturbance, Mr. Scott. I demand to know why."

Scott was a big fellow, uncouth, rough, always sure that he was in the right. He mistook Riel's mildness for timidity. "You demand!" he sneered. "What right have you to demand anything of me?"

"I am the President of the Provisional Government," Louis said. "Therein lies my right."

"The Provisional Government! A mob of half-breeds, doing what they damn well please. You should be hung, all of you. You *will* be hung! I do not recognize your Provisional Government, sir."

The guards on either side stirred ominously. They itched to finish giving this fellow the beating he deserved. But Riel, though breathing hard himself now, made a sign that they were to control themselves, and they obeyed.

"It has the consent of the people here—*all* the people, now, Mr. Scott."

"All the people?" Scott challenged. "It seems to me everything around here is run by you half-breed scum."

Riel stiffened. If the man persisted in his attitude of superiority —an attitude which anyone could see was not justified—the guards would take matters into their own hands. If they did, anarchy might replace the Government at Red River. He must prevent that at all costs.

"Everything around here is run by a Government which derives its authority from the people. If you don't recognize that voluntarily, perhaps we will have to force you to. I won't tolerate your brand of bullying here."

"You wouldn't dare to try anything on me, Riel. And you know it."

"You are making a grave mistake, Scott. I am entrusted with the task of maintaining order here. I will not flinch from my duty. Neither you nor anyone else can swerve me from my path. Once again—why did you cause a disturbance today?"

Scott spat contemptuously on the bare floor. "I'm not going to answer you, Mr. Half-breed. What do you plan to do about it, eh?" He glanced at his guards. "And it'll take more than another beating to make me change my mind."

Louis felt his temper leap within him. A little more of this— a very little more—and he would explode. Then his guards would explode, too, and pandemonium would break loose. Yet the one thing he could not afford to tolerate was mob violence. By giving his enemies a chance to say that government at Red River was a hollow sham, it would endanger every achievement he and his followers had made.

"Take him back to his cell," he ordered quietly. "I will consider what must be done."

"You haven't got the guts to do anything, Riel; and you know it."

By a supreme effort that left him trembling, Louis made himself refrain from striking the man across his grinning face. "Take him away," he ordered again. Then he turned, deliberately, to stare at the dirty snow outside his window.

He must learn, as a leader, how to draw himself apart. The guards must not read the thoughts hammering in his aching head. Yet the effort it took to control himself was almost more than he could sustain. He breathed deeply, paced about the room with measured steps until he had calmed down. Then he returned to his desk and considered the case anew.

This fellow Scott must be punished for his bully-boy behaviour. But he must be punished *legally*, by the full authority of the Government at Red River. The métis leader realized, sitting there, that the fact of Scott's misbehaviour was dangerous. This challenge must be met; if Riel ignored it his Council would divide against him, his own authority would backfire in his face. Then *everyone* would suffer. But could not time be applied as a remedy? Would it not be possible to leave Scott languishing for a while in jail?

A fist hammered at the door. Louis turned to face the room. "Yes?" he called wearily. Then, with more authority: *"Entrez."*

It was Paul Proulx, a member of the Council, and he looked grave. "Your prisoner is still bent on trouble, Louis," he announced. "Ceaselessly, he taunts the guards. 'You are a pack of cowards,' he jeers. And he tells them you will not dare to punish him. They are beginning to believe him, Louis. Something must be done."

Riel nodded. "You are right; something must be done. What do you suggest, my friend?"

"The guards say he must be shot."

"We have committed no violence here so far. It would be a pity to start it now." Louis spoke in a matter-of-fact tone, as a leader should speak when discussing questions of moment with his lieutenants; yet inside he felt vaguely sick. It was true that he had threatened, some time ago, to shoot Boulton. But he had been bluffing then to shock the Canadians into recognizing his authority. This Scott affair was something else again. "I was hoping we could leave him in jail to cool off," he suggested quietly.

"I don't think that would be acceptable to our men."

"I will leave him till tomorrow, then I will go to see him. Perhaps in the meantime he will cool down."

"And if he doesn't?"

"If he doesn't?" Louis shrugged. "We will have to cross that bridge when we come to it, *mon ami*."

In the morning Riel did as he had said he would. After breakfast he made his way to the jail. He had always been sensitive to other people's moods; this morning he could feel that everyone at the fort was restless, expectant, watching him to see how he would conduct himself. What Proulx had said was the truth; Scott had made his mark. Riel's own men were losing confidence in him now.

Assuredly, then, the prisoner must be punished. And yet . . .

He walked to the door of Scott's cell. The métis guards moved in behind him, like bloodhounds, to hover close by and listen to their chief. They were outdoor men, accustomed to hard, rough living and the direct sort of discipline that such a life demands. When one of their number committed a serious offence on the buffalo hunts, his case was dealt with quickly in the presence of the whole camp. The president of the hunt and his elected captains, acting on behalf of the whole community, heard the complaint, listened to the offender's excuses, pronounced sentence and saw that it was carried out. Under such circumstances everyone could be sure that justice would always be done.

Louis was their President now; yet he seemed reluctant to act the part. What was the matter with him? Was he weak, lacking courage, as Scott insisted? If he was, they had better get themselves another leader, quickly; for weakness in a leader was a dangerous thing. They would observe closely how the President handled his prisoner today. In that way they would learn what must be done.

When Louis appeared, Scott came to the door of his cell. He was as impenitent, as hot-headed, as he had been yesterday. Even when the guards began calling out that he must be shot, he maintained utter contempt for them all. Pressing close to the bars, Louis warned him in a low voice that they meant what they said. But Scott only replied: "You métis are a pack of cowards. You would not dare to shoot me." Quite evidently he believed this from the bottom of his narrow, fiery heart.

Scott's words were like a slap on the face, publicly administered, to Riel. There could be no backing away, now. Suddenly, Louis knew what he must do. No one man could be allowed to jeopardize an honest movement of a whole people. He, as President, must see to it that justice was done. His men were right; as their leader he must do his duty, whether it was personally distasteful to him or not. Turning away, he declared, loudly enough for everyone to hear, that the Council would be called to decide on Scott's fate. Then he made his way back to his office.

Later that day the Council decided that a court martial should be assembled to pass judgment on Scott's conduct as a prisoner. Riel himself was not a member of the court, but was present to lodge the charges against Scott and again in his capacity as a witness. The prisoner had defied the authority of the Provisional Government; he had fought with his guards and insulted Riel.

Confronted with these accusations, Scott refused to make a coherent defence, treated the whole proceedings with utter contempt. All seven members of the court, after hearing the evidence, found him guilty. Four of them called for a sentence of death and two favoured exile; the odd man declared that he would, reluctantly, agree with the majority. While the matter of exile was being discussed, Scott sneered: "If you escort me to the border I will be back at Red River before you." So it was decided, definitely, that he must be shot. Sentence was passed. The prisoner was returned to his cell.

That evening Father Lestanc from St. Boniface Cathedral, Rev. Mr. Young, a Protestant minister, and Donald A. Smith all pleaded with Riel on behalf of the prisoner, but to no avail. Scott had been given his chance; he had failed to make use of it. If Louis pardoned him now his own followers would become unmanageable, the other prisoners would become restless again, the people of Red River would listen to the blandishments of the Canadian party once more and be persuaded to sell their birthright cheap. In short, chaos would result—and for what purpose? To spare the life of a man whose actions had repeatedly shown him to be incorrigible. No! Sentence had been passed; let it be carried out. Scott must be shot in the morning. He, Louis Riel, would not shirk the responsibility with which his office as President had burdened him.

On the following day, March 4, 1870, a firing squad under the command of André Nault carried out the sentence against Scott. It is worth quoting an eyewitness account, because rumours still persist that Riel, "the fiendish half-breed chief", wounded Scott himself and buried him alive. In Nault's own words, this is how it was done:

Three bullets, two of which took effect in the chest, struck Scott and he fell. Before I had time to make sure whether he was dead, one Guillemette, who was a little intoxicated, ran to the body, turned it over, and discharged his revolver at its head. The body was placed in a casket and taken to the bastion. After a while some people came to tell me that they could hear groans from the bastion. I went to investigate and remained near the body for two and a half hours. All I could hear was the wind hissing through the buildings. The body was taken out of the Fort by Elzéar Goulet and Elzéar Lagimodière. The reason why the burial of Scott was kept secret was fear that the Orangemen would make a sort of pilgrimage ground of it.

VIII

IN WRITING
WE HAVE NOTHING

IT seems that everywhere within the colony Scott's court
martial was accepted as a necessary condition to the establishment of peace. Though the carrying out of the sentence
was regretted in almost all quarters, it was not resented
widely in Red River. Not even the elected representative from
Portage la Prairie, in which constituency the dead man had lived,
thought it necessary to lodge a formal protest when he took his
place in the new Assembly.

On March 9, 1870, five days after the firing squad had done
its work, Bishop Taché arrived in St. Boniface. He brought with
him a commission from the Canadian Government. When Riel
learned of this he was instantly suspicious. He sent for his Adjutant-General.

"Lépine," he said thoughtfully, "I understand that His Excellency has returned."

"That is so, *mon Président*. He arrived last night, just at
sundown. Everyone will be comforted to know that our Bishop
is among us again."

For a moment Riel sat, digesting this; then he spoke with
exaggerated casualness. "No doubt what you say is true, Ambroise. And yet, the question has arisen in my mind: is he our
friend still, or is he now a Canadian spy?"

Lépine was shocked by the suggestion. "What do you mean,
Louis? He has always been our friend."

"When he went away he was our friend," Louis agreed, "but now, they tell me he has returned with a Canadian commission in his pocket. Would a Catholic bishop cut short his stay in Rome simply to run an errand for the Canadian Government? Not likely, unless—"

"Unless what, Louis?"

Riel frowned. "He was the most influential man in the West before I began my political career. Perhaps he resents my success. Perhaps he has made some kind of deal with Ottawa, eh?"

Lépine seemed stunned. "That does not sound like him, Louis. Bishop Taché would not do a thing like that."

"I hope you are right." The voice was dry, matter-of-fact; it did not sound convinced, and yet Riel knew he would like to believe that Lépine was right. "All the same," he went on with authority, "he accepted a Canadian commission. He showed it at the border. Does that not prove he has entered our land as a servant of Canada instead of as the Bishop of St. Boniface?"

Looking out the window, groping in his mind for words that would calm his chief and resolve his own growing doubts, Lépine watched smoke curl upwards from the Bishop's chimney across the Red. At first he watched it idly, for it was a familiar sight; then it registered consciously and suggested to him a course of action. "Why don't we ride over to the other side and ask him where he stands?" he asked.

Riel stiffened. "I cannot have it said that I crawled on my hands and knees to an emissary of Macdonald. You forget—I am the President of the Government of Assiniboia!"

"But, Louis, you and the Bishop are old friends."

Riel's eyes flashed dangerously. "We *were* friends, before he went away. In those days he was the leader of his flock and I was one of his lambs. But *I* am the leader here now. Like everyone else, he must acknowledge that fact. In order that he may understand this—in order that everyone may *know* he understands it, too—I think it would be wise for us to provide a military guard for his residence. Yes, that is what we must do!"

When Lépine made no comment, he went on: "You are my Adjutant-General, Ambroise. I am sure that Taché will be honoured by your presence. But whether he is honoured or not, you must do as I say. Take ten men and mount a guard before his palace. Let no one enter to leave without a thorough inspection. Remain on duty there until he acknowledges the Provisional Government. Do you understand?"

"Of course I understand, but—" Lépine protested.

"Do you recognize me as your President, Ambroise?" Riel challenged loudly.

"Yes, but—"

"Either you carry out my orders or I'll find someone else who will." As suddenly as it had come, the fire seemed to go out of the métis chief's body. He shivered, as if doused with a bucket of cold water; then he came across to Lépine, put a hand on his shoulder. "You see?" he said quietly. "Already the influence of the Bishop is causing division in our ranks. If we are to achieve what we set out to achieve, we must not be divided, old friend."

But the influence of the Bishop did not cause division in their ranks. Later that day Lépine and a small party of men crossed the frozen river and took up positions before his residence. Taché came outside, gave the guards his blessing. When he learned from Lépine the reason for the soldiers' presence, he expressed nothing but sadness that there should be so little trust in this world. For twenty-five of his forty-seven years he had devoted all his energies to missionary and charitable work among the métis and Indians. For the past twenty years he had been their bishop. And yet, because of a piece of paper which he brought with him from Canada, his people distrusted him and questioned his motives!

114

Immediately after the guards arrived, he sent word to Riel that he would meet with the newly elected legislature when it assembled on the 15th. Before them he would explain the nature of his commission. Then, as a reminder that he was still the Bishop of St. Boniface, he withdrew the services that one of his chaplains had been providing at Fort Garry.

Six days later Taché addressed the new Provisional Government, giving them assurance of the good intentions of the Canadian Cabinet. Macdonald had told him that an amnesty would be extended to those who were involved in the troubles in the North-west. After receiving a copy of Riel's published Bill of Rights, which Taché had come upon in St. Paul and sent to him, the Honourable Joseph Howe had replied by telegraph: "Proposition in main satisfactory, but let delegates come here to settle details."

"These things are all right as far as they go," Riel declared, interrupting the Bishop at this point. "But much has happened here in the last little while. How can we be sure that Macdonald's promises and Howe's words still hold good?"

"I saw the Prime Minister on February 9th," Bishop Taché replied. "I brought up this very point. I told him that blamable acts had been committed, that others might be committed before my arrival here. He assured me it would make no difference to his attitude about an amnesty."

"But he gave you nothing in writing to that effect?" Riel asked.

"Only this." Taché drew a letter from beneath the folds of his soutane. "When there is time I will supply you with a copy for your official records. Meanwhile, let me draw your attention to this paragraph, in which Sir John says: 'In case a delegation is appointed to proceed to Ottawa, you can assure them they will be kindly received.' Is this not assurance enough that the Prime Minister is favourably disposed?"

Many members of the Legislative Assembly seemed satisfied that it was. Riel was not. He insisted that discussion on the Bill of Rights be reopened, that a clause be inserted in it providing that "none of the members of the Provisional Government or any of those acting under them be in any way liable or responsible with regard to the movement or any actions which led to the present negotiations". To this the other legislators agreed.

When this piece of business had been dealt with, Riel reopened the question of provincial status. Both he and the Bishop urged that the Bill be further amended to include, for the protection of their land rights, a demand that the settlement enter Confederation with all the rights, powers and responsibilities of the other provinces. Because Donald A. Smith was no longer present to provide resistance to the measure (he had decided that his influence could be better employed in Ottawa, and had left for the East), it was adopted by the Legislature.

From this the members turned to the question of releasing the few prisoners who still remained in jail. Quickly they agreed that the time had arrived when these men could be freed without endangering the well-established peace; that an amnesty could be proclaimed for all who had taken up arms against Riel.

Afterwards, Louis and his Cabinet had lunch with the Bishop. It was probably at this time, over mugs of steaming tea, that Taché introduced the question of revenue for schools. This matter had been overlooked by the legislators. Now, at his suggestion one further amendment was made to the Bill of Rights. A clause was inserted to provide that "the schools shall be separate and the public money for schools shall be distributed among the different religious denominations in proportion to their religious populations, according to the system in the Province of Quebec." This was not a revolutionary provision. To incorporate it in their Bill must have seemed, to the men gathered there, a fair and reasonable thing to do. Their action was more an outline of procedure than the enunciation of a principle, for all the schools in the West were under the wing of one denomination or another.

On March 23rd, two of the delegates—Father Ritchot and A. H. Scott—set out for Ottawa. The next day Judge Black, the third delegate, followed. With him travelled Major Boulton, the former prisoner of Riel, and Colonel de Salaberry, who had been one of the original envoys from the East. Soon after they left, the Union Jack was raised above Fort Garry in place of the métis flag, and, although O'Donoghue protested, Riel would not haul it down. The people settled themselves hopefully to endure the dreary season of nature's promises, given and withdrawn, that in the Red River Valley of the North serves as spring.

At last, caressed by alien winds from the south and warmed by the high-swinging sun, the river's ice melted, the drab prairie stirred and became once more a vital, growing thing. As its surface firmed enough for travelling, the métis of Red River departed on their spring buffalo hunt; as it dried enough to work, the farmers of Red River made ready their fields with ploughs and oxen for the summer's crop. Reminded in a thousand ways of its glorious past, the jaded Company again took heart. Shrugging its still elegant shoulders, it acknowledged the Provisional Government as the *de facto* power in the land, then joyfully took up its ancient role of trader, banker and merchant extraordinary throughout the land.

To the people of Red River the alarms of winter were half-forgotten nightmares now. Great issues that had seemed to dominate their winter lives appeared in the light of spring to be mere blobs of grey in the middle-distant past. Though everyone knew, in a detached, unfeeling sort of way, that their future would be sealed soon now, no one was burdened by this knowledge. Instead, all were bewitched by the sensuality of the new season; for such is the magic of April after a winter on the plains.

On the 17th of the month Governor Mactavish roused himself from his sick-bed and departed for Britain, where he was to die. Riel and his Council were left alone to rule in the name of the people. All the basic decisions had been made; all the steps necessary for their implementation had been taken. Martial law had been replaced by a code of laws laid down by the new Legislative Assembly. Mere routine performance of duty was the order of the day.

By this time Louis would have been justified in considering himself a successful politician. He had conceived a program, which the people had accepted; with the departure of the delegates for Ottawa he had tasted the satisfaction of seeing it, so far as it came under his control, fulfilled. Now, if these delegates were favourably received by the Canadian Cabinet—and Bishop Taché's assurances indicated that they would be—his beloved people would enter Confederation with their future well-being assured. Perhaps he would be offered a Cabinet post; perhaps he would be invited to settle down to a pleasant public life as the Government's specialist in western affairs. Meanwhile, like everyone else, he must wait and see what developed from the meeting of the delegates with the Cabinet in Ottawa.

It was good to have a spell of relative quietness. It was good to have time to think of oneself for a change. His winter's work had been successful, but it had been a constant strain, too. Late in February, during the worst of the trouble with the Canadian prisoners at Fort Garry, it had caused a reaction in Louis; he had collapsed with a brain fever. For three days he had lain desperately ill. A priest had given him the last sacraments of the Church, his mother and sisters had hurried to his side; but, miraculously, the crisis had passed and within a week he had seemed almost his old self again.

But as President of the Provisional Government of Assiniboia, he was still overworked. The internal pressures of his job might have eased lately, but the external ones had not, nor were they likely to until an agreement had been reached with Ottawa over the matter of confederation. O'Donoghue was not the only one who had mistaken his political actions for a revolutionary movement against established sovereignty. Robinson, the editor of the *New Nation*, had more than hinted that annexation would be the most desirable outcome of the present situation. All sorts of people in the United States had written him letters, offering him aid. It had not been easy to steer a true course through the tides and currents to which his judgment had been subjected.

One evening, as he sat thinking of these problems, two strangers were ushered into his presence. They were nondescript fellows of about middle age, well enough dressed to look prosperous, yet possessing an indefinable air of shiftiness about them. If their eyes had been a fraction sharper, their hands a degree or two more dexterous, he might have mistaken them for riverboat gamblers. As it was, he did not know what they were, or whom they represented. But as soon as he was alone with them he began to find out.

"Ever hear of Jay Cooke, Mr. Riel?" one of the men asked, nipping the end from a cigar and preparing to light it.

Fascinated by his offhand drawl, Riel shook his head.

"Ever hear of the Northern Pacific Railway Company?" the other man queried.

"But, of course. That is, when I was working in St. Paul I heard people say—"

"Well, Jay Cooke *is* the Northern Pacific Railway, Mr. Riel," the first man announced. "And he's starting construction this spring. Soon he'll have track laid all the way to Puget Sound on the Pacific Coast. It'll make a big difference to this part of the world. Don't you agree, Mr. Riel?"

Louis wondered what all this had to do with him. "I—I suppose it will," he agreed non-committally.

"Too bad you and your people are going to be on the wrong side of the border to benefit by it."

"What do you mean?" But Louis knew very well what the man meant. This was annexation talk, pure and simple. He had heard it too many times not to recognize it now. And he knew that the wisest thing to do was to let these fellows talk themselves out without offering opposition.

The first man, his cigar lit at last and jammed into a corner of his mouth, went on: "We have been given to believe that you are definitely throwing in your lot with Canada. Is our information correct, sir?"

Louis shrugged. "It all depends on how our delegates are received. They're on their way to Ottawa now."

Like a veteran actor, the second man picked up his cue. "I can tell you how they'll be received, Mr. Riel. They'll be eaten alive." From his pocket he pulled a folded newspaper. Opening it, he tossed it down on the desk before Riel. "And here's my proof—right there on the front page of the Toronto *Globe*."

Louis smoothed the paper with the back of his hand. In the middle was a news item that had been marked in ink with an *X*. It was an extract from the minutes of some meeting in Toronto; and as he read it, a sickening feeling of apprehension mounted inside him. This is what it said:

Whereas Brother Scott, a member of our Order, was cruelly murdered by the enemies of our Queen, country and religion, therefore be it resolved that while we sympathize with the relatives of our deceased Brother, we, the members of the Loyal Orange Lodge No. 404, call upon the government to avenge his death, pledging ourselves to assist in rescuing the Red River Territory from those who have turned it over to Popery, and bring justice to the murderers of our countrymen.

"Rich stuff, eh?" the cigar smoker said. "And there's more on the inside if you'd care to read it."

Louis turned the page. Inside he found an editorial demanding that the delegates from Red River be hanged! He thought: This is why we must have our amnesty in writing. If we don't stop this sort of thing right now, a great number of innocent people will suffer.

The smoker shook his head, removed the cigar from his mouth. "I've never seen the like of it, anywhere," he said with unctuous sympathy. "Here, you are the President of this whole rich Territory. Yet in Toronto they call you a murderer." His lips twisted in a sarcastic sneer. "And they expect you to confederate with *them*!"

Louis cleared his throat. "This is Orange Lodge stuff," he said quietly. "Nobody *murdered* Scott. A court martial found him guilty of a crime that demanded the death penalty; he was executed before a firing squad. It had to be done, for the safety of the colony. These people do not understand."

"They don't *want* to understand. They never will. You realize that if they get their way everyone who associated with you will be made to suffer, too."

"That—that could happen. But we have assurances of an amnesty," Riel countered weakly.

"In writing?"

Louis shook his head. "In writing we have nothing."

"I thought as much," the first man said. Then he leaned towards the métis chief and his tone became confidential. "And that's why we came here to talk to you."

From the other side his partner closed in, too, so that Louis began to feel trapped between the pair. "You see, we are special agents of Jay Cooke, Mr. Riel," the voice went on, "which is as good as to say we're special emissaries from the Government of the United States. Old Jay, he handled the Union's bond issues during the war; he's Ulysses S. Grant's right-hand man. When we tell you *he* authorized us to come and see you—well, it's the same as telling you that the President himself has approved the proposition."

The second man—the one who had produced the copy of the *Globe*—spoke up persuasively. "Our boss owns a lot of land, Mr. Riel. A lot of land indeed! But he's always interested in acquiring a little more. Particularly this colony of Assiniboia. If you were to help him get it he'd make it worth your while, and there'd be no need of an amnesty then."

Louis glared at him. "Serpents! Snakes! Devils!" he shouted. "Get this into your cheap commercial heads: I have my differences with the Canadian politicians, yes, but I am a man of honour! I'm loyal to my Queen! I don't suppose you'd understand a thing like loyalty—you cringing, avaricious vermin!"

Life settled down again to dull routine. Then, on June 17th, Father Ritchot returned to Red River with a copy of the new Manitoba Act. It had been passed by both houses of Parliament and signed more than a month before by the Governor-General, Sir John Young. For political reasons the amnesty clause contained in Riel's Bill of Rights had been left out of the Act, but the Governor-General had assured Father Ritchot that Her Majesty intended "to wipe a sponge over all that had taken place in the North-west". As he spoke in the name of the Queen, one had to believe that he meant what he said.

Apart from this omission, the Act was acceptable enough. There was to be a new province known as Manitoba—which, in the Cree language, means "the god who speaks". Its people were to govern themselves by means of a Legislative Council and Assembly; they were to send elected representatives to sit in the Parliament of Canada. The provincial boundaries would be roughly the same as those of the old colony of Assiniboia. The rest of Rupert's Land—the vast bulk of the British North-west—would become a territory governed by Ottawa and administered from Fort Garry.

The public lands of the new province were to be controlled by the federal Government, so that they could be apportioned as subsidies to the railroad-builders, financiers, and immigrants now interested in the West; but existing land titles would be guaranteed and a grant of 1,400,000 acres would be made to the unmarried children of the métis. In this way the present inhabitants of the West would be kept content.

French was to be recognized along with English as an official language; the educational rights held by various denominations at the time of union were to be guaranteed. In short, Manitoba, though deprived of the right to control its own lands, was to retain the balance between English and French nationalities on which Confederation rested. It was perhaps the best compromise one could legitimately have hoped for at this time.

The Act was to become effective on July 15th. In the meantime, Riel was to carry on in his present capacity. Father Ritchot was explicit on this point; he had asked the Governor-General who was to govern the country pending the arrival of the Lieutenant-Governor, and "if he was to name somebody to do so. Sir John answered: 'No, let Mr. Riel continue to maintain order and govern the country as he has done up to the present moment.' He asked me if I thought Riel was sufficiently powerful to maintain order. I said I thought he was. Then he answered: 'Let him continue until the Governor arrives.'"

Could anything have been more indicative of goodwill? Everyone was overjoyed. The rights of the people of Red River had been acknowledged! The inhabitants were to become Canadians with no strings attached. When the Legislature of Assiniboia met it ratified the agreement, thereby accepting the terms of confederation. Everyone's faith in common sense and justice was restored.

And yet—privately Riel was alarmed by three features of this deal. One of these was the official silence on the amnesty question. According to Father Ritchot, Macdonald now maintained that, as Canada had no jurisdiction at the time of the "troubles", the Canadian Government could not consider the matter—it was something to be decided by the Queen. Another was the news that a military expedition under Colonel Garnet Wolseley had already set out from the East and was making its way to Red River over the old water route of the North West Company. Although Sir Georges Cartier had assured Father Ritchot that the soldiers were coming west solely to impress Americans and Indians with the power of Canada, the priest, having experienced the temper of Ontario, was convinced that they were marching against the French métis.

It was this temper of Ontario that provided Riel with his third reason for alarm. When Father Ritchot and A. H. Scott had arrived in Ottawa, they had been arrested as accomplices in the "murder" of Thomas Scott. Shortly thereafter they had been released and received by the Canadian Cabinet; but if such feeling continued to burn in Canada's most powerful province, the future might be black indeed—in spite of all Macdonald's smooth assurances to the contrary.

When Riel discussed his doubts with Father Ritchot and the Bishop, Taché reassured him. A complete and general amnesty had been promised. These things took time to arrange; politics always involved more than met the eye. Perhaps the Bishop was right. Macdonald must perform on a tightrope held in the air by the voters of Ontario and Quebec; no doubt he would find some way of declaring an amnesty without losing his footing. Ontario might be after métis blood, but Quebec was not; and more than likely the Canadian Cabinet was stalling while it cast about for some face-saving formula acceptable in both provinces. As the Bishop said, he would have to wait trustfully and see. And in the meantime, to prove his loyalty, he would govern the colony to the best of his ability until relieved of his duties by the new Canadian Lieutenant-Governor.

But on June 26th Bishop Taché called Louis to his residence. The prelate looked worried; he wore his travelling clothes.

"My son," he began, pacing up and down his office, "I have been considering this matter of an amnesty. I have questioned Father Ritchot more fully since the day you and he were here. It has occurred to me that, should his fears prove well founded, you and I will be made to look like public liars in the eyes of our people."

Riel smiled. The Bishop had said "our people". For the first time he had acknowledged the political arm, as represented by Riel, on terms of equality with the Church. "Yes, Your Excellency. What you say is true."

"*Eh bien*," the Bishop went on, "I have decided to go east again and clarify the whole matter once and for all. It is my duty to do so. If necessary I will go to the highest authority in the land and demand an explanation. Then I will communicate with you and there will be no more room for doubt."

"I am sure all the people will be grateful, as will I," Louis acknowledged with a bow.

That afternoon the Bishop departed and Louis went back to his task. June gave place to July. Then one evening a strange thing happened at Fort Garry. The river boat *International* arrived from the South, as it did three or four times a season. No sooner was it moored securely to the wharf than the captain sought out Louis and handed him a piece of paper which had been found in one of the cabins. It was a proclamation, and it announced to the world that, though Canadian forces were marching west now, the people of Red River had nothing to fear from them. It was signed in the name of Colonel Wolseley, the English commander of the force.

The following afternoon Lépine turned up with an identical copy. Beside him was a stranger, a military-looking man in his early thirties, whom he had discovered in the lower part of the settlement.

"He admits posting this notice, *mon Président*," the Adjutant-General announced gravely. "I thought you might like to question him."

"Thank you, Ambroise," Louis replied. Then, to the man who stood before him: "Are you a representative of Canada, sir? Did someone send you here to post this proclamation?"

"My name is Butler, Mr. Riel—Captain William Francis Butler. I've been travelling through the States attached to Colonel Wolseley's staff."

"Why did you not bring this thing to me," Louis asked, "instead of going behind my back to the people?"

"I did not think you would co-operate. I thought it best that I post the proclamation myself to make sure that the people here were informed of the peaceful nature of the expedition that is on its way."

Louis laughed. "You know we have no intention of resisting the Canadians, Captain Butler. We have signed a treaty with them. We are ready to receive their representatives with open arms. To prove it, I'll have this thing published in the *Nation*."

"All the same," Lépine muttered darkly, "our forces would be willing and able to fight the Canadians if the necessity arose."

"The necessity will not arise," Riel cut in sharply. "We have a treaty. That is all we ever wanted."

Butler smiled. "I will tell Colonel Wolseley this when I rejoin him, sir. He will be pleased to hear it. I am told that his troops are not of the best. It is just as well that he will not have to trust them in a fight—especially against seasoned men like your own."

Louis accepted this statement as nothing more than a pretty compliment. After telling Captain Butler that he hoped he would be comfortable during his stay in Red River, he dismissed the incident from his mind.

But the next day Lépine brought it up again. "That Captain Butler, Louis—you heard him say the Canadian troops had no intention of fighting, did you not?"

Louis nodded. "I did."

"Well, last night he must have visited all the taverns in Winnipeg. Everywhere people are saying that in spite of his proclamation Wolseley intends to hang every métis in the colony when he arrives. There hasn't been talk like that around here for months. It caused quite a stir, I can tell you."

Riel shrugged. "This is just drunken chatter. Such things are said in taverns."

"Perhaps it isn't, Louis. I know you don't want to believe it, but perhaps it's the truth."

Riel frowned, got up from behind his desk, began pacing up and down. After a few minutes he stopped and turned to face Lépine. "Ambroise," he said quietly, "you may be right. This whole thing begins to fit together. First we find the proclamation which tells us that we have nothing to fear. Then we discover the captain in our midst. He takes pains to inform us that we can beat the Canadian force if we want to fight. Now, you report that he has been spreading fear among the people—in other words, giving them a reason for wanting to fight. Perhaps our friend Butler is an *agent provocateur*. Perhaps he has been planted in our midst to encourage us to fight. You know, there are people in Ontario—a lot of people, I'm afraid—who would like nothing better than an excuse to use these troops against us."

"And there are people here who would like nothing better

than an excuse to fight the Canadians," Lépine said quietly. "And I am one of them."

Louis shook his head. "No, Ambroise, we must not take the bait. We have signed a treaty in good faith. We must abide by it. There will be no fighting as far as I am concerned."

"We signed a treaty, yes. But what about the amnesty question? The Manitoba Act is of no use to us if we are all to be shot."

Riel spoke gently. "I am the President here, and I say there will be no resistance. You must trust my judgment, Ambroise, just as I must trust the judgment of Bishop Taché. But I tell you what you can do—you can send some men to find this Captain Butler and bring him to me now. In view of what you have told me, it might be prudent to have another little chat with him and find out what he's *really* up to."

But Captain Butler was not to be found. During the night he had disappeared eastward to join the Canadian forces as they toiled through north-western Ontario towards Fort Garry.

On July 15, 1870, the Territory became a part of Canada. As no Canadian representative had arrived to take it over, Riel and his Provisional Government continued to administer the land. According to Bishop Taché, who wrote to Louis from the East, the new Lieutenant-Governor would be among them soon. He was a good man and utterly unlike McDougall. His name was Adams G. Archibald; he was a native Nova Scotian. Everyone could have faith in both his ability and his integrity. Above all, he would be fair to all factions, for he had not been embroiled in the controversies of Quebec and Ontario about the métis.

The plan was that Archibald would proceed to Red River through the United States, and assume his duties at Fort Garry before Wolseley and the troops arrived. In this way there would be no suggestion that forces from Canada had imposed Canadian rule on the local inhabitants against their will. In this way, too, it would be made abundantly clear that the soldiers were there to do nothing more than "show the flag" for the benefit of American annexationists and restless Indians. Thus, neither the métis nor anyone else would have cause for the slightest concern.

Louis was much cheered. He had always maintained that the vast majority of the Canadian people were reasonable men. Now by their conduct they were going to prove that he was right. His faith and that of the Bishop would be more than justified.

At about this time another letter arrived in the settlement. It was from Colonel Wolseley, addressed both to the Bishop and to the Hudson's Bay Company officials, and it requested that a notice be posted advertising for 250 men who would be willing to work on "Mr. Snow's road" to the North-west Angle. These men were to be paid five shillings a day as axe-men and labourers. Surely this was another excellent indication of the Government's peaceful intentions. As soon as they had been assured that by so doing they would not hasten their own destruction, many métis signed on for the work.

Presently a second letter arrived from Bishop Taché. It reported that Sir John A. Macdonald had been prevailed upon by Dr. Schultz and the Orange Order to change his plans; the new Lieutenant-Governor would go west through Canada, overtake the troops, and arrive at Fort Garry with them. There must be no peaceful intercourse with the with the "murderers" of Thomas Scott. As a matter of principle, confederation must be imposed on the métis by Canadian troops. Then, and only then, would the civil arm of Canada be allowed to assume its already acknowledged place in the West.

Time was running out; opportunities for influencing Canadian policy were evaporating before the Provisional Government's eyes. The advancing forces were entering the Lake of the Woods country now. Through spies, Riel kept close track of their progress. Again and again Lépine begged him for permission to ambush them and demand an amnesty while he could. His answer was always the same: Bishop Taché was working on the question in the East; they must retain their faith in him. Riel even sent several natives to Wolseley to offer themselves as guides.

At last one day it seemed as if this faith was justified. Word came from the Bishop that Archibald had departed for the West on schedule. Before leaving he had, on his own initiative, modified his plans; he had promised that, instead of overtaking the troops, he would rendezvous with Louis at the North-west Angle of the Lake of the Woods and journey with him overland to Fort Garry. In this way he would arrive well ahead of the soldiers, for Wolseley was committed to following the longer route down the Winnipeg River to the plains; "Mr. Snow's road" via the North-west Angle would not be completed in time.

Riel was elated. His point had been won. In spite of Schultz and the plottings of the Orange Order, he would hand over the reins of authority voluntarily to the civil arm of the Canadian Government, as he had agreed by treaty to do. There would be no grounds whatever for claiming that a military expedition had "secured" the country; there would be no justification for inflicting reprisals on his beloved métis. The amnesty question would *have* to be decided in his favour by the Queen!

His elation was short-lived. Though he rode down to the rendezvous, the arrangement misfired. Long afterwards he learned that the new Lieutenant-Governor had lost his way; at the time he thought the man had gone back on his word. With a heavy heart he returned to Fort Garry to inform his Cabinet of his failure.

On August 23rd Bishop Taché arrived home. Immediately, Riel crossed the river to see him. His spirits were very low, for he was sure that if the Bishop carried good news he would have sent it ahead by messenger. Taché looked grave as he greeted Louis at his door.

"The amnesty?" Louis asked, coming inside.

The Bishop shook his head. "Pressure from Ontario was too great. Macdonald dared not give me anything in writing. The rendezvous with Archibald was our last hope."

As he stood there, an emotion of strange bitter-sweetness swept through Riel, and he felt very tired. "It does not matter what happens now," he said quietly. "The rights of the métis are assured by the Manitoba Act; it is what I wanted; my mission is finished." And looking around the familiar room—at the books and the desk and the Bishop's big chair, at all the solid things to which he had been introduced when he came here first to study as a boy—he thought: "Everything is slipping away. This is the emptiness an old man must feel when he is about to die!"

Taché moved close, put his hand on Louis' shoulder. "Courage, my son. A Christian must always have courage." Then: "The Canadian army is approaching; it must be very near by now. But Colonel Wolseley, the British commanding officer, is under strict orders from London to treat you all gently."

Louis smiled. "That is more than one has a right to expect, Your Excellency. Wolseley may be an English gentleman. Many of his soldiers are Canadians, though; and Canada is too young a nation to be reasonable, I fear." He straightened himself, bowed stiffly. "Thank you for all your efforts. No one could have done more. And now, I must return to the fort."

Without another word he left the room and crossed the river to Fort Garry. As he reached his quarters the wind shifted to the north-west and it began to rain. Alone, defeated, yet quite sure still that what he had done was right, he listened to the drops of water drumming on the window-panes. It was as if all the world were weeping for his fate.

There was nothing more to be done, really, and yet the thing must be played out to its end. Summoning his colleagues, Louis told them what the Bishop had said. Then he advised them to disperse to their homes and lie low. "I myself will remain here in case some word of peace is sent ahead by Wolseley," he concluded. But he did not believe this would happen now. Without fuss, he told Louis Schmidt to gather together his chief papers and take them away for safe-keeping.

Late that night, with Baptiste Nault and two others, he rode out in the rain towards the north. On the east side of the Red, O'Donoghue and two men did the same. Though they saw camp-fires in the distance, darkness hid the disposition of the enemy's troops. Early in the morning they returned and lay down in their sodden clothes for a few hours' sleep.

Just after dawn James Stewart, a native of Red River, rode into the fort to announce that Wolseley was advancing and taking prisoners as he came. "The soldiers swear they will shoot all the Frenchmen who had anything to do with the execution of Scott," he warned.

"Then we must flee," Riel announced, looking at Lépine. "If they find us here they'll take it out on every poor métis in the land."

"We should have attacked them while we could," the Adjutant-General countered fiercely.

"Perhaps there'll be another day," O'Donoghue put in hopefully.

Riel laughed. It was a harsh laugh, containing no mirth. "Perhaps there will," he agreed. "But in the meantime we would be wise to keep out of sight. Come on, all of you."

Some of the men rode off towards the south. Riel, with Lépine and O'Donoghue, slid down the river's muddy bank to the ferry. Silently, they cast it loose, crossed over to the St. Boniface shore. As they arrived on the eastern bank the green-coated imperial riflemen, in the van of Wolseley's force, came into sight. Without a word Lépine cut the cables spanning the river, to prevent pursuit.

"Now you know what it costs to trust Canadians," he said as he straightened from his task.

"Yes, now I know," Louis agreed. "But it does not matter, for my work is done."

IX

BLAKE'S
BLOOD MONEY

THE following weeks were a nightmare to Louis Riel. During the first few days after the arrival of the troops he, Lépine and O'Donoghue fled to the village of St. Joseph thirty miles west of Pembina, in the United States. There Louis had time to review the situation. Would the Canadians honour their pledges of peace?

Soon it became quite evident that they would not. In spite of the peaceful tone that had run through the despatch brought by Butler to Red River a bare month before, Colonel Wolseley now issued an order of the day to his soldiers which began: "The leaders of the banditti, who recently oppressed Her Majesty's loyal subjects in Red River, having fled as you advanced to the Fort . . . you have not therefore had an opportunity for glory."

What could such a statement mean, if it was not an admission of warlike intent? Was this not positive proof that the Canadians had been sustained by dreams of vengeance all during their long journey westward? And—an even more shattering thought—was it still possible to believe, in the face of such evidence, that Bishop Taché had not known all along the true temper of these troops? The Bishop himself now admitted, in a letter sent to Louis at St. Joseph, that things were not going as he would like them to; that there was no sign of an amnesty anywhere; that Louis must not think of returning to Red River just yet. Precipitate action might lead to a calamity; time was required for sanity to return.

Yes, time was certainly required for sanity to return. And yet —would not time also be required, by those who were jealous of Riel, to dethrone him in the hearts of the métis? He must remain for a while in the United States; that was only common sense. But he must maintain contact with his people, as well. He must use the pages of the *New Nation* to express his own ideas, to explain the policies he had in mind. On September 2nd he wrote to Joseph Royal, a sympathetic young Quebec lawyer who had arrived recently in the West, telling him that the newspaper now belonged to him.

As time passed, more news flowed southward to him. In a letter from Joseph Dubuc, another young *Canadien* with political ambitions who had taken up residence at Red River, Louis learned that warrants had been issued against him and Lépine. Now, to all intents and purposes, the amnesty question seemed settled indeed—but in the wrong way.

When Colonel Wolseley and his British regulars departed for the East, the Canadian troops who remained behind began behaving like an undisciplined mob. According to report, they went about the settlement terrorizing everyone; they haunted the saloons, shouting "Kill big Taché!" and swearing that they would wipe the French half-breeds from the face of the earth; they roamed the province in bands, beating up anyone whose face was dark enough to suggest some Indian blood.

Was this the peaceful force that Macdonald had promised Father Ritchot? Was this the manner in which the Queen wiped a sponge over all that had taken place in the North-west? Before Archibald arrived at Fort Garry, Donald A. Smith, who had come west again with the soldiers, had acted temporarily in his place. He had sat there, in full authority, watching it all—yet doing nothing to restrain the troops!

One day some Canadians recognized Elzéar Goulet, a member of the firing squad that had executed Thomas Scott. They came upon him outside the Red Saloon in Winnipeg. Though he had been merely a soldier carrying out the orders of his superior officers, they chased him to the Red River; when he tried to swim to the safety of the other side, they stoned him to death.

The man who brought this shocking news said that Madame Goulet, after the body of her husband was recovered and brought home, had made her children kneel beside it and pray for forgiveness for the murderers. But, hearing this, Riel could find no room for such Christian thoughts in his own full heart. Why did these self-styled custodians of civilization conduct themselves like barbarians? Why did the Canadian authorities refuse to preserve the peace, as he and his colleagues had done? Why was the justice promised by the Manitoba Act being turned deliberately into a mockery?

After this Louis could remain inactive no longer. He was the people's leader still; he must do something to help them now. Secretly, he summoned his followers to a meeting at St. Norbert. About forty of the more courageous métis answered his call. He himself rode north to the rendezvous. When they were all assembled he declared that some way must be found to put an end to the persecution of the people. Though everyone agreed, no one knew what should be done.

It was the opportunity for which O'Donoghue had been waiting. A full year had passed since Riel was named the métis leader. Now it appeared that his policies had failed. When the others had revealed their poverty of ideas, the Irish-American rose and, with a stirring speech, proposed that they petition the President of the United States to take possession of the whole North-west. Only by becoming American citizens, he told them, could they hope to escape the wrath of Perfidious Albion. When

Riel declared, as he had before, that he refused to be a party to such a scheme, the whole meeting turned against him. What was the use of maintaining their allegiance to the Queen? they asked. What was the sense in continuing to hope for some settlement of the amnesty question, when the Canadians had proved their bad faith consistently at every turn?

Now Riel could feel his hold on the métis evaporating into thin air. If he was to remain their leader, he must do something, and quickly, to justify his position. Yet O'Donoghue's proposal was madness; under no circumstances would he agree to it. Rising to his feet again, he suggested that they send a resolution to President Grant, not asking for annexation as O'Donoghue desired, but begging him to use his good offices in an appeal for justice to the Queen. After some debate the meeting decided that this was what should be done. Because he was an American citizen and claimed to have met the President, they chose O'Donoghue to go to Washington on their behalf.

It appears that, following this meeting, Louis made a furtive visit to his mother in St. Vital. Then he returned to hiding in the United States. From Joseph Dubuc he learned that events were advancing without him; a census was being taken, preparatory to an election of representatives to the new Manitoba Legislative Assembly. Slowly Archibald, the new Lieutenant-Governor, was gaining control of the situation; under his guidance, twenty-four electoral divisions had been formed from the parishes along the rivers, twelve English and twelve French.

Men whom Riel knew would be contesting seats. Marc Girard and Louis Schmidt would be running in St. Boniface, Dubuc in Baie St. Paul, Royal in White Horse Plains. This must have been bitter knowledge to receive; and yet he must have known that feeling was still too high for him to join them, for, when he was asked by the citizens of St. Vital to stand as their candidate, he refused "because of circumstances". Judging from a letter he wrote to Bannatyne towards the end of December, he realized that it would be best to accept the advice of Sir Georges Cartier, passed on to him by Joseph Royal, to submit to a voluntary exile "for three or four years" for the sake of the cause he represented.

Whatever his motives for refusing to re-enter politics at this time, he was exhausted and despondent now. In February he became so ill that his mother, taking with her young Charles and Alexandre, went secretly to be by his side. Not until mid-April was he on his feet again. By May he was sufficiently recovered to insist that he return, exile or no exile, to help with seeding on the family's farm.

It was a changed Red River to which he came back. Elections for the new Manitoba Legislature had been held and Archibald had appointed a Cabinet to help him rule. On January 12, 1871, this body met and in it such old-time métis as Louis Schmidt sat down with men like Dr. Schultz and Donald A. Smith. From all the evidence it seems that these ancient antagonists were now trying honestly to pull together for the general good, although Schultz was heard, on more than one occasion, to speak of "poor Scott" and the sufferings of the other Canadian prisoners of Riel during the previous year. A new man from the East, H. J. Clarke, had been made Attorney-General, and some of his English-speaking contemporaries accused him of thinking that "he was the law, instead of the legal director". Nevertheless he served a useful purpose, for with a heavy hand he began at once to crack down on the lawless characters among the Canadian volunteers.

Thus peace returned gradually to the community, and by the spring of 1871 all seemed tranquil at last. The Canadian volunteers had been disbanded; those who remained in the West were settling on the land. Immigrants were pouring in with wives and families and taking up homesteads on the prairie beyond the rivers. Before the summer had ended, more than seven thousand new-comers were installed in the tiny province.

Riel watched it all, but remained quietly on the farm. For the most part the influx was absorbed in an orderly and civilized manner; only one group of easterners made themselves conspicuous by the violence of their behaviour. Deliberately squatting on river-land claimed by a band of Catholic métis, while the latter were absent on the summer buffalo hunt, they renamed their district The Boyne and defied anyone to turn them out. If they were looking for trouble they almost found it, for when the dark-skinned old-timers returned the intruders were immediately challenged at gun-point. But Governor Archibald refused to be intimidated either by métis arms or by people from Ontario who "seem to feel as if the French half-breeds should be wiped off the face of the globe" (as he wrote to Macdonald at about this time). Swiftly he moved to forestall possible violence. Firmly he acted to win métis confidence and persuade them to set aside their guns. Then he insisted that the matter be settled on the basis of law. Because of his impartiality and the trust it inspired, the second "Battle of the Boyne" was never fought.

All during the summer Riel lived inconspicuously at home. Though the amnesty question was no nearer settlement than it had been, he was not molested in any way. On the ground that the Manitoba Act did not empower the courts of the new province to take retroactive action, Governor Archibald repeatedly refused to sign a warrant for his arrest. Riel began to hope that there might be a future for him in his beloved West. When, on September 22nd, Taché was formally elevated to the archbishopric, Louis chose the occasion to come out of retirement for the first time. From the steps of St. Boniface Cathedral he delivered a public speech in praise of his lifelong friend. Though his action provoked criticism on both sides of the river, no incidents followed in its wake and he began to regain confidence in himself.

Once more he was the leader of the métis race; he would serve to the best of his ability in peace as he had in war. But how would he begin his new career?

Suddenly an opportunity presented itself. It began to be rumoured that O'Donoghue was about to lead an armed attack against Manitoba. Having been ignored by Washington when he went there for aid, the ex-treasurer of Riel's Provisional Government had turned to the Fenian Society for help. (This was an Irish-American organization whose aim it was to overthrow British rule wherever it might be found.) From its members he had received lavish promises, some money, and modern arms. Now, accompanied by one of the Fenian leaders—a character known as "General" John J. O'Neill—he was touring Minnesota trying to recruit followers for the cause; he had announced publicly that he would attack Fort Garry with a force of 3,300 men. No one knew how serious the threat might be. Potentially, it could be very serious indeed, for he was calling on the métis to join him.

It was impossible to be sure how the people of mixed blood would react; overnight the atmosphere at the Forks became electric. As Archibald well knew, the métis had ample reason to feel restless still. They had been mistreated badly by Canadians who had said they came in peace. They had failed as yet to receive a square inch of the 1,400,000 acres of land that had been promised them—though the Hudson's Bay Company had been paid its £300,000, and others, like Dr. Schultz, had received generous compensation for losses sustained during the recent trouble. It might well be that beneath their calm exteriors, sufficient resentment lingered to prompt them to answer O'Donoghue's mad call.

Appalled by the prospect of renewed conflict among the people, Governor Archibald cast about him for a means of keeping Manitoba quiet. Reluctantly he came to the conclusion that, though it might prove disastrous to his political future, he must call upon Riel to help him. At his request a meeting between the métis chief and Archbishop Taché was arranged. It took place at Father Ritchot's house in St. Norbert.

Louis was almost his old self again as he assured his friend that he would keep the métis in line. Their grievances were very real, he said. It was natural to fear that some of them might succumb to the temptations offered by O'Donoghue. But he was their acknowledged leader still, and in his opinion the majority would listen to his advice. He would call a meeting and point out to his people that the Fenian Society was condemned by the Church, and that they would be wise to use this incident as an opportunity to demonstrate their loyalty to the Crown. Surely, by rallying to the flag now they could smooth the whole path of their future. If they remained loyal, they would put the Queen, and Ottawa, under an obligation to decide the amnesty question in their favour.

For the first time since his Government had collapsed, Louis began to move about the upper part of the settlement quite openly. Though he remained out of Winnipeg and stayed away from places where Ontario immigrants might recognize him, he went quietly about the business that he had promised he would attend to. He was received by his own people with open arms. The magic of his name, of his personality, had not diminished; he was able to persuade the whole métis nation to accept his views. Through Father Ritchot (Archbishop Taché had departed for the East once again) he assured Governor Archibald in due course that all would be well.

According to reports received at Fort Garry, the Fenian invasion was imminent now; Manitoba lay in mortal danger of attack. Hurriedly, disbanded Canadian volunteers were recalled to the colours. In Fort Garry they were drilled and armed; then, under Colonel Irvine, they were despatched to the southern frontier. The force was small; it consisted of infantry only. There was no cavalry and there were no reserves. After pondering these facts, Governor Archibald decided on further action. It might be suicide politically, but the survival of the country seemed to be at stake: he would summon Father Ritchot to his side once again, request him to arrange that the military forces of the métis be marshalled in the service of the Queen. He saw the priest; the priest, in turn, called upon Riel, who said he would do what he could. With the help of Ambroise Lépine (who had returned to Manitoba by this time, too), Louis soon raised a troop of three hundred men. On October 8th he paraded these men, with their horses, before St. Boniface Cathedral.

Though the Governor dared not acknowledge formally that he had communicated with the fugitive métis chief, he was grateful nevertheless for his help, and he wanted to demonstrate the fact. Accordingly, he crossed the river that morning and inspected the assembled force. But he did it with the Nelson touch. In front of everyone he shook hands with Riel, Lépine and Pierre Parenteau. Riel was introduced simply as the man "chosen by the French métis for their leader"; the two lieutenants were referred to as "prominent men". With a smile he told them he was grateful for their support. Knowing what he meant, they bowed and assured him they would stand by until required.

At this time few Ontario-born Canadians would have tolerated the idea of Archibald acknowledging openly the "murderer of Thomas Scott". In what he did he showed personal and political courage of a high order, for there was still an abundance of feeling abroad among the immigrants. One instance will serve to illustrate this point. On the second night of their march to the south, while encamped near St. Norbert, several of the Canadian volunteers plotted unsuccessfully to murder Father Ritchot in his rectory—simply because they knew he had been an emissary of the Provisional Government the previous year! Their plot was discovered in time to be quietly circumvented; but, had it not been, had it succeeded, God only knows what the métis would have done to their new compatriots in revenge.

The Fenian scare petered out; no shots were ever fired in Manitoba's defence. Before either the Canadian volunteers or the métis troops arrived within miles of the border, O'Donoghue, O'Neill, and thirty-seven other hotheads were lodged in an American jail. O'Neill and most of his men were captured by the U.S. cavalry on the Canadian side of the boundary. O'Donoghue was taken prisoner by some local métis and delivered to the authorities at Pembina. Thus, the whole flimsy bubble burst harmlessly on the empty north-western plain. But it *could* have been serious; people expected it to be serious; and, challenged by the threat of it, the métis had proved themselves by coming in solidly on the side of Canada.

At the height of the Fenian scare Lieutenant-Governor Archibald had said: "Should Mr. Riel come forward as suggested, he need be under no apprehension that his liberty will be interfered with in any way. It is hardly necessary to add that the co-operation of the French half-breeds and their leaders in support of the Crown and under the present circumstances will be very welcome and cannot be looked upon otherwise than as entitling them to favourable consideration." Consoling words, these; brave ones, too. Words strong enough to give hope to a hunted man. But the crisis had faded now, and with it all hope.

The flame of hatred had been rekindled in Ontario, where, at about the same time as the Fenian unrest, an election had taken place. Edward Blake, the leader of the Liberal Party there, began his campaign by offering a reward of five thousand dollars for Riel's head. Accusing the federal Conservatives of failing to punish anyone for the "cold-blooded murder of an Ontario citizen", he exploited ruthlessly the popular feeling around him. Though the issue had nothing whatever to do with provincial affairs, it served the Liberals well. With a huge majority they were swept into power, and Blake's offer of blood-money became provincial law soon thereafter. The news was published abroad, read with avid interest—even joy—in some quarters. In the West, dozens of immigrants from Ontario became eager to try for the reward.

On December 8th, while Louis was attending a meeting of the St. Jean-Baptiste Association at St. Boniface College, a band of men forced their way into his mother's house. Not finding him there, they attempted to set the building on fire, but were prevented from doing so by a party of métis who happened to be passing by. When Mrs. Riel, a widow with seven children still under that roof, appealed to the police for aid, she was ignored. Hearing this, the métis swore publicly that they would defend with arms anyone molested by Canadians. It appeared as if the "war" had begun all over again!

At about this time Archbishop Taché arrived home. He had spent November in the East, trying once again without success to persuade the federal Government to settle the amnesty question. By now, even he was willing to admit that the situation defied a political solution. While Quebec, as much as Ontario, had refused to accept the shooting of Thomas Scott as a legal function of a legal government in the North-west, it insisted that Mair, Schultz, and others from Ontario shared the blame and were using excitement over the execution to cloak their own past exploitation of the métis. In other words, as illegal acts had been committed by both sides, would it not be wise simply to forgive and forget at this stage? To the citizens of Ontario this was anathema. There could be no question of exercising charity here; there could be no consideration of motives or circumstances. An English-speaking, Anglo-Saxon Protestant had been "murdered" by French-speaking, half-breed Catholics. The naked action spoke irrevocably for itself and cried to Heaven for vengeance.

Now politics under *any* form of government is the art of achieving that which it is possible to achieve. In the matter of an amnesty for Riel and his chief lieutenants, it had become impossible politically to achieve a thing. The House of Commons was threatened with a fatal rift, was overshadowed by that worst menace of all—a division along racial-religious lines. Even to attempt to deal with the question might tear the new nation apart.

Though democracy is an admirable philosophy of government, it cannot function effectively as a *form* of government under such circumstances. Unless its adherents are men of integrity, seeking the common good, its processes will grind to a halt. Moreover, it presupposes that basic norms of society, basic standards and values, are shared by the members of the community on whose behalf it functions. It presupposes a disposition towards honesty, both in those who cast votes and those who receive them; it will not operate effectively unless reasonably accurate information is available about the issues at stake.

Because none of these conditions were present, Sir John Macdonald and Sir Georges Cartier, his deputy in the Cabinet, were faced with an impossible task, and they knew it. The integrity of the people was misplaced; they were not thinking of the common good—that is, the good of Canada as a whole. Confederation was barely four years old, and their loyalties still flowed along rigidly sectional lines. To make matters worse, the citizens of Ontario and Quebec had been indoctrinated for generations with tales that could not fail to make them distrust one another. Their historic development, from which they derived their standards of value, their concepts of the norm, had been radically different ever since that sixteenth-century rift in the minds of European men known as the Reformation. And—a final source of misunderstanding—the news they had received about the goings-on in the North-west had been shaded by the political opinions of the editors who presented it. Thus there was a deadlock, complete and fundamental, which only time and the re-birth of goodwill might dissolve.

Now, Macdonald knew this, for he was nothing if not a very able politician. He knew also that he must get on with the development of the West or run the risk of losing British Columbia for all time. Compared with his vision of a nation stretching from set to sea, Riel and the few thousand métis who followed him counted for nothing at all. If it became necessary to offer them as human sacrifices to the god of progress—in reparation for the blunders that Ottawa had committed the previous year—he would not hesitate to do so. But it was not necessary yet; there were two further manoeuvres he might employ before considering such an alternative.

First, he would continue to deny that his Government was competent to rule on the amnesty question (because it had exercised no jurisdiction in the territory at the time of Scott's death) and try to prevail upon Britain to decide Riel's fate. Second, he would attempt to bribe Riel to leave the country, in the hope that without the irritant the blister would soon disappear. This manoeuvre especially would require the utmost secrecy and delicacy of execution, for it could cause explosions politically if noised abroad. Undoubtedly the man best suited for the job was Taché, the Archbishop of St. Boniface, whom both he and the métis chief trusted implicitly. He would put it up to him, throwing in a hint that if Riel left Canada it might become possible to tackle the amnesty question in earnest. Astutely, Macdonald reasoned that Taché, who wanted only peace for his flock, would find the proposition irresistible.

The Archbishop saw Macdonald; he agreed to co-operate. As soon as he returned to Red River he sent for Riel and Lépine. Sitting in his study, the two métis faced him expectantly. As he stood with his back to the window, they were able to see beyond him to the out-of-doors, where snowflakes floated gracefully downwards in the motionless air as the dull grey afternoon turned slowly into night. They were able to see across the river where, a mile away, the lights of Winnipeg already blinked their message of warmth, security and peace to the people of the plains. They were able to see all this and, seeing it, to feel comforted and full of anticipation. Just to gaze at the scene made them hopeful that the nightmare through which they were passing would fade with the fading day and leave them in peace at last.

With the Archbishop's first words they were shocked out of their reverie. "I'm afraid I bear no good news, my sons," he said quietly. "I have seen Sir John Macdonald. There is no immediate chance of an amnesty for either of you. In fact, I have summoned you here only to ask of you further sacrifices on behalf of the métis people."

Lépine laughed harshly. "I thought it would be something like this. You never could trust the Canadians."

"But Governor Archibald assured us—" Riel began.

"I know what Governor Archibald said," Taché cut in. "I know also that he spoke without authority. Now, you will listen, please, while I tell you what Sir John has asked me to say."

A trifle stiffly the Archbishop moved to his chair; then he sat down, stared in front of him silently for a long moment. Presently he cleared his throat and began: "There is no chance whatever of an amnesty for either of you. Sir John feels that politically it is out of the question at the present time. I must admit that, after hearing all the facts, I agree with him—though it is his own fault that things have come to such a pass. Time will be required for feelings to cool, for the voters of Ontario and Quebec to develop a sense of proportion about your activities. That is why Sir John considers it imperative, if the rest of our people are to be pardoned, for you both to leave the country for a while. He appreciates the inconvenience this will cause and is quite willing to provide you with compensation."

"How much?" Lépine demanded with his customary bluntness.

"A thousand dollars, divided between you."

There was a moment's silence, then Riel came to life. "*Non!*" he said firmly. "I will not do it, Your Excellency! I will accept no bribes. My place is among my own people, and with them I must remain."

Taché smiled. "Louis, it is because I am aware of your love for the people that I dare ask you to comply with Sir John's request. He is right, you know. Your presence here can only cause trouble, and trouble can only bring reprisals in its wake. But if you go away perhaps things will gradually calm down."

"What you are saying is that I am a millstone around the neck of my people," Riel accused, his voice thick with emotion.

The Archbishop nodded. "That is the bitter truth, Louis. It is necessary that we face up to it."

All his life Lépine had been accustomed to facing facts. He recognized, now, that what Taché said made sense. He cleared his throat. "We might as well take the money, Louis," he advised. "We'll never get anything better out of the Canadians; of that I'm sure."

Sitting motionless, breathing hard, Riel studied the beadwork on his moccasins and the bishop's polished floor. For a moment more he clung to his dream of destiny; then with a sigh he relaxed his hold. "I am willing to do anything that will help my people," he said wearily, "provided it does not make them think that I have accepted a Canadian bribe." He looked pleadingly at Taché. "If you, as my Bishop, request me to leave the country temporarily, so that the amnesty question may be settled once and for all, I will do so. But I must have your request in writing; I must possess proof to show that I have not abandoned my people in their hour of need."

"I will write such a letter willingly," the Archbishop said quietly.

"One more thing," Louis went on. "Mother is a widow. She has four young girls and three young boys to feed. If I leave at the request of the Canadian Government I will be unable to help her in any way. It seems to me that someone should pay for her keep while I am gone."

"As the Archbishop has said, Louis, there is that thousand dollars," Lépine reminded him.

"Five hundred for you and five hundred for me!" Riel said scornfully. "What good is a thousand dollars to us? What everyone forgets is that the Canadian Government owes me a good deal more than that! Didn't I administer the country for them last year, from July 15th until Wolseley arrived, without compensation? Haven't they said things about me that any court would consider slanderous?"

"Calm yourself, Louis. I'm sure the difficulty about money can be overcome," the Archbishop said smoothly. "But it would be as well not to go into these other matters just now. Leave it with me for a few days, will you?" He stood up. The others, knowing the interview had come to an end, arose too. After bidding their host good-bye they left the room.

A few days later Taché sent for them again. The difficulty *had* been overcome; a total of four thousand dollars was now available for the support of their families. (The additional three thousand dollars had been added from the coffers of the Hudson's Bay Company, thanks to Donald A. Smith, who had arranged the transaction at Fort Garry.) The Archbishop told them this, then suggested that Riel and Lépine should take five hundred dollars in cash, allowing him to retain the balance to support their families while they were away. They agreed to all he proposed, and, the matter being settled, slipped across the border to exile in the United States. The date of their departure was February 20, 1872.

Part Two

PROPHET OF THE NEW WORLD

X

THE MEMBER
FOR PROVENCHER

DURING the rest of the winter of 1872-1873 and much of the following summer, Riel remained in exile. It was an interval during which frustration, and sometimes actual physical danger, cut deeply into his self-confidence. On March 19th he wrote Archbishop Taché from St. Paul, telling him that he and Lépine had arrived there fifteen days ago, and that Schultz had arrived on the 16th and, with Dr. Bown, had attempted to steal his papers. On April 2nd he wrote his mother, saying, among other things: "I fear my letters are intercepted."

If he had imagined that, by accepting Macdonald's money, he would find peace, he was soon disillusioned. Adventurers hunted him for the bounty his capture would earn them; after narrowly escaping a dozen times, he became convinced that enemies lay in wait for him everywhere. His nerves became jaded; gradually he began to carry with him wherever he went an abiding sense of apprehension. Presently he took to identifying himself with the boy David of Biblical times, who, before he became King of Israel, had been forced to live alone, in exile, in the wilderness. Occasionally he even signed his letters "Louis David".

The news from Red River would have convinced the most stolid of men that Riel's decision to go into exile had been wrong. Day after day events were proving beyond a doubt that his gesture had been an utterly futile one. On April 16th he heard that Alexander Mackenzie, the Liberal leader in Ottawa, had brought up the "Scott affair" in the House of Commons. On April 22nd he learned in a letter from Father Dugas that Schultz and other members of the "loyal" party had burned Archibald and Riel in effigy. Five days later he was informed that Maxime Lépine, André Nault, and Pierre Laveille had been attacked by a group of Canadian ex-volunteers while leaving Fort Garry, after going there to see the Lieutenant-Governor about métis timber rights. He learned, also, that there was a movement afoot to elect him to the House of Commons as Member for the new constituency of Provencher.

Immediately, Louis wrote to his friend Joseph Dubuc, saying that he would like to sit in the Commons on behalf of his people "if no federal law prevents it". But he added that he was reluctant to consider the matter seriously. And yet he must have considered very seriously whether or not he could be of service in the political world. The métis needed strong representation in Ottawa—of that there could be no doubt. Day after day they were being pushed further aside by an influx of immigrants from the East; steadily they were losing their sense of identity as a people; and because the amnesty question had not been decided, they lived constantly with the fear that they might be pronounced outlaws at any time. For them and for their children, hope was fading fast.

On the national scene politicians were still bending truth in the interests of expediency. Blake, in Ontario, still offered a reward for the "murderer's" head. Macdonald, who was in trouble with the farmers of Ontario over a treaty he had been forced by Britain to sign with Washington, and with Orangemen everywhere because of Archibald's reasonable conduct towards the métis, still took pains to be all things to all men. "I wish to God I could catch him!" he would shout to the voters of Ontario—who had no inkling, yet, of the money he had advanced to Riel. Then, moving across the border into Quebec, he would vow to the voters there that it was the Ontario Liberals alone who were to blame for frightening Riel away! Such have always been the vagaries of our more "practical" politicians.

Riel resolved to put an end to the farce. In midsummer, with Lépine, he returned quietly to St. Vital. By this time the first Parliament of Canada had come to the end of its life; a general election was about to be held. After much soul-searching, Louis let it be known that he would allow his name to stand as a candidate in his own constituency of Provencher. Because of his local popularity, no one dared at this moment to prevent his offering himself at the polls. If he were elected, so he reasoned, he would be able to rely on parliamentary immunity to protect him while he publicly presented the métis case.

The voters in Provencher were almost solidly métis; the only other candidate who had offered himself was Clarke, Manitoba's Attorney-General, and Riel was confident he could defeat him without difficulty. If he was right, he did not get the opportunity to prove it; for he was persuaded to withdraw his name as a candidate before the contest had well begun.

Now in those days elections were not held simultaneously across the country, as they are today. Thus, before the people of Manitoba cast their ballots, the contest in the East had already been decided—and Sir Georges Cartier, Macdonald's key French-Canadian Cabinet minister, had met defeat in Montreal East. This was a serious blow to the Conservative ministry, who were anxious to get on with the nation-building task they had just begun. As a counter-stroke, Macdonald and Cartier, using the services of Archibald and Taché, approached both candidates in Provencher and asked them to step aside in the interests of the country as a whole. If they would consent to do so, they were told, Cartier could be elected by acclamation in the new riding.

Both men acquiesced; it seemed to them self-evident that it would be good for the West in every way to have a Cabinet minister representing them in Ottawa. In coming to his decision Riel was influenced for the last time by the old argument, passed on by Taché from Sir Georges, that if he would sacrifice himself the amnesty question, and certain other vexing local issues, might more readily be settled in the métis' favour.

In due time, when Cartier had been elected unopposed, Macdonald and his colleagues settled in for what they confidently expected to be another five years in office. They planned to populate the West, build up industry in the East, and make a start on the railroad to the Pacific Coast. Almost immediately Sir Georges became too ill to carry on in active politics. He departed to England for treatment. In the following May, still on the far side of the Atlantic, he died. Thus, no one will ever know whether or not he intended to honour his promises to Riel.

By now it was apparent that the changes that had taken place in Manitoba were permanent. To the métis, it was as if black snow-clouds of winter, so long threatening on the horizon, had moved at last to engulf their Red River Valley. For them, there was no hope for the future now; indeed, even the English-speaking old-timers of Kildonan and St. Andrews Parishes had begun to withdraw defensively within themselves. Before the year was done Alexander Morris had replaced the benevolent Archibald as Lieutenant-Governor of Manitoba. No longer did the chief executive make a point of surrounding himself with moderate men; no longer did he ensure that a balance was maintained between French and English, Catholic and Protestant, sections of the community. Such was the pressure of immigration from Ontario that it would have been impossible to do so even had he wished to try.

While the French-speaking population sank into a permanent eclipse, all attempts at duality vis-à-vis French and English groups was abandoned. There had been almost no immigration from Quebec during the past few years—French-Canadian emigration had been directed for a long time now towards the adjacent New England states—but there had been a constant flood of immigration from Ontario. There was no room any more for métis hunters, or for potato-patch farmers of any race or creed. At last, on September 15, 1873, came the crowning blow, indicative of the political strength of the new-comers. Bowing to pressure exerted on him by popular clamour, Morris authorized warrants for the arrest of "Louis Riel, Ambrose [*sic*] Lépine, and others".

While all these changes were taking place and strangers from Ontario were combing the countryside, vying with each other for Blake's five-thousand-dollar reward, Riel and Lépine hid among friends. All during the winter and the following summer they evaded capture. The métis might be poor and utterly depressed, but they would not betray their leaders, no matter how much the reward. A blank look, a shrug, an obscure phrase muttered in French or Cree, was all the reply any of them would give to questions about the fugitive pair. Nowhere, except among the Scottish Highlanders after their uprising on behalf of Charles Stuart in 1745, can be found an example of such loyalty.

The death of Sir Georges Cartier meant, of course, a by-election in Provencher; and so, on July 19th, Joseph Royal, Joseph Dubuc, M. A. Girard, A. A. C. La Rivière, and other prominent local men wrote to Louis pledging their support if he would submit himself as a candidate. On August 2nd Riel replied that he would accept their offer; if elected, he would go to Ottawa and endeavour to make the Government live up to its promises of 1870.

Promptly, his old acquaintance Bannatyne came forward to offer his support. While Louis hid in a dummy haystack at Vermette's Point, across the Red River from St. Norbert, with magnificent defiance the métis population nominated him as their candidate. Though Macdonald and Governor Morris were appalled, they could do nothing to check the march of events—for this time Archbishop Taché refused to intervene.

On September 17th Lépine was recognized, arrested, and committed to stand trial for the murder of Thomas Scott. On October 13th Riel was elected to Parliament by acclamation. Without showing himself in public, Louis slipped away from the colony to begin his parliamentary career. Though he did not know it, his life at Red River had come to an end.

On October 17th, four days after his election, Dubuc had written Louis and outlined the plan decided upon to get him safely to his destination. Sufficient money for the journey had been collected; a companion named Tasse had been instructed to rendezvous with him at Fargo, in the United States. From there they must travel to Duluth—it was deemed safer than St. Paul—and take an American boat to Milwaukee or Chicago. From Chicago, Louis must go to Montreal or Terrebonne, relying on friends in either of these places to get him to Ottawa somehow.

This was cloak-and-dagger stuff; the journey was accomplished with such secrecy that even today it is impossible to know about it in detail. Of only one thing can we be sure—Louis' health must have given way under the strain of it all. After making one abortive attempt to present himself in the House of Commons, he went to New York State, to an Oblate seminary at Plattsburg, on the edge of Lake Champlain. From November 4th until January 23rd of the following year he spent most of his time there, resting.

But he cannot have been confined to his bed. From letters written at this time we know that once, at least, he journeyed to Montreal, where he met the aged Bishop Bourget; that, while staying for a few days with the religious community that staffed the asylum at Longue Pointe, he "astonished everyone by running into the dining-room, scantily clad, and announcing that he was the Holy Ghost". (Was this extraordinary behaviour suggested to his unsettled mind by the saying, current at the time, that he was driving his enemies into a frenzy because he was invisible to them?)

For most of this period, however, he remained at Plattsburg, occasionally visiting Father Fabien Barnabé, the parish priest in the nearby village of Keeseville; and here another influence began to quicken him. On his first visit to Father Barnabé, he met the priest's sister, Evelina, who kept house with her mother in the rectory. She was a lovely, gentle creature, and for the first time Louis experienced the healing power of a woman's affection.

It must have been a strange courtship. There was no real blending of minds or personalities here, and both knew that marriage, at least for the moment, was out of the question. Because he had given himself so thoroughly to his cause, there was nothing left in Louis for the girl he loved; but she did not seem to mind. He was handsome, he was lonely, he needed her; she found fulfilment in giving him whatever he was able to receive—and he was able to receive peace, at least for a time. While autumn gave place grudgingly to winter, they walked together along the banks of the Ausable River. He remained preoccupied with his dreams, with his hopes for the future of his beloved people; yet to have her at his side while he talked was like a balm to his troubled mind.

But the season was autumn, not spring, and this Indian-summer love affair had no real promise in it. Presently, like a prophecy of things to come, the first chill winds of winter reached them from out of the North. They came in the form of a letter from Louis Masson, the Conservative Member of Parliament for Terrebonne, Quebec. The Government of Sir John Macdonald had been forced to resign. Alexander Mackenzie, the Liberal Party's leader, had been asked by the Governor-General to form a government in its place. It would be best for Riel to stay where he was until the situation in Ottawa had clarified itself.

Then came another letter to say that Parliament had been dissolved, that a general election was to be held as soon as possible. Finally, word came that many old members had lost their seats and, though the Liberals would command a majority in the new House, Riel himself had been re-elected by the constituents of Provencher to represent them. Full of hope, Louis left New York to resume his journey into the political world.

Macdonald's Government had been forced to resign over what history now refers to as the "Pacific Scandal". In the heat of a bitter election fight, desperately short of party funds, his judgment made hazy by alcohol and fatigue, the "Father of Confederation" had done an incredibly stupid thing: he had accepted large donations of money from Sir Hugh Allan, a Montreal financier with whom he was negotiating a contract to build the Canadian railway to the West. This had occured in 1872, the year that Louis had stepped aside so that Cartier could run in Manitoba.

Allan's syndicate had ousted some wealthy Americans, former associates, who had revealed these dealings by way of revenge, and the facts had been proved subsequently by a royal commission empanelled to study the case. Though the inquiry did not claim that Macdonald had been deliberately dishonest or that he had attempted to feather his own nest, it did suggest that he had been almost criminally irresponsible, and public indignation had demanded that he step aside.

It is interesting to find that Jay Cooke, whose agents had tried to bribe Riel in 1870, seems to have been the power behind these American capitalists. It is pleasant to observe that he failed to gain control of the West by this means, as he had failed in his annexation scheme with Riel; but it is less pleasant to note that it was Macdonald's reputation, not Jay Cooke's, that suffered in the defeat.

Towards the end of January therefore, Louis bade *au revoir* to his friends in Plattsburg and to Evelina in Keeseville; then he returned secretly to Canada. For a time he stayed with the Mercier family in St. Hyacinthe, Quebec, and was affected for the rest of his life by the experience. They were charming people, the Merciers and their friends, and kindness itself to the métis chief; but they provided the worst possible influence to which he could have been exposed at this time.

The head of the family, Honoré Mercier, was thirty-four years of age in 1874. Though a brilliant lawyer, his chief interest lay in provincial politics, and his second in the Church. In politics he was what was then known as a *castor*, which meant that he stood for out-and-out French-Canadian nationalism. He was opposed to the whole idea of confederation; he hoped to turn Quebec into a Church-dominated, self-contained fortress, in the vain hope that by doing so he could shield its people from the English-speaking Protestant world. Just as the Orangemen of Ontario were more British than the English and more Protestant than John Calvin, he and his followers were more Gallic than the French and more Catholic than the Pope.

To further their objective, this group worked hand in hand with such reactionary figures as the aged Bishop Bourget of Montreal (by whom Riel had been profoundly impressed) and Alphonse Desjardin, the editor of *Le Nouveau Monde*. These latter men stood for the ultramontane movement within the Church, a movement that in other parts of the world was soon to wane. Though originally it had arisen in Europe as a protest against undue meddling in ecclesiastical affairs by government, it had been twisted until now, in Quebec, it stood for the domination of the State by the Church. Archbishop Taschereau would ultimately, with Rome's help, destroy the influence of these men, but at the moment they were still to be reckoned with. It was inevitable that to them Louis would seem a priceless prize and be adopted quite naturally as one of their own.

In conference with them, Riel soon abandoned all remaining notions that, once safely in Ottawa, he could rely on parliamentary immunity to protect him while he argued the métis cause. According to them he was in graver danger in eastern Canada than he had been in the West; Macdonald had been defeated as much by indignant Orangemen, who blamed him for Riel's continued freedom, as by feelings of honest revulsion over his relationship with Sir Hugh Allan. English-speaking Canadians were still out for Louis' blood—and they would continue to be until they had spilled it.

To back up their views, his new friends pointed out that in Mackenzie's Cabinet now was the same Edward Blake who, when Premier of Ontario, had posted the reward for Riel's head. Neither Louis nor any other French-speaking Canadian could hope for justice within the framework of confederation, now. Nevertheless, they hastened to add, he must hold fast to his sacred mission. The new Parliament would open on March 27th. As the elected representative of the métis people, he must go to Ottawa and be ready to strike a blow that would awaken the nation.

Secretly, he moved to Hull, across the Ottawa River from the capital, where he waited for an opportunity to act.

Now the ice was out of the river and the snow was almost gone. Back in the Gatineau Hills—as if to provide an omen for the happy days ahead—parties of *habitants* made syrup from the sap of the maple trees, and in Ottawa a young man named Wilfrid Laurier arose in the House of Commons to deliver his maiden speech.

It was March 30, 1874. The time had come to act! Louis Riel and Dr. Jean-Baptiste Fiset, the re-elected member for Rimouski, walked quietly towards the office of the Clerk of the House. At this hour of the afternoon, though the juniors were back at their desks again, dreaming of the end of the day, most senior government officials still lingered over their lunch. No one paid heed to this solitary pair; no one suspected what they were up to yet. However, when they got to the door of the Clerk's office, just to be on the safe side, Riel hung back while Fiset entered and prepared the way.

Standing there in the deserted corridor, Louis must have felt nervous and vaguely ill, but exalted too. Dr. Fiset was beckoning to him to enter the ill-lit room. Stiffly—for the matter must be undertaken with dignity—he complied. Before the Clerk's desk he repeated the formula of the oath: "I do swear that I will be faithful and bear allegiance to Her Majesty Queen Victoria." Then he signed the book where Fiset's finger showed him he should sign. Turning on his heel, he started for the door. The exaltation within him had risen to obliterate his nervousness; the feeling of achievement had superseded all else. He had struck his blow of defiance; he had signed the Members' Roll! Though a price of five thousand dollars was upon his head, he had shown the world that he was not afraid. The métis cause would live on because he, Riel, lived for it.

Behind him he heard Dr. Fiset say good-day to the Clerk of the House. Remembering his manners, he forced himself to pause at the door, half turned, and bowed to the man who had sworn him in. Then the doctor was beside him and together they walked away.

That evening, in a gas-lit room in Hull, Louis wondered, no doubt, what exactly he had achieved. He had signed the register, he had defied the world; but now all Ottawa bristled with policemen and he was as much a fugitive as he had ever been. He was through and so were the métis, and he might as well admit it, to himself and to God.

But Dr. Fiset refused to sympathize with him. He did not seem to care how Louis felt about this afternoon. He was a seasoned politician. To him, the signing had been a success, for it had reminded people that the Liberals were no nearer to settling the amnesty question than the Conservatives had been before them. He was positively bubbling with good spirits as he told Louis of what was going on in the capital now. A rising of the people was feared—mounted guards had been posted in front of the city's armouries. Everyone had expected Riel himself to appear in the House this evening; the galleries had been crowded with spectators hoping to catch a glimpse of him. Lady Dufferin, the wife of the Governor-General, had been present with her entire dinner party. The whole thing had been a great show. In short, their action had stirred the political pot, and anything could happen as a result.

Indeed, they *had* stirred the political pot! On the debating floor Conservative members from Quebec had demanded an amnesty for the métis, while Conservative members from Ontario had silently cursed them for doing so. On the other side of the House, Liberal members had chuckled with glee at this spectacle of disunity in the ranks of the opposition. For a moment it had seemed as if they might propose that Sir John alone should be blamed for Riel's actions and the "rebels" be pardoned for all they had done. But the more sober among them had realized that such a move would be bad politics in the long run, and had dissuaded their colleagues in the nick of time. It might win them support from a few wavering French-Canadian members, they had pointed out, but it would alienate them from the voters of Ontario—and it was from Ontario that the Liberals drew their most solid support.

Thus, gradually, as English-speaking Conservatives and Liberals were drawn together, the matter had become a non-party issue; and, at the strategic moment, Mackenzie Bowell, the Conservative Member from North Hastings, who was Grand Master of the Orange Lodge, had risen to move that Riel be ordered to attend or lose his seat. The majority of the House had voted in favour of this motion. (If Riel did attend, as had been clearly pointed out from the floor, he would be arrested on the warrant sworn out against him in Manitoba for the murder of Thomas Scott, and sent back to Winnipeg to stand trial.)

"But I tell you, Louis, we caused a great stir!" Dr. Fiset concluded happily.

Riel shrugged. "To what avail?" he asked despondently. "It got us nowhere."

He was right; it had got them nowhere. But it *had* started a process that Sir John Macdonald and Archbishop Taché had striven for years to avoid. It had delivered Parliament into the hands of the hotheads, it had divided the chamber along racial-religious lines. And now the rift must widen before it could begin to heal. Before they were finished, the Quebec "national-ists" would almost have their way, the Ontario Orangemen would almost achieve their dream; Canada would come close to being ripped asunder, and the spirit of co-operation that had prompted confederation in the first place would come close to being dealt a mortal blow. But at the time no one seemed to care except Riel—and he cared only because he thought all the hatred and bitterness around him was directed against him and his métis race.

During April, while French-Canadian Members of the House of Commons muttered that Riel *must* take his seat, and mass meetings of French Canadians resolved to defend him against physical harm if he tried, Louis hid out in Hull. On one occasion, when he crossed over to Ottawa to attend church, he was recognized; but he was not arrested. For all their show with soldiery and police, this Government had no more desire than had Macdonald's to bring upon themselves the embarrassment of capturing him. Finally, it was ruled that, as he had failed to obey an order of the House, in that he had not taken his seat when commanded to do so, he should be expelled from Parliament. To this the Conservatives added the pious observation that, if he was guilty of any crime in the North-west, the Liberals should proceed against him; if he was not, they should have the courage to say so and let him take his seat.

The order of expulsion was passed on April 15th, with 124 votes for and 68 against. By this time the whole question of an amnesty had been referred to a Select Committee of the House. A French-Canadian Member now proposed an amendment to defer Riel's expulsion until the committee had reported; another *Canadien* moved that the question of amnesty be referred to the Queen; both moves met defeat. After this there was nothing for Louis to do but to prepare a written defence for his friends in Parliament to present on his behalf. While the committee sat, Provencher elected Riel for the third time to the seat from which he had been expelled; and he remained hidden, praying that justice would at last prevail.

But it was late in the day for justice now. In due course the committee reported that the execution of Scott had been the act of a *de facto* government, that Taché and others had been justified in believing themselves authorized to promise an amnesty, that Governor Archibald's appeal to Riel for aid in 1871 had implied that he was not liable to arrest and punishment. But the Government did not dare to wipe the slate clean. Instead it concocted a compromise by which the Governor-General, now Lord Dufferin, would grant a full amnesty to all rank-and-file métis who had participated in the trouble, at the same time ruling that Riel and Lépine must lose their civil rights and suffer banishment for five years, and that O'Donoghue be banished for life. With that, Parliament turned its frock-coated back on the subject and addressed itself to other matters as quickly as it could.

At about this time Lépine's trial was finally concluded in Winnipeg. After the question of the court's jurisdiction had been settled (Lépine's lawyers had questioned the right of a Manitoba court to try a man for something done before there was a Manitoba), he was found guilty of the murder of Thomas Scott and sentenced to be hanged. The Governor-General commuted the sentence to two years' imprisonment or five years' banishment, and used the occasion to announce that the same treatment would be given Riel should he come forward to stand trial. But Louis would not come forward; no longer did he trust anyone connected with the official world. Lépine elected the jail term.

These developments had solved the political issue, at least for the time being, but they had killed all métis hopes for justice in the West. Without personal leadership the half-breeds were doomed to disintegration, to watching in agony while hordes of immigrants trampled underfoot the rights they had fought for and won. And they would have no leadership now, for the only man who could have given it to them was in exile. Defeated, hopeless, without either money or health, he had fled to the refuge of Keeseville.

XI

RISE, LOUIS DAVID RIEL

B Y December, 1874, Louis was in Washington, D.C., looking for a job. He had been sent there by Father Barnabé with a letter of introduction to Major Edmond Mallet, a prominent French Canadian, who was Inspector of Indian Agencies for the American West and a friend of President Grant. When Riel arrived he had been full of hope that some position might be found for him as a government agent to Indian tribes, but by now it was apparent that this would not be so. Everyone had extended sympathy to him, many had given him hand-outs that he might be fed and clothed; yet no one had offered him a job and no one was likely to do so. What could he do? For a man of his temperament, life without important work was hardly worth while.

Despondent, lonely, unsure of himself, he decided one day to walk to Mount Vernon to see the home of the first President. He found it peaceful there. With its gracefully pillared white house towering over the Potomac, its trees planted by Washington himself, its plain brick tomb containing the relics of the man who had led his people to justice and freedom, the estate created a profound impression on his mind. After seeing it all he sat down on a bench to rest. Gradually a conviction of purpose in life returned and filled his soul.

Perhaps he fell asleep. There is no eyewitness account of what occured that December afternoon. Louis explained it afterward simply by saying that he had had a vision; God had come to him, as he had to Moses so many years before, in the form of a burning bush. He had said to him: "Rise, Louis David Riel. You have a mission to perform. Go to Montreal and tell Bishop Bourget that he is to be the Pope of the new world!" Weeping with joy, Louis had risen and walked in to Washington, where he made ready to return to Montreal.

Bishop Bourget was an old man, soon to retire. A valiant fighter, he had quarrelled often with both civil leaders and his fellow-bishops in Quebec. No doubt he felt a genuine sympathy for the brilliant young métis leader who, it seemed to him, had been pushed aside—as he himself was being pushed aside—by a gang of almost pagan politicians. In any event, when Louis sought him out secretly in Montreal to tell him of his experience at Mount Vernon, Bourget counselled him to have courage, for God was always on the side of right and His cause must triumph in the end. Then he gave him a thousand dollars and sent him back, with his blessing, to the United States.

Did Bourget believe that Louis had experienced a genuine vision? It is impossible to say, but it is very unlikely. Had Louis told him the second part of his "message", the Bishop would have thought him mad; for, to the end of his days, Bourget was a loyal Catholic and, no matter how numerous his personal disappointments had been, he could not have believed for a moment that God desired him to lead the Church in North America into schism. In any event, whatever words passed between them, Louis felt calmer when he had accomplished his mission.

During the winter and the following spring he dwelt peacefully in the United States, using Keeseville as his headquarters as he had before. As for the money presented to him by Bishop Bourget, it was soon gone. In a characteristic gesture of generosity, Louis gave it to a blind Italian beggar who came to his attention the next time he was in Washington.

During the summer of 1875 Riel journeyed westward to St. Paul in search of employment; but before he went he must have written, asking for advice, to Bishop Bourget, for the Bishop wrote him on July 14th as follows:

Dear Mr. Riel,

I received your letter yesterday and I was greatly touched, for that letter proves to me that you are animated by good motives and at the same time tormented in your mind by other inclinations or something which I do not understand, which makes you undecided in carrying out the duties imposed upon you by the obedience in which you live.

So I have the intimate conviction that you will receive in this world, and sooner than you think, the reward for all those mental and moral sacrifices you make, a thousand times more crushing than the sacrifices of material and visible life.

But God, who has always led you and assisted you until the present hour, will not abandon you in the dark hours of your life, for He has given you a mission which you must fulfil entirely.

By the Grace of God, you will persevere in the way which has been traced out for you. This is to say, you must not withhold anything you possess. You will desire above all things to know God and to show forth His glory. You will work unceasingly for the honour of your religion, the salvation of souls, and the good of society. And you will sanctify yourself in desiring heartily the sanctification of others.

As you asked me, I offered your letter to God, praying Him to confirm you in noble aspirations, and that He will protect you to the end. May your faith increase in strength, in order that you may never hesitate in the face of the difficulties which life presents to us in all its aspects.

Take care of your health and follow the advice of your doctor. Place yourself in the hands of Divine Providence, and believe that nothing happens in this world without this order or this permission.

Be ready for all emergencies which may come, keeping an unalterable peace of mind. I bless you and remain yours. . .

Quite obviously, the letter was meant to be nothing more than a message of encouragement. But to Louis it came to possess fantastic significance. For the rest of his life he carried it (with another one, also from the Bishop) on his person. As far as he was concerned, it assured him that he possessed a mission which he must fulfil; that he would succeed because, as the Bishop had said, he was right and God would not abandon him!

In the summer of 1875 he went to St. Paul to look for a job. But this city was too close to Manitoba for comfort and there were too many Manitobans visiting it constantly. After several nasty incidents, Louis fled eastward again to the same purposeless round of jobs at manual labour which he had experienced before.

By this time the stimulus that he had received from his "vision" had spent itself. Once again he was dejected, despondent, and possessed by unnamed fears. Back in Washington, on December 8th, he experienced a complete breakdown while attending Mass at St. Patrick's Church.

It was the Feast of the Immaculate Conception. The congregation had just risen, for the celebrant had begun the Credo. As Riel himself later wrote:

While the people were still standing, and me with them, I suddenly felt in my heart a joy so intense that to hide my face from my neighbours I covered it with my handkerchief, my hands on my mouth and eyes. In spite of my precautions, a boy of twelve just in front of me saw my great joy. Two minutes later this great sweep of joy was followed by a great sorrow of the soul. With an effort I tried to suppress my sobs, but my sobs and tears made a terrible noise in the church. My pain was as intense as my joy. It too passed in a little time, but my spirit was full of this thought: "The joys and sorrows of man are short."

For the past five years Louis had existed at a high emotional pitch; he had known frustration repeatedly, most often when success seemed within his grasp. All along he had been possessed by a sense of mission. Gradually, due to his temperament and the rebuffs he had experienced, this had become a conviction of *divine* mission—a conviction reinforced by his experience at Mount Vernon and his relationship with Bishop Bourget. Now, as his reason left him completely, he became convinced that he was one of a trio of bulls who were destined to remake the world. There was a white bull, a black bull, and a red bull. He himself was the red bull. The white bull was Count Chambord, the surviving Bourbon claimant to the throne of France; the black bull was Don Carlos, the thwarted, half-mad son of Philip II of Spain, who had been dead for four hundred years. When possessed by the notion that he was the red bull, Riel roared and tried to destroy whatever he found at hand.

Now Louis was incapable of looking after himself. As soon as he broke down in church, Major Mallet took him, with the aid of a guard, to the home of Father Primeau in Suncook, New Hampshire. After a while, when he began to show signs of improvement, Father Primeau moved him to Keeseville. But another bad spell came upon him, in which he frightened Evelina and her mother and tried to escape from his guard. In a letter to Major Mallet, Father Primeau expressed the utter hopelessness that all Louis' friends began to experience at this time.

"The poor young fellow! When I tell him that what he imagines is unreasonable, he weeps. 'Is it necessary to perform miracles to convince you?' he asks. 'Command me then.'" Primeau added: "What we expected has come true. His role is finished. Only a miracle can bring him back to normal."

Reluctantly, the Barnabés decided to notify John Lee, whose wife was a sister of Riel's father and in whose house Louis had stayed after leaving college in Montreal years before. Towards the end of January, or early in February, of 1876, Lee arrived and took his lunatic nephew with him to his home.

Riel was an exile; he had no right to return to Canada. John Lee must take care to ensure that no one recognized him. On the train, when Louis cried and made a noise, he told the other travellers that his nephew was a poor lunatic and asked them to excuse him. But Louis attracted so much attention that Lee became alarmed and sent a telegram to arrange for a carriage to meet them at St. Lambert, across the river from Montreal. At a later date, he wrote:

We crossed the river on ice, and, mounting the bank to pass the church [Bonsecours], Louis tried to throw himself from the carriage so that he could enter the church. Only by promising him that we would go to church after lunch was I able to calm him.

For the next six nights he did not sleep, cried, saying always that he was a prophet and had a mission to fulfil. He had contortions like a man in a rage. After six days he became calmer but tried to get outside, even threatening to throw himself out of the window, saying he wished to go to church. . . . After four or five weeks he seemed to get better, still begging to go to church. I consented when he promised to act sensibly. But he interrupted the Mass to contradict the priest. There was a commotion and I took Louis out. The priest called for silence, saying that it was nothing, just a poor lunatic.

It was important that the true identity of the "poor lunatic" remain unknown. As an exile, he was breaking the law by being anywhere in Canada; those who harboured him were breaking the law, too, and inviting reprisals. After this experience it must have taken great courage on the part of the Lees to persist in their self-imposed task of rehabilitation—courage and a good deal of physical and mental strength. But they were not young, and after a time the point was reached when they could no longer cope. To quote Lee's account:

Later he tore up his clothes, and would not say why. He tried to escape through the window to go to church, and when I remonstrated with him for his craziness, he said: "No, I'm not crazy. Never say I am crazy. I have a mission to fulfil and I am a prophet. I am sent from God!" His manner was of the fanatically exalted. But finally we were all tired out. I went to Dr. Lachapelle [who was a friend of Louis', probably introduced through the Massons or the Merciers] to ask him to admit Louis to an asylum. Lachapelle made the necessary arrangements.

I told no one, but took him there under the pretext of going for a ride to Longue Pointe [where the asylum of St. Jean-de-Dieu was situated]. I told him that his friend Dr. Lachapelle was going there to see him. I promised to return to see him next day.

This man, who had conceived the Manitoba Act and forced its passage through Parliament, was now documented by name and number in the asylum at Longue Pointe. He was registered under the name of Louis R. David, to protect the authorities, who pretended they did not know he was really Riel; he was allotted the number 565. Then the doors of the institution closed behind him and, to the outside world, he became as if dead.

From the start there was trouble. As Dr. Howard, the Superintendent, wrote:

He was a fine-looking man with a spiritual face. He had a dignified air, and I could hardly believe he had committed crimes of which he was accused. I felt a great pity for him. I went towards him to shake hands. "I am glad to see you, Mr. David. I am Doctor Howard," I said.

"Why do you call me David?" he demanded. "My name is Louis David Riel." Taking a book from his pocket, he opened it. "See, there is my name. My beloved sister [Sara] wrote it." The Sister Superior [afraid, no doubt, of Orange retaliation for harbouring this exile] grabbed the book and tore out the page, tearing it into bits. "You are known here as Monsieur David," she said, and a terrible scene followed. It took us all to get Louis Riel to his room, such was his rage. He finally stopped weeping and said: "This book was a gift from my sister on my birthday. Wherever I have gone, I have carried it with me." After that Louis still insisted that his name was Riel.

During the two and a half months he spent at Longue Pointe, he was by no means a docile patient. He wrote a lot of "thoughts" and some poetry, and stacked his output in a corner of his room. When he imagined that someone had stolen these papers, he made a scene and had to be restrained in a strait jacket. On one occasion he ran amuck in the chapel, said later that he had done so to show the Sister Superior that he was to be treated like a gentleman. On another occasion he stood against the wall, his arms extended as if he were on a cross, to prove to the nuns that he was Christ crucified.

The date of his admission was March 6, 1876. On May 19th he was moved to Beauport, near Quebec City, where there was less likelihood of Orangemen discovering him. When he was being moved he made a scene and had to be forced on the boat. His uncle, John Lee, was watching. "It was a pity to see," he wrote.

At Beauport Louis was admitted under the name of La-Rochelle. For some time he alternated between violence and the more peaceful pastime of writing. Sometimes he would ignore everyone. "At Beauport I found him more melancholy than at Longue Pointe," wrote Lee after a visit. Sometimes he would imagine himself to be a prophet, a pope, a priest or a king. But little by little he became more balanced. As he himself wrote when he was released the following year:

I had come to believe myself a prophet. It seemed to me that the papacy should leave the moth-eaten soil of Europe for the New World. I saw the light of civilization grow from the Orient, the Euphrates, Palestine, Rome. . . . It seemed to me that it was America's turn, and I believed that I had an important role to play in the new order of things. By pen and sword I tried to make converts.

However, one day, tired of fighting opposition, I asked myself if I was right or if everyone else was right. At that moment, the light came to me. Today I am better, I laugh myself at my hallucinations of my brain. I have a free spirit, but when one speaks to me of the métis, those poor tragic people, the fanatic Orangemen, of the brave hunters who are treated like savages, who are of my blood, of my religion, who have chosen me as their leader, who love me, and whom I love as brothers, ah, alas! my blood boils, my head gets on fire, and it is wiser if I speak of other things.

On several occasions during the summer and autumn of 1877 he was allowed to go "outside" for short visits to friends. During one of these he met Wilfrid Laurier at Three Rivers. Laurier was much impressed by the métis chief, found him fluent and well informed on American and European affairs. But he also found him unbalanced and inclined to boast vaguely of the "great mission . . . which a heavenly vision had urged him to undertake".

On January 21, 1878, he left the institution for good. The doctors said he was cured, but they warned him that he must avoid becoming involved in questions of politics or religion if he wished to remain so. He went back to Keeseville, New York. When he arrived there Father Barnabé wrote Major Mallet to say: "I am convinced that a little rest will make him perfectly well. His spirits show the most perfect lucidity, the greatest flexibility. Truly one would say that he had never been feeble-minded, if we did not know it as a certainty."

The good priest seems to have taken it for granted that Louis would settle down now among his *Canadien* friends in the eastern United States. These people rallied around him, made several attempts to get him a job. For a while he lived on his own, trying to establish himself in one or another of the large sea-coast cities. In the fall Father Barnabé wrote: "There must be a better position than journalist in New York. . . . Do not be discouraged. . . . I shall pray for you." Evelina wrote him on his birthday and asked him to pray that she should accompany him on his journey through life; and Aunt Lucy Lee, in Montreal, wrote him to say how pleased she was to hear that he was enjoying the best of health. But nothing seems to have suited him, and early in 1879 he decided to move west once again.

He had been away for a long time; perhaps his enemies had forgotten about him and would leave him alone. Settling in the village of St. Joseph, where he had hidden with Lépine during the winter of 1870-71, he occupied himself with farm-labourer's work, with poetry-writing, and with dreaming of gathering all the scattered métis people into one co-operative colony somewhere. His mother came down from Red River to see him, bringing with her one of his sisters and a new brother-in-law. "It was a great joy to see Mother again," he wrote to Father Barnabé in April, "and to meet my brother-in-law Lavalle; my sister Octavie has good taste."

It was a great joy, too, to be back in the West. There could be no doubt at all that Louis was made for this big country, for the undulating plains, the distant horizons that lay all about him now. On May 13th, Evelina wrote him from Keeseville, saying: "Last spring I saw you so often helping Mr. Content [a neighbour]. This year you are so far away. . . . I am anxious to cut the lilacs and offer one to you; we were so happy together. . . . I am afraid you will repent your choice, as I do not have the qualities you desire in a wife. . . . Take care of your health . . . write often."

But Louis did not write often; evidently the more he thought about the future, the more he pushed the memory of this girl to the back of his mind. There were so many other matters to consider. He was almost thirty-five years of age now; other men were making their mark in life, while he frittered away his time at lowly tasks. As Lépine had informed him in a letter at about this time, Dubuc was now a judge, Royal was a Member of the Canadian Parliament. Yet he himself had no position in which he could serve. He must put down his roots again among the people he was destined to lead. He must give up all idea of marrying a woman who by her upbringing would be incapable of sharing with him the sort of life he had been called upon to live.

Early in 1880, his period of exile came to an end. Instead of returning to Red River to live, he broke off his engagement to Evelina Barnabé and moved to Montana, to the country around Fort Shaw. There he joined a roving band of métis and became a hunter and trader, trading with Fort Benton and Helena, which was the capital of the territory. Living close to nature, among people of his own kind, Louis must have thought he had found his niche in life at last.

XII

A GREAT DAY
FOR THE MÉTIS NATION

BY 1884 about twenty-five of these métis families had settled around the Jesuits' Mission of St. Peter, nineteen miles south of Fort Shaw. There, under the guidance of Father Damiani, they were trying to learn how to combine farming with the life of hunting and trapping which they had always known. Louis quickly became a leader here; he wrote to his brother Joseph: "[I am] the master of the school, with the Reverend Jesuit Fathers, who have been kind to me during the long time that I have dwelt in their mission." Yet he was more than just "the master of the school". Once again he was the champion of the métis race, and once again he was at the centre of controversy in an area that was being overrun by immigrant white men.

Almost from the moment of his arrival in their midst, Louis saw that these métis of Montana were going under, as the métis of Manitoba had gone under while he was away. The buffalo were disappearing under a hail of white man's lead, the small game was being ruthlessly exploited by men bent on quick returns. Indian and métis horses and other livestock were being rustled by young toughs whom no one seemed interested in curbing.

"Even the officials of the country [connive with those who] pillage them," Louis wrote indignantly to the *Helena Weekly Herald*, as early as 1882. And in September of that year he sought out United States Marshal A. C. Botkin and threatened to invoke higher authority in Washington if no one would do anything locally about the situation. He followed up this threat by laying evidence before the marshal to the effect that one Simon Pepin, a trader, was illegally selling liquor to the métis and Indians, and charging that this was contrary to the federal Liquor Act. The case was thrown out of court, on the ground that while Pepin had sold liquor to the métis, it had not been proved that he had sold it to the Indians—and the métis, being part white, were not denied by law the right to purchase liquor.

When Botkin decided to campaign for a seat in Congress on the Republican ticket, Riel was asked to back him; and after the elections of 1882 were over, the victorious Democrats accused Riel of delivering métis votes for money. He declared in a letter to the *Herald* that the half-breeds had voted for Botkin simply because the Republicans had promised to use their influence on behalf of the métis. As a result of the incident, both Riel and Botkin made many enemies; and the former was arrested on a trumped-up charge of having had British métis vote for Botkin.

To secure evidence for his defence, and to attend the wedding of his sister Henriette to J. M. Poitras, Louis went to St. Vital in July of 1883. Armed with affidavits from the Postmaster, the Deputy of Customs, and the Judge of Probate in Pembina, he was able to disprove the charges against him—but only after fighting the case right through to the session of April, 1884, at his own expense.

As he had been everywhere else, Riel became a controversial figure in Montana. "I am accused of being a turbulent man," he wrote to the *Herald* at one point. "Such slurs give me the opportunity to say that . . . the principal meaning of my struggles . . . is honesty in public affairs. . . . Shrewd politicians have more than once tried to compromise with me. And because

I have always refused to give up my moral strength and my influence for their thousands of dollars [here he overlooks his deal with Taché], they have taken their revenge in calling me a rebel . . . and I see these men have brothers in Montana."

No one could deny him the right to say these things, for in May of 1880, at Fort Benton, he had declared his intention of becoming a citizen of the United States. And on March 16, 1883, he had become a citizen under the name of Louis David Riel. Botkin said much later that he had received his naturalization certificate with "almost childish delight".

He and his wife had become citizens on the same day. Her name was Marguerite-Monet Bellehumeur; she was a pretty little thing and she looked after his wants with loyal care. When he met her, soon after he arrived in Montana, he had been inspired to write a poem about her:

> *Priez Dieu qu'il donne à Marguerite*
> *Un esprit de plus et plus franc.*
> *Sauvez ma femme humble et petite,*
> *Sauvez son coeur obéissant.*

He had accompanied her father on trading expeditions to Fort Benton, at the head of navigation on the Missouri, and to Helena. The simple life had agreed with him; its peacefulness had been a tonic after the years in the East. Marguerite was a docile little creature of eighteen, with the shy manners of her Cree mother. Before witnesses, she and Riel had pledged themselves to each other and moved into the same tent. Seven months later—on March 9, 1882, at Carroll—this Indian form of marriage had been followed by the religious ceremony performed by Father Damiani. And now they had a two-year-old son, Jean, and a baby daughter, Marie-Angélique, and had settled at St. Peter's Mission, where they had a little house and a cow.

They lived a simple life, and yet it was interesting enough to keep Louis well occupied. As if to clarify his own mind, he wrote endless papers about the past; he also dashed off articles on matters of contemporary interest, such as the one entitled "The Spots of the Sun" that he wrote at Fort Assiniboine in 1881:

The present and actual state of the Sun is that of incandescence. After comparing the different hypotheses of astronomers, this seems to be the simplest and most probably true way to account for its great heat and its brilliant light. [Then, going on to explain that sun spots are nothing more than islands, or continents, formed by the cooling process of evaporation, he concluded:] Perhaps have I [sic] well explained what they are—if so, my thanksgiving to God, who created me and who gave me good sense to understand and to explain His work.

And he planned, endlessly, for the future. Botkin wrote, years later:

It was not of a little interest to listen as he unfolded his dream of a half-breed republic. . . . His project was to gather the half-breeds from the United States and all the British Provinces of North America and so build a nation . . . [with] a republican form of government. The Catholic religion was to be recognized . . . as the faith of the people, but there was to be a repudiation of Rome. Riel was to head this unique experiment . . . but . . . there was no taint of self-seeking in his efforts for freedom, justice and humanity.

He would unite all the métis in the world into one vibrant nation! In spite of his American citizenship, he would not

183

forget his Canadian brethren. When the time came to act, he would include them in his plans.

For a while he had almost forgotten them, to be sure. As he had worked to organize his people in Montana into an effective political unit, he had had little time to think of the Canadian métis. But when he had gone to St. Vital for Henriette's wedding and joined the other relatives gathered there, he had been reminded of their plight. He had learned, at first hand, how conditions were among his people in the North West Territories, where métis from Red River had gone during the past few years. And since then he had thought about them a great deal and had decided definitely that they should not be ignored.

Perhaps, instead of bringing them here, he would go to Canada again and do what he could for them there. In spite of all he had gained for them in 1869-70, they needed help now —of that he was very sure. After the transfer they had tried to adapt themselves to the changed conditions at Red River, but very few indeed had succeeded. Though they were as children concerning the ways of the world, they had been given almost no official help during this period of adjustment through which the forces of civilization were making it necessary for them to pass.

In 1870 the Government had bragged that 1,400,000 acres would be set aside for them under the terms of the transfer; but the actual land involved had not for a long time begun to change hands. Instead, each métis had been issued scrip entitling him to a 240-acre holding of land—when and if it was surveyed. No one had received his property before 1873; the allotments had not been completed until 1879. By that time it had been far too late for most of the half-breeds. The scrip with which they had been issued was transferable; those to whom it had been given were without sufficient resources to wait for their land to be made ready. So, when invited to do so, they had sold their scrip to speculators for a fraction of its worth. Then, swindled of their stake in the new order, they had drifted westward to recapture their traditional ways of life on the plains. Settling along the Saskatchewan, they had tried to become hunters and trip-men and potato-patch farmers, as of old. But the peace and security which they sought had been whisked forever beyond the horizon of their lives.

For a long time the hunting had been going from bad to worse on the prairies. Suddenly, in one dreadful season, all remaining game vanished from the plain. It is thought that it was deliberately destroyed by the actions of "civilized" men. When the American chief, Sitting Bull, fled to Canada with his Sioux after Custer's "last stand"—and took to raiding across the border from his British sanctuary—the U.S. Army decided on tactics of attrition, so it was said. Finding themselves prevented by the boundary line from continuing a full-scale war against these Indians, its commanders had attempted to starve them into submission. First they exterminated what was left of the northern buffalo herd when it grazed into U.S. territory; then they sent agents into Canada to fire the prairie from Wood Mountain to the Rockies, so that all game in the area would be destroyed.

Be this as it may, the game had disappeared—and the métis and Indians who lived off the land were faced, without warning, with the prospect of starvation. The Canadian Government had made arrangements to feed the Indians in return for a promise to retire to reservations and behave, but no one had moved to help the métis. And things were indeed serious for them now.

Huddled along the Saskatchewan, they were trying their best to sustain themselves off the land. But they were not skilled farmers, and their best was not good enough. If someone would teach them how to work their farms, if someone would give them seed grain and animal breeding stock and implements, they might work themselves out of their difficulties; but no one—with the exceptions of the missionary priests, the Oblates of Mary Immaculate, Archbishop Taché, and the Anglican Bishop McLean—was showing the slightest interest in their plight. In fact, they had been abandoned by everyone who had temporal power.

To heighten their conviction of abandonment, they found it impossible to get clear title to their land. White immigrants from the East were filling the country all around; sooner or later there would be trouble in the North-west, as there had been at Red River, and for almost indentical reasons. They had sent petition after petition to the Government, but each of them had been ignored. (Canada being a democratic country, its politicians could not be expected to show much interest in Canadians who, because they lived in the "territories", were without a vote.) According to report, the situation had grown grim indeed; it would not improve until the métis united once again under a leader who knew how to reach officialdom's ear.

Riel had made the Government pay attention in 1869, and last year his cousin, Napoléon Nault, had asked him whether he would be interested in reassuming his old role. Riel had shrugged. "I am very busy in Montana," he had replied with diffidence. But he had added: "I might return to Canada if it was shown that I was needed there." Then he had gone back to St. Peter's to teach school.

One day recently he had received an anonymous letter which said: "Do not imagine that you will begin the work when you get here; I tell you it is all done. The thing is decided; it is your presence that is needed. . . . You have no idea how great is your influence . . . the whole race is calling for you." And when they sent for him—or if God gave him some other sign—

he would go to his people and lead them, as Moses had done, to the promised land.

In his journal he had written: "I ask for glory, great and holy in this world, greater and splendid, all beautiful in Heaven. Ask for glory, saith the Lord, through Louis David Riel, His prophet in the New World."

There were times when he *knew* he was a prophet, other times when he was not so sure, and yet other times when it didn't seem to matter after all. Often he had argued the matter with the Jesuit priests. Whenever he told them he intended to found a new religion, they scoffed at him; steadfastly, they refused to concede that he already possessed ecclesiastical justification for his views. On January 2, 1876, Bishop Bourget had written to him:

For my part I pray God . . . to guide you in all your ways, so that you will never wander from the path which Divine Providence has traced out for you and for our greatest good and that of your country and people. One must hope and ask that the time of mercy arrive for this desolate country. . . . The Faith . . . will raise it sooner or later . . . in order to cover it with honour and good. Be blessed, then, of God and men and have patience in your woes.

In a previous letter the Bishop had said, "You have a mission," and now, "Divine Providence has traced out for you a path"; yet the priests refused to believe in him! In fact they had declared him sinful for talking in such a manner, and had suggested that, as penance, he should write to Bishop Bourget and ask him exactly what it was he had meant by his letters. Well, he had written the Bishop; and in the meantime he would continue to pray, for it soothed his restless soul.

It was the afternoon of June 4, 1884, and he was praying in

187

the mission's chapel when the delegates from Canada arrived to seek him out. A woman went in and told him that Gabriel Dumont and three other men were outside, that they wished to see him. While they unhitched their horses he finished his prayers; then he joined them.

Gabriel Dumont, the leader of the métis people who had settled on the Saskatchewan, was a man of about Riel's own age. Sharp-eyed, powerful of frame, heavily moustached, he epitomized most of the characteristics that were admirable in the half-breed race. Though he could neither read nor write, he had been a fearless buffalo hunter and Indian fighter since his early 'teens. At the age of thirteen, he had been one of sixty-three métis, led by Father Laflèche, who had fought off a thousand warlike Sioux. As a young man of twenty-five he had been chosen to represent the métis in negotiations with this same Indian tribe—negotiations that resulted in a treaty of friendship advantageous to both factions.

He and Riel had not met before, though they had known of each other and admired each other's reputation from afar. During the trouble at Red River in 1869-70, Dumont had sent word to Fort Garry that if he were needed he would come to Riel's aid with five hundred men. But he had not been needed, and he had remained out on the plains. As soon as it became apparent to him that Archbishop Taché and Riel had been hoodwinked by the Canadians, he had visited all the Indian tribes of the West with the object of uniting them, should the occasion demand it, with the métis race for their mutual defence. Between 1873 and 1875 he had ruled the métis of the St. Laurent district, on the South Saskatchewan River, as their elected president. Though the Mounted Police had forced him to give up this position when white men began to homestead in the area, he was still the acknowledged leader of his people, and he came now to speak on their behalf.

The three half-breeds who accompanied Gabriel Dumont were Moise Ouellette, Michel Dumas and James Isbister. They had been elected at a joint meeting of the French and English métis and instructed to seek Riel out and to invite him formally to return to the Canadian North-west. They brought with them a formal resolution, which they handed to Louis. It read as follows:

We, the French and English natives of the North-west, knowing that Louis Riel made a bargain with the Government of Canada in 1870, which bargain is contained mostly in the Manitoba Act, and this meeting not knowing the contents of the Manitoba Act, we have thought it advisable that a delegation be sent to the said Louis Riel, and have his assistance to bring all matters referred to in the above resolution in proper shape and form before the Government of Canada, so that our just demands be granted.

When Louis had read this he protested that he could give them whatever advice they required without journeying seven hundred miles to the Saskatchewan. Dumont hastened to assure him that he was needed in person in their midst. A fresh outlook was required; some new strategy would have to be evolved if the Government was ever to be persuaded to sit up and take notice of the West. Why, only this spring, a motion to "consider the condition, complaints and demands of Manitoba and the North West Territories" had been defeated in the House of Commons by a vote of 116 to 57!

In the opinion of these métis, the Lieutenant-Governor of the Territories was more interested in dealing in townsites for his own profit than he was in the people; the Minister of the Interior, at Ottawa, was just as bad. What was needed was a magnetic leader who could make the politicians pay attention for a change.

Riel refused to give them a definite answer on the spot. He would think about it overnight, make known his decision in the morning. And yet, as he talked with these men, he must have known himself that his mind was already made up. The métis at Red River had sold their lands in exchange for the Manitoba Act. But these people of the Saskatchewan had made no treaties; thus, through their Indian mothers, they were still entitled to one-half of all the land in the West. And, this being so, they were entitled to a cash payment of many millions of dollars from any government that proposed to take it away from them. And also, there was the matter of Riel's personal claims that had never been attended to. . . .

That evening he sat down and wrote a formal reply to the delegates camped outside his door:

The communities in which you live have sent you as their delegation to ask my advice on various difficulties which have rendered the British North-west as yet unhappy under the Ottawa Government. You invite me to go and stay among you, your hope being that I for one could help better in some ways your condition.

Cordial and pressing is your invitation. You want me and my family to accompany you. I am at liberty to excuse myself and say no; yet you are waiting for me, so that I have only to get ready, and your letters of delegation give me the assurance that a family welcome awaits me in the midst of those who have sent for me.

Your personal visit does me credit, and causes great pleasure, but on account of its representative character, your coming to me had the proportions of a remarkable fact. I record it as one of the gratifications of my life. It is a good event, which my family will remember, and I pray to God that your delegation may become a blessing to me among the blessings of my fortieth year.

To be frank is shortest. I doubt whether my advice given to you on this soil concerning Canadian territory could cross the border and retain any influence.

But there is another view. The Canadian Government owes me 250 acres of land, according to the Manitoba Act. They also owe me five valuable lots on account of hay, timber and river frontage. These lots are mine according to the same 31st clause of the Manitoba Treaty. Besides, if they only pay attention a minute they will easily find that they owe me something else.

These my claims against them are such as to hold good notwithstanding that I have become an American citizen.

Considering then your interests and mine, I accept your kind invitation. I will go and spend some time amongst you. By petitioning the Government with you, perhaps we will all have the good fortune of getting something. But my intention is to come back early this fall.

Montana has a pretty numerous half-breed element. If we count with them the white men interested in the half-breed welfare, by being themselves head of half-breed families, I believe it is safe to assert that the half-breed element in Montana is pretty strong. I am only just getting acquainted with that element. I am one of those who would like to unite and direct its vote so as to make it profitable to themselves and useful to their friends. However, I have made acquaintances and friends among whom I like to live. I start with you, but to come back in September.

I have the honour, gentlemen delegates, to be

Your humble servant,
Louis Riel

And so, on the 27th of June, 1884, Gabriel Dumont led his little party of visitors from Montana along the trail running parallel to the right bank of the South Saskatchewan River. They crossed a patch of level pasture, leaving the river behind, its steep banked waters sparkling in the afternoon sun; just ahead stood a clump of poplars which hid the snaked descent into Fish Creek, or Tourond's Crossing. Beyond lay the homeward trail. In this parkland country north of the prairie, nature's yellow-green mantle proclaimed new hope, new purpose, everywhere. Soon the travellers would forget the dust and heat, the mosquito-filled nights of the journey they had just completed; and each would feel a sense of accomplishment glowing within him; and everyone would say once again that Gabriel Dumont had done what he had set out to do.

He was a born leader, this Dumont. And as he returned now to his home and his wife Magdeleine and his aged father, he was bringing with him Louis Riel, the one man who could politically reactivate the métis cause.

Three weeks in the open air seemed to have cleared the shadows from Riel's mind. He looked younger, more full of zest, than he had for a long time. He felt as well as he looked. Sitting up there in the wagon with the horse's reins in his hands, Marguerite beside him with wee Marie-Angélique in her arms, and little Jean behind him, he felt totally free of that gathering sense of destiny that had haunted him at St. Peter's. He could almost imagine himself as an ordinary man, travelling with his wife and family to this new land. Perhaps, if all went well, he would settle in Canada again.

"We'll stop and say hello to old Tourond. He farms on the other side of the ravine," Dumont called. Then: "Better check your brakes, Louis. The path gets steep after this next bend."

They had entered the bush now; the trail had swung them to the left. As they reached the edge of the ravine it forced them to make a sharp right turn. Below in the woods lay a creek with a pole bridge across it and a second right turn at its northern side; then a steep rise to the open ground beyond. At the bottom of the dip, just as they were crossing the bridge, Dumont turned in his saddle. "Can you imagine a better place for an ambush?" he shouted to Louis above the clatter of the horses' hooves. "With fifty men I could hold off an army in here."

As they began climbing the northern side of the ravine the horses drew their quarters under them, straining against the grade. Coming to the top of the hill, the little party broke suddenly onto open ground. Before them were the whitewashed buildings of Tourond's farm, and between them and these buildings was a huge throng. People, dogs and children were milling about among the horses and wagons, all forming a kaleidoscope of colours beneath the smiling sun. The women wore their gayest bonnets, the men broad *assomption* belts and brightly tinted shirts. It seemed as if the entire métis nation had turned out to greet Riel!

"Sainte Marie!" Dumont cried. "Now *there's* a welcoming committee fit for a king!"

Louis turned to his wife. His eyes were shining as if he had caught a glimpse of the Beatific Vision. "They have not forgotten me," he murmured, reaching for her hand.

"I had expected they would want to organize a welcome for you," said Dumont; "that's why I sent Moise Ouellette on ahead yesterday with the news. But *this*—this is really something, eh?"

Louis nodded. He was too full of emotion to speak.

Now the crowd had seen him. Cheering people surged out onto the trail and ran towards them. One of the horses Riel was driving reared up at the unexpected sight, and Dumont had to seize its bridle to steady it. James Isbister, who normally rode at the rear, came up to help him. The crowd was all around them now, calling out to acquaintances and staring respectfully at the Riels. Several old friends from Red River came up and shook Louis' hand. He had not felt so much a part of things for years.

Presently Dumont, who had dismounted, shouldered his way to the Riels' wagon. Beside him was a wiry-looking old man with an enormous moustache. "Louis! Madame Riel!" Gabriel called. "I would like to present you to my father, Isidore Dumont, the mightiest hunter of them all!"

Old Isidore Dumont climbed up into the wagon behind the Riels. Panting, he leaned forward and shook their hands. Then he bent down to shake hands with little Jean, who was standing behind his parents in the back. "I knew your grandfather," he said to the little boy. "I hope you turn out to be as fine a man as he was."

Now the old fellow was standing upright again, his arms above his head, calling for silence. "My friends," he began as soon as he could make himself heard, "my son Gabriel has persuaded M. Riel and his family to live among us for a little while. This is a great day for the métis nation! What he did before, M. Riel can do again. With his help, I tell you, we will make the Government sit up and pay attention to our just demands. Then, once again, our nation will be free!"

The crowd cheered wildly. Sitting there, the centre of it all, Louis must have felt like a hero in a golden chariot rather than a penniless school-teacher on a shabby old wagon. He rose to acknowledge the people's acclaim.

"Dear friends," he said with herculean self-control, "my wife and I are overwhelmed by the warmth of your welcome. We thank God for the friendship you extend to us and pray earnestly that we can be of some service to you in return." Then he sat down, amid thunderous applause.

Now Gabriel Dumont caught the attention of the crowd.

"My father tells me," he shouted, "that there are fifty wagon-loads of you assembled here. This is indeed a tribute to Monsieur and Madame Riel. They will remember it always, the welcome you have given them here at Tourand's farm. But Madame Riel especially is tired after her long journey. She loves you all, but she desires nothing so much at this moment as to rest for a little while. So, with your permission, we will continue on to my house forthwith. There will be plenty more opportunities to demonstrate your sentiments. The Riels will be among us all summer. For a few days they will stay with me; afterwards, they will take up residence at the home of their cousin, Charles Nolin. For the time being—no more speeches, please; but you are welcome to form up behind us and make of our progress a parade."

"It went very well, eh?" Louis asked eagerly. "I am glad that I made the decision to come here. These people are happy to see me; of that there is no possible doubt."

"Yes, they are happy to see you, Louis," Dumont said evenly. "We all have come to believe that you are our only hope. But a word of warning, Louis: the police—some of the clergy, too —may not be so overjoyed. They've had things their own way for a long time here."

"Did I say anything to which they could object?" Louis challenged indignantly. "They will soon see for themselves that I am a reasonable man. Good men have always agreed with what I do. When I speak to the clergy I will mollify their hearts."

Suddenly, a frown came to his face. "Where is my old friend Ambroise Lépine today?" he asked. "I was told that he lives in these parts. Is that not true?"

"It's true enough, Louis," Dumont said. "But Lépine—well, he was condemned to death, remember? He was ordered to be hanged. When they lifted the death sentence, after his trial, he promised that he would not take up politics again. He has told me that he intends to honour that pledge."

"I wish he could be persuaded to change his mind," Riel muttered.

Dumont shrugged. With a grunt he turned and swung himself into the saddle. In his opinion they could get along without Lépine; he had decided this long ago, and he was not the sort of man to stand all day in the roadway rehashing decisions that had already been made. Giving his mare a kick, he turned her head towards home. As if in a dream, Riel took up his reins and followed.

They arrived at Dumont's farm before supper-time. Gabriel's wife Magdeleine greeted them in the yard outside. At her urging, Marguerite Riel and the children went with her directly indoors, but Louis and the two Dumont men remained to wave at the people as they paraded by.

When the last cart had passed the three men went inside, washed up and sat down to eat. "For this and all Thy gifts we thank Thee, God," Louis prayed, before he began his supper. But he was not thinking of the food in front of him as he offered thanks. He was thinking of the crowd, and of the opportunities to serve his people that had revealed themselves today.

XIII

WE MUST
AGITATE PEACEFULLY

BATOCHE is a tiny village on the east bank of the South Saskatchewan River, situated at a ferrying-point some seven or eight miles below the crossing where Gabriel Dumont lived. Nowadays, a person has difficulty deciding where it begins and ends, for its houses lie scattered among the poplars to the north and south beside the dusty municipal road. In 1884 one's task would have been simpler by far; gunfire and soldiers' torches had not done their work by then. The few traders' stores, all the métis dwellings, lay grouped together still as they ought to lie—cradled peacefully beneath the steep wooded bank that guided the river's ancient course, on the flat ground beside the water's edge. Their focal point was the ferry cable and a two-storey wooden building put up by Xavier Batoche.

Behind and above this village, on the tip of high ground that juts towards the south, were the little church of St. Anthony of Padua, the priest's house, and the village cemetery. These alone remain today, fulfilling their functions as of old. They give one the illusion that they have sprung from the sandy-loam soil on which they rest. In themselves they are quite ordinary landmarks—the simple, steepled place of worship with its high-pitched roof, the square, snug house of the priest, the pitifully adequate resting-place for the bones of the local dead

—yet an aura of history clings to them still. They are the only relics remaining to link us with Louis Riel and his last stand in the North-west.

The house of Charles Nolin, Louis' cousin, lay in this settlement, near the south end. It was a two-storey structure, with a verandah running along the side facing the river. Into it the Riels settled comfortably for the summer months.

Immediately it became apparent that Louis was to be accepted by the métis rank and file almost as their Anointed One. As one of the delegates who had fetched him from Montana wrote: "The humble condition of his home reminded us of the opportunities he had had . . . to become rich . . . and how at all risks he had stood firm [for] his people. We know how much he wrought for Manitoba and how much he struggled for the whole North-west; and, seeing how little he had worked for himself, we came back . . . with twice as much confidence in him as we had on leaving." His manner was so disarming that even Father Moulin, the village priest, looked upon him with approval and invited him almost as soon as he arrived to speak to a gathering in the church.

To Father Fourmond, the incumbent at St. Laurent—a village a few miles to the north and across the river, westward, from Batoche—Louis said: "I left with the blessing of the good Jesuit Fathers of Montana. I have come on my arrival to claim, very humbly, that of the Reverend Oblate Fathers at St. Laurent. I do not wish to undertake anything without the direction of the clergy and without their advice."

It was Father Fourmond who wrote of him that year: "I admire the faith that breathes in all his words, the sweetness that characterizes his physiognomy and his elocution . . . his aspect, representing good faith, humility, modesty, suddenly animated by a terrible fire . . . when his ideas are opposed. The rights of his people are to him sacred. . . . *Voilà un homme convaincu.*" All in all, nothing could have seemed more auspicious than the atmosphere that prevailed.

Early in July the first organizational meeting was held at Nolin's house. Before the meeting, Louis and his cousin sat outside on the verandah discussing the things that were on their minds. It was a beautiful morning and pleasant to be alive.

"Louis," Nolin began with a gravity out of keeping with the spirit of the day, "I have been watching you and I am worried. You seem to have lost your fire. People who had not met you in the old days say that you are nothing but a world-weary school-teacher. Do you know that?"

"So?"

"So—perhaps it's not important, but if I were you I'd give 'em hell when you speak to them today. That's what they'll expect—that's what they'll want to hear, you know." This man was a seasoned politician; he had been the Minister of Agriculture in the provincial Government during the brief period when the French-speaking citizens of Manitoba counted in public affairs. He had moved to Batoche, along with Maxime Lépine and Michel Dumas, a bare two years before. He spoke confidently, as a man of the world who believed that he knew what he was talking about.

"What do you want me to tell them?" Riel challenged quietly. "That I have a divine mission? That I intend to destroy England and Canada—and Rome and the Pope too? These things are true—they are prophecies; I have written them in a book; but it would be foolishness for me to reveal them to the people just now."

Nolin smiled thinly. "I did not know that you could prophesy —still."

"Of course I can prophecy—I am a prophet. If you don't believe me I'll show you the letters I got from Bishop Bourget confirming the fact."

"That won't be necessary, Louis. I believe you; and I'm sure that the rest of the people will, too. You are going to tell them about this plan of yours? You are going to tell them today?"

Riel glanced at him scornfully. "Of course I'm not going to tell them today! What do you take me for, anyhow? I did not come seven hundred miles to be thrown into jail. I came because I am the leader of the métis nation, and that nation sent for me. I came because they and I have certain legitimate claims against the Government in Ottawa for which we both have a right to demand recognition. This is not the time to talk about destroying things. This is a time for organizing ourselves peacefully and making a detailed investigation of our needs. We must agitate, yes; but we must agitate peacefully. Above all, we must impress the authorities with our moderation and good sense. Once I have got it started the process may take five years, it may take ten. I would be stupid to stir up our people, to 'give 'em hell', as you suggest, right at the start."

"We've had our bellyful of petitions and demands, Louis. Nothing ever comes of them," Nolin grumbled.

"And nothing ever *will* come of them, until we have achieved representative government. Our first objective must be to gain representation in both the North West Council and the Canadian Parliament."

Nolin shook his head. "You're a dreamer, Louis. We won't get anywhere unless we make the Government realize they've *got* to negotiate with us." A sly expression came to his face. "Those prophecies of yours might come in handy; we might use 'em to show old Macdonald what trouble he'd be in if *all* the métis and Indians in the West turned against him at the same time. There are quite a few people around here who are expecting you to issue a call to arms."

"There are quite a few people who will be disappointed,

then," Riel snapped. "I have come here to do two things: to help the métis nation achieve their rights through constitutional means, and to force the Government to recognize my personal claims against it. I cannot help it if I'm a prophet, if I foresee disaster ahead for those who oppose me. The point is, it would be foolish to provoke any more trouble than we have to. I thought I had made that perfectly clear when I accepted your invitation to return here."

Nolin shrugged but made no comment. They sat in silence until people began arriving for the meeting.

Delegates had journeyed to Batoche from as far north as Prince Albert and as far west as Fort Carlton. For the most part they were a mixed bag of French and English métis. One of the latter, William Comarty, presided over the meeting; Riel's old friend, Louis Schmidt, acted as its secretary. The atmosphere was one of good-fellowship and hope. Everyone seemed pleased to have Riel in their midst. When he rose to speak, Louis repeated publicly the points he had made to his cousin in private; and, notwithstanding Nolin's warning, his audience seemed eager to work as a team with him.

Following the speeches a plan of action was evolved. Delegates were selected from the crowd and made responsible for organizing in their districts smaller gatherings at which local grievances could be aired. When sufficient time had elapsed for these gatherings to be held, the various lists of grievances they produced would be co-ordinated and used as a basis for a métis bill of rights. Ultimately, the bill would be sent to the North West Council and the Parliament of Canada, on behalf of the whole métis nation.

When the meeting had come to an end Louis was tired, but filled with satisfaction and good humour, too. He turned to Louis Schmidt, who was beside him with his book of notes. "Thank you for keeping a record of all this," he said. "It's like old times, working together again, eh?" Then: "But if I am to accomplish anything during my short summer here, I will have need of a permanent secretary from now on. Have you any suggestions, old friend?"

A shadow of distress came over Schmidt's face. "I'd like to take the job myself, Louis," he began, "but—"

"Not on your life, my friend! You've got steady employment in Prince Albert; I couldn't allow you to give it up—not even for a cause such as ours."

Schmidt looked relieved. "Leave it with me, Louis, will you?" he said. Then: "It's not the easiest thing in the world to find a qualified person in these parts. Perhaps I'll think of someone in a day or two."

It was natural that Schmidt should beg off. He was a married man now, with a growing family, and he was just beginning to re-establish himself in this new land. After being elected by acclamation to represent the people of St. Boniface in the Manitoba Legislature of 1870, it had seemed to him that he was off to a flying start under the new régime. On the strength of the future's promise he had courted and won the hand of Justine Laviolette, an eighteen-year-old girl who claimed descent from Champlain, the founder of Three Rivers, Quebec.

In 1873 he had become a license commissioner for the province and secretary-treasurer of the St. Boniface Catholic School. After being defeated in the next election, because the boundaries of the constituency had been redefined, he had offered himself successfully in St. François-Xavier East and had sat in the Assembly of 1878 until it was prorogued. Then, losing heart as he saw what was happening all around him, he had moved with his wife and three children to the St. Laurent district on the Saskatchewan, and had taken up land on the left bank of the river.

The previous year he had given up farming to accept a position in a lawyer's office in Prince Albert. Though one of the men behind the movement to bring Riel back to the Northwest, he did not feel that he could devote all his time to the cause.

It might not have seemed to be the easiest thing in the world to find a qualified person to act as secretary for Riel; and yet, in actuality, it was not difficult. Three days after the meeting at Nolin's house, another meeting was held at the settlement of Red Deer Hill, ten miles south of Prince Albert. Saying much the same sort of thing as he had at Batoche, Louis spoke before a predominantly English-speaking audience and was favourably received. It was here that he met William Henry Jackson and arranged with him to take on the jcb of secretary.

Young Jackson was in his mid-twenties, rather too delicate-looking to fit in naturally with this environment; yet he had good qualifications. He was a graduate of the University of Toronto; he had acted as secretary for the local farmers' union. His father was a farmer near Prince Albert; his brother Thomas was a druggist in the town. The family had moved from Ontario at about the same time Louis Schmidt left Manitoba. They were all in the forefront of local agitation against conditions as they existed in the West.

After arranging with Jackson that he should come and join him at Batoche, Louis rode homeward with his cousin, Charles Nolin.

"That was a good day's work, *mon cousin*," Nolin said as they rode along. "The wheels are in motion at last."

Louis nodded. "I think it went very well," he agreed. Thinking of the new connection he had made with the English-Canadian faction through Henry Jackson, he added: "Before we are through everyone will be on our side. Then, even without a call to arms, Sir John Macdonald will gladly listen to what I have to say."

Nolin shrugged. "I hope you are right, Louis. And, who knows? Perhaps you are."

Prince Albert, where Henry Jackson came from, was by far the most important settlement in the area. With a population of seven hundred people, most of whom were Ontario-born immigrants, it was the distributing centre for a large section of the North-west. Until recently it had been a real boom town, but the pendulum of fortune had swung the other way and its inhabitants were now experiencing a period of painful readjustment.

Crops had been poor during the past two seasons, and trade had fallen off as a result. To compound the effects of these misfortunes, the Government had announced its decision that the main line of the transcontinental railway must take a southerly route. The original survey had called for the track to pass through Prince Albert and Edmonton on its way to the Pacific's shore. Now, local farmers knew they would have to transport their produce more than two hundred miles to the railhead; local merchants and real-estate operators knew they would have to wait indefinitely to realize the profits that had seemed to them in the bag. In brief, all the immigrants who had come to this district with high hopes were bitterly disappointed.

On the reservations nearby disgruntled, half-starved Indians ate rations of bacon and flour doled out to them by officials whom they did not trust. And the métis? We know already of the ferment in the métis' minds. To sum up, the area was a stew-pot of discontent—a simmering, bubbling cauldron, on which the lid of autocratic rule had been tightly jammed. Unless someone loosened this lid, an explosion was bound to occur sooner or later.

In Batoche Louis Riel grew more and more confident that he could harness these pressures to work for him rather than to go off with a bang, directionless, into thin air. If he played his cards right the métis would do whatever he suggested; the Indians would follow him, too, if called upon to do so by Gabriel Dumont. Once he had united all the restless people in the region under his personal control, the whole territory would be on his side. Faced with such a situation, the Government must pay him heed. Then the métis would achieve their rights, the Indians would be treated as human beings, trade would improve, and the local whites would prosper. The task of gathering lists of grievances, of co-ordinating them, of persuading all the people to agree to the same bill of rights, would take time; but it could result in victory in the end.

But despite his success at Red Deer Hill, despite the arrival of a petition, signed by eighty-four persons—all but six of them pure white—he was reluctant to make a direct appeal to the people of Prince Albert. He had been hounded too often by *les anglais* to feel sure of his reception among them now. Finally, after being urged to do so by the parish priest of that town, he drove northward to Prince Albert and delivered a speech so moderate in tone that Louis Schmidt could only shake his head and say: "He lacked his former fire; his declarations were somewhat vague."

Louis Schmidt may have been disappointed by the tenor of his old friend's speech, but many others among those who heard it were not. Suddenly, Riel found himself a celebrity among the very people whom he had feared for so long. The experience seemed most rewarding. "Not long ago," he wrote to his brother Joseph in St. Vital, "I was a humble schoolmaster. . . . Here, today, I am the most popular among public men on the Saskatchewan. . . . Bankers invite me to their table . . . they applaud me with the crowd. And the wicked rich, who regarded me with pity in past times, are at present alarmed. It opens their eyes with astonishment; they are

alarmed; it annoys them. What has made all this happen?
Dear Joseph! . . . You know that it is God. . . . I was asked to
speak at an assembly of citizens at Prince Albert . . . before
five hundred people. . . . There I saw the mysterious power
of God."

He was popular, then. His cause was receiving infusions of
enthusiasm everywhere. Yet not quite everywhere; for the
priests whom he had asked to bless him were, almost from the
start, fearful of the excitement stirred up by his presence.
Though they had been pleasantly surprised by the moderation
of his words, they remained apprehensive about the future and
the part he would play in creating it. One day Father Alexis
André, the Superior of the Oblate missionaries—the priest who
had, years before, taken Schmidt with him when he went to
work among the Sioux—came to call and tell Louis what was
on his mind.

The priest was bearded and rugged as his native Breton coast,
his boots were scuffed and dusty, his cassock had long since
faded from black to iron grey; but his shrewd, kindly eyes were
as clear still, and as challenging, as a trumpet's call.

"M. Riel," he began in French when they had seated themselves on the verandah of Charles Nolin's house, "I am on my
way from Prince Albert to the West, to meet with Bishop
Grandin. I am glad I caught you at home."

"Everyone has heard of your exploits, Father. I am very
pleased to meet you."

"To be honest, Monsieur, I am less than pleased to meet you!
I would have preferred it had you decided to remain in Montana." The priest shrugged. "But you are here, and there is
no use regretting the fact. In many ways you have surprised us
by your moderation, M. Riel. I myself heard you speak at
Prince Albert. Tell me, Monsieur; now that you are here, what
do you plan to do?"

"I plan to save the métis nation," Louis replied loftily. "In fact I have already begun my task. That makes us allies, does it not?"

Father André accepted the challenge. "All the children of God should be allies, M. Riel," he said mildly. Then: "Though I am not concerned about the métis 'nation', I am vitally concerned with the soul of each métis. Even during these difficult times each soul must be kept alive, nourished, encouraged to grow in grace, just as each body must be respected as a temple of the Holy Spirit. It will take these poor people several generations to learn how to live in the white man's world."

Riel frowned. "That's just the point, *mon père*; this is *not* the white man's world. It is *our* world! None of the métis of the North-west have signed a treaty with Canada. None of them have—"

"What you say may or may not be true, Monsieur," the priest cut in. "But at best it is an academic point. The thing that is happening here is as old as history itself. Neither the métis nor the Indians would stand a chance if they tried to oppose it. A current has set against them. Their only hope is to drift with it until they learn how to swim. If they are to survive, there must be no bloodshed, M. Riel!"

Louis squirmed like a schoolboy. "Father, I agree with you from the bottom of my heart." He fished inside a pocket of his trousers, brought out a folded piece of paper, which he handed to the priest. "Perhaps, if you read this, you will be reassured."

It was a manifesto, issued over the signature of the local Settlers' Union, calling upon the people of the Prince Albert district for their political support. "We are starting a movement . . . ," it began, "with a view to attaining Provincial Legislatures for the North West Territories and, if possible, the control of our own resources. . . . Riel has united the half-breed element solidly in our favour. . . . [He] has warned them against the danger of being separated from the whites. . . . Riel has been painted in blacker colours than he deserves. . . . It is better to accept his services as long as he works for us. . . . As long as both elements work on the square . . . there will be no clash, but a marked advance towards justice in the North-west." It was signed for the union by William Henry Jackson, the young man who had recently consented to be secretary to Louis Riel.

"You see, Father, we are all on the same side now. You have nothing to fear, believe me."

"I'll be the judge of what I have and have not to fear, Monsieur," the priest snapped. Then, less testily: "My chief concern is for you. I am not convinced that you recognize for what they are the forces at work in this land. When you spoke recently at Prince Albert, the moderation of your tone was gratifying. But—in spite of what this manifesto may say—did you know that there are men in that town who would like nothing better than to see you inspire a rising, who say quite openly that it would be good for trade if you forced the Government to send in five hundred police? Did you know that, eh?"

He paused dramatically. When Louis gave no reply, he went on. "These same men say our people should ignore what we priests have to say—because we counsel moderation and they hope for violence to break out! They are evil men, Monsieur. Most of them are members of the Liberal Party. Their only aim is to discredit the present Government."

He spoke more gently now. "I pray that you will recognize them for what they are and understand why they are encouraging you. I pray that you will realize they are thinking only of their own pockets and the political advantages to be gained." His voice hardened. "Many of your English-Canadian allies hope to use you, M. Riel."

Louis was not impressed. "They may hope to use me, *mon père*," he countered gaily, "but I hope to use them, too. So we are even, eh?" He stood up, began pacing up and down. Then he perched himself on the verandah's edge, began tracing out patterns in the dusty earth with his moccasined toes. "Of one thing you can be very sure, Father," he said thoughtfully. "I will not fall into their trap, I promise you. And when I have shown my people how to attain peacefully the rights that are their due, I will go back to Montana whence I came."

The priest stood up. "I think you mean that, M. Riel. I will take you at your word." Then: "I hear you are preparing a petition, as you did at Red River long ago. Both the Bishop and I would be interested in seeing it when it is complete."

Riel stood up, too. "You shall see it then, *mon père*. If we work together much can be achieved. If not—"

"M. Riel," Father André cut in with the incisiveness of etching acid, "you must understand this: there will be no question of the Church working with you. Not this time! In 1870, when Archbishop Taché championed your cause, he accomplished next to nothing for his pains; yet he was greatly criticized in Ontario for the efforts he made. Believe me, he will not expose himself to such criticism again. He cannot afford to, for he and Bishop Grandin are almost the sole remaining spokesmen available to the Indians and the métis. If their voices were discredited there would be no one left who could speak in Ottawa for the natives here." The priest shook his head. "Compared with the broader picture, the long-term view of what is happening in the West, your goals seem unimportant, believe me."

Louis turned away to conceal his anger. His goals were unimportant, were they? Who said so—Taché? That Archbishop! Sitting in St. Boniface, acting as if he ran the world; still up to his old game of pretending to be all things to all men! What good had Taché ever done his cause? If it hadn't been for

Taché's meddling in 1870, he and Lépine might have beaten the Canadian Army once and for all!

Suddenly, he longed to shout and pound the table, to proclaim that he had only one true friend among the clergy; that this friend was Bishop Bourget of Montreal, who had given him money and written him letters years ago; that he couldn't care less about Taché, or Bishop Grandin, or the Church's "long-term" view. But with an effort he controlled himself. If he wished to retain the confidence of the people he must play along with this priest, he must keep *all* the priests on his side, for they wielded great influence in these parts.

"*Mon père*," he murmured, pretending to be contrite, "I understand and accept your point of view. Thank you for the words of advice."

With that the two men shook hands. The priest continued his journey westward to meet Bishop Grandin at his headquarters in St. Albert, a tiny métis village near Edmonton.

The weeks of summer slipped by. While Dumont talked of rights to the Indians on the reserves, Riel addressed himself to the task of welding the métis into one co-ordinated group. At the same time, through Jackson, he systematically increased his contacts with the English-Canadian element living around Prince Albert. Occasionally he spoke from a public platform, and whenever he did so he took care to preach moderation, to insist that his only objective was to help the people help themselves. He took care, too, to show respect, always, to the priests. And yet everywhere he went he encountered a subtle braking force that slowed the momentum of enthusiasm which he was trying to build up. He could recognize it as the work of the priests and could feel it as an unseen eddy of distrust that blew first here, then there, to snuff out the flames that he and Dumont had lit.

Yet, in spite of the priests, his work was progressing steadily —if a little more slowly than he would have desired. The claims of the métis were being recorded, agreed to and forwarded to him to be incorporated into his bill of rights. He would demand representative government and provincial status on behalf of the people; he would insist that they must have title to the land on which they squatted, that acreage be set aside before it was too late for their children and children's children, that more government contracts be awarded to residents of the territory and less to great impersonal concerns like the Hudson's Bay Company. These were sensible demands; they added up to nothing more than elementary justice for all. When they were all written down and codified the people would approve of them, for sure.

"But what if the Government refuses to consider them?" Dumont asked one day.

Riel shrugged. "When the final draft is agreed to, my work here will be done. In September I will return to Montana. What the people do after that is their concern, not mine."

Dumont scowled. "That's just evading the issue, Louis, and you know it. Without your presence here, without your leadership, this movement will disintegrate just as all the others have done. We need a bill of rights, sure; but we need continuous agitation here, too, in order to make the Government pay attention to our demands. For you to talk about leaving us now—why, it's almost treason! You are our leader, Louis. We *need* you."

Louis smiled. It was good to be told one was indispensable. "I will stay for a while longer, *mon ami*. You need have no fears that I will desert you in mid-stream."

Dumont looked relieved. "That is gratifying to hear, Louis. There have been rumours—" He did not finish the sentence. Then he asked: "But what about it? If the Government refuses to consider our demands—what then?"

Riel looked at him, shrugged again. Gabriel always wanted to have everything planned out in detail. He had no faith in intuition, it seemed. "You are an experienced campaigner," Louis said. "You know that one cannot cross one's bridges until one comes to them." It was an incomplete answer and Louis knew it; yet he was not prepared to amplify it just now.

Two weeks later he received evidence that the priests were not the only ones who were worried about his activities in the territory. One day Bishop Grandin arrived in the district and requested that Louis ride over to St. Laurent to meet him. With the Bishop were Fathers André, Fourmond, and Vegreville; also Amedée Forget, who said he represented Lieutenant-Governor Dewdney, the Governor of the whole North-west.

Forget was blunt. "I have arranged this meeting, M. Riel, to offer you a position on the North West Council—a position in which you would have ample opportunity to serve the cause of your people."

Riel was taken by surprise. "I did not know there were any positions open on the Council right now."

Bishop Grandin spoke up: "There aren't, Monsieur. That is —there weren't, until Raoul Bréland volunteered to step down and let you take his place."

Louis flushed scarlet. Another bribe! But he controlled himself. "Raoul Bréland?" he asked mildly. "Why should he step down, Your Excellency? Is he not performing his duties satisfactorily?"

"Yes, but—"

"Then why take his position away from him and give it to me?" Riel shook his head and smiled. "I could not accept this offer. It would be an injustice," he said.

"A seat in the Senate, perhaps?" Forget asked quietly.

Riel laughed. "The Senate, no less! I doubt very much if you could deliver such a prize."

"What is it that you are after, Riel?" Father Fourmond asked impatiently. He was the priest at St. Laurent. It was in his rectory that the meeting was being held.

"As I have said publicly, I want only two things, *mon père*. I want justice for my people; I want recognition for my personal claims against the Government."

"And if you achieve these things you will go back to Montana?" Father André asked.

"That's what I told you, *mon père*. I am a man of my word."

The Bishop sighed. "*Eh bien*," he said, "leave it with me. We will see what can be done."

"I thought the Church had decided to remain aloof from my cause, Your Excellency. That is what Father André told me." Louis could not resist the jibe.

The Bishop frowned. "The Church has great sympathy for the plight of her children. She will do all she can to support them in their struggle for justice—so long as that struggle breaks no constitutional bounds. But what upsets us about you is that we cannot see an end to the movement you are trying to start. Already we have made strong representations to Sir John Macdonald and he has ignored them. What happens if he ignores yours too? With the people all stirred up, God knows where it might lead. The Church will not condone revolution, Monsieur. If you or anyone else crosses that line, the sacraments will be refused to you. Do I make myself clear?"

Riel inclined his head. "Perfectly, Your Excellency. In reply, I can only repeat: I have no intention of starting a revolution."

"Just make sure that events don't run away with you, that's all, my son."

"Your Excellency, I will try." Then (an idea had just come to his head): "While riding over here it occurred to me that our movement would be more assured of success if it were to become a definite political unit, that this political unit should have the blessing of the Church. The title that comes to mind is the *Union Métisse de St. Joseph*. Would you consent to the use of that name for such an enterprise?"

213

"I would—provided you agree to the conditions we have already discussed," Bishop Grandin replied after a moment's hesitation.

Louis bowed. "Thank you, Your Excellency. I appreciate your support. All the people will appreciate it, too. You will have no cause to regret this decision."

Everyone shook hands; Louis took his leave. Afterwards, Bishop Grandin wrote in his journal: "Riel gives me the impression of a man greatly exaggerated, both in religion and politics. I fear he will become insane. Several fathers share my feelings, as well as many of the métis, but the majority of the latter regard him as an oracle."

On September 24th, when the métis people came together for a formal service of dedication to St. Joseph, Louis took advantage of the occasion to address the throng. Outside the church he said, among other things: "Myself, like the others, . . . can act wrongly. Well! May the priests have the courage to correct me, reprimand me, even denounce me. The Church has that right. It is for it to advise us charitably, so that we are made to lead a Christian life." Then, stepping down from his perch on the church's steps, he took up a collection for the missionary work of the priests.

September and October slipped by. At meeting after meeting Riel, Dumont, Charles Nolin, Napoleon Nault and others worked to reconcile local differences of opinion, so that gradually all elements of the métis population became ready to agree to the same wording of the proposed petition. Soon all that would remain to be done would be to complete a final draft, to send it off to the Secretary of State in Ottawa, to wait—while increasing steadily the clamour of agitation in the area—until the Government gave its reply.

XIV

I WILL
INVADE THIS LAND

ARLY in November the Riel family moved to a house made available to them in Batoche by Moise Ouellette. Probably they did this because of pressure exerted on them by Charles Nolin, with whom they had been staying since July. It is one thing to put up guests for the summer months; quite another to accept the prospect of having them on one's hands indefinitely!

Towards the end of that month Father Vegreville, the parish priest of St. Louis, came to Batoche. For some reason or other he spent the night in the Ouellette's home. The following morning a meeting of the *Union Métisse* got under way. Both Riel and his young secretary Jackson attended, as did other leaders of the métis people. When he was invited to sit in on the discussions, Father Vegreville accepted.

The purpose of the meeting was to review the union's activities and decide on future action. The priest sat quietly on the fringe of the group, more interested in observing the progress of the work than in meddling in this business. It was a bleak day outside; the ground had frozen solid overnight, and snow clouds—black at the centre, sea-grey along their swirling edges—rode low on the north-west wind; but around the iron heater in Ouellette's front room it was warmer than midsummer, and everyone was charged with a feeling of security, of high confidence.

"This time we will not fail," exulted Charles Nolin as they came to the end of the draft wording of their petition. "All the people are united by the magic of my cousin's name."

Riel smiled like a happy child. It pleased him to hear his beliefs confirmed by another man. Though he had been tired of late, tired and increasingly keyed-up with an accumulation of strain that refused to be shaken off by a good night's sleep, this morning he had awakened with a conviction that his mission would succeed.

"My brother is arranging for Louis to address another meeting in Prince Albert," young Jackson announced proudly.

"That's splendid," said Gabriel Dumont. "And the Indian chiefs are behind us to a man." Riel nodded dreamily. "Every English Canadian, every Indian agent, will soon be despatching telegrams to Ottawa on our behalf. I prophesy that when this begins to happen Sir John Macdonald will pay attention to our demands."

"The priests are afraid he'll react by sending in more police," Napoleon Nault warned, glancing in the direction of Father Vegreville.

"The priests!" Dumont jeered. "What do they know about it? The plain fact of the matter is that this is none of their affair. And anyhow," he added slyly. "they were born afraid. That's why they wear skirts all the time—isn't that true, Father?"

Father Vegreville flushed with indignation. "That is not true, M. Dumont. You have no right to say such things."

"I was only jesting, *mon père*. But still, this is none of your affair."

"That's right, Gabriel," Louis put in eagerly. "It *is* none of his affair. And who is this man to tell you that you have no right? He is a priest—that is answer enough, I suppose. Well—let me tell you something: the priests are always meddling in matters that don't concern them." (This from the man who had publicly invited them to "meddle".) "I think it is because they resent seeing anyone but themselves wield power."

As he spoke he felt as if he were about to discover the solution to all his problems—as if, buried deep within him, lay the key to life itself. Suddenly, with a breath-taking rush of certainty, he knew what it was he wanted to explain.

"It's because they think they're God's chosen instruments," he announced. "But what happens when God chooses someone else to advance His plans—eh?" He drew himself up, stared deliberately at Father Vegreville. "I will tell you something, Father. I am a prophet. God has spoken to *me*! But none of you, except Bishop Bourget of Montreal, has so far acknowledged the fact." He turned to Dumont, frowning. "What they are afraid of is that I will lead the people to their destiny and rob the priests of their power."

Father Vegreville said nothing. He was aware that this strange métis leader had at one time been mad; now, he began to suspect, the madness had returned—and, if it had, what was the sense of reasoning with a lunatic?

"Now, Louis, could this be true?" Nault asked, greatly distressed.

"Of course it's true! God has revealed it to me."

Casually Dumont lit his pipe. As far as he was concerned, the proof of the pudding always lay in the eating; and certainly Louis had shown so far that he was no ordinary man. If he claimed to be a prophet, well—perhaps he *was* a prophet! "The priests perform their functions in the churches," he said casually. "You perform your function in the world. They should understand this and leave you alone."

"But the bishops?" Nault persisted. "They would be angry if they heard you talking like this—and they have great influence in Ottawa. Would it be wise to anger them at this time, when we are about to send off our petition?"

Riel reacted as if he had been stung. With a gasp he sprang to his feet. "The bishops! The Government! Ottawa!" he shouted angrily. "In 1870 I believed all that; I do not believe it now! The whole thing is a plot, *mes amis.* Sir John Macdonald and the Pope—they are in it together." He laughed harshly, began to pace about the room. "But this time they will not succeed." He glared at Father Vegreville. "We are taught to address you as Father," he cried, "but you should be known simply as a servant of God. I know this, for God has revealed it to me. Another thing," he went on, turning again to the assembled men, "the priests and the bishops think of nothing but money and their own comfort. They should be made to work with their hands, as did the apostles!

"Rome is through—this has been revealed to me. She is a tired old harlot; she has nothing left to offer today. Civilization has grown from the Orient, from Palestine, from Rome. Now it is America's turn! We, the new nation of the western world, will lead the way—under Bishop Bourget and me it will be achieved!" He threw up his hands dramatically. "There is nothing novel in what I say. God disclosed it to me long ago."

With shining eyes young Henry Jackson sat watching his chief. "The Protestants, too?" he asked anxiously. "Will they be admitted to the new order of things?"

Louis stared at his secretary for a long moment. "The Protestants, of course," he said quietly, "and the Irish—and the Jews—and the Poles. This is my mission. Everyone will be admitted, I promise you." Suddenly, he glowered. "I will invade this land, divide it up and invite all nations to settle here."

For a long moment there was silence. It was as if everyone expected the priest to take up the challenge from here. But Father Vegreville was a man of great self-control; wisely, he held his peace.

Presently, Charles Nolin cleared his throat. "Truly, this is a vision worth fighting for, Louis," he said quietly. "If Sir John Macdonald knows what is good for him, he will ignore us no longer."

Dumont nodded. "This time we are determined to succeed."

With that the meeting came to an end. Louis felt buoyed up with vitality, as if some weight that had been crushing him had suddenly been lifted. Eagerly, he rushed over to Father Vegreville, shook hands with him, wished him a pleasant journey home. It was then that the priest became utterly convinced that Riel's illness had truly returned.

The work of the *Union* progressed. By December 16th the petition was ready. To foster the impression that it came from all the people of the area—though most of the English Canadians had not formally agreed to its terms—it was forwarded to the Secretary of State, the Honourable J. A. Chapleau, over the signature of W. H. Jackson, who styled himself "Secretary of the General Committee". Now there was nothing to do but wait for a reply. In a little while, success or failure would be achieved. With increasing intensity Riel turned his energies to prayer.

All his life Louis had been a devout church-goer. It had long been his custom, when possible, to attend daily Mass, to take communion at frequent intervals. In view of his outburst against the clergy and the authority of the Pope, his parish priest, Father Moulin, must now decide whether or not he should be denied the sacraments. If he had sinned deliberately, one course of action would be called for; if he was a madman, and therefore not accountable for his actions, another would be in order. At their next regular meeting, held at St. Laurent, the priest asked his fellow-missionaries for advice. Knowing that this would happen, Father André, the superior, had requested Louis to hold himself ready to attend.

In due course Riel was summoned before the fathers. He was

tired, he was jaded; the strain of his activities gripped him constantly now. The moment Father André brought up the subject of his outburst, Riel exploded. Loudly he began to rave in much the same language he had used before. The priest made no attempt to argue with him; but presently, when the torrent of abuse had come to an end, he said: "Louis, you know I cannot agree with what you say; but please believe me when I tell you that all of us have nothing but love for you in our hearts."

With these words a feeling of peace descended like warm rain on Louis' head. Sobbing, he went down on one knee. "Forgive me, Father," he begged, "and give me your blessing."

"I will do that, my son," Father André said gravely. "But in return I must ask you to do something for me. I must ask you to come with me to the chapel, to swear before all these priests and in the presence of the Blessed Sacrament that you will never lead a revolt against the Government or the Church. Will you do that for me, please?"

Louis nodded. "I will."

On the way back from the chapel, Father André drew him aside. "You must try to live up to your oath, my son. Pray hard for the strength to do so. Now, a word about another matter. Some time ago you informed Bishop Grandin that if you could get the Government to accept your petition you would go back to Montana; yet I am aware that you have personal claims against the Government, too. What do these claims amount to? Perhaps I can arrange for them to be passed on, in your behalf, to Ottawa."

Louis thought with pleasure: the Government has asked him to do this. Indeed, it is beginning to pay attention to my demands! "Well, *mon père*," he said, "here is how I see it. In the first place, this Government owes me a quarter section of land. It also owes me some more land on account of hay, timber and river frontage of which I was deprived. All this is so, according to the Manitoba Act. In addition, it has never paid me anything for my services in 1869-70, when I ran the country for it for many months; neither has it paid me for the help I gave Governor Archibald in 1871."

"So—they owe you an enormous sum! Well, I think I would agree that you have some claim. What would you say if I tried to get it for you?"

Riel shrugged. "I doubt very much if you can get it—but you may try."

"And if I succeed you will go home?"

"If you succeed, I will go home," Louis agreed.

"People would be quick to say you were betraying your fellow-métis," the priest warned. "This is a factor which I must in fairness point out."

Louis frowned. "In that case they would be lying," he said. "The way I look at it, if the Government sets a precedent by acknowledging *my* claim, they will have to acknowledge all the others, too. Is that not so, *mon père?*"

Father André shrugged. "Perhaps."

"Of course it's so! And besides, when I get home I will start a newspaper; I will use it to make known the plight of my people, to fight their fight." (The thought had just come to him, but already he could see himself as a crusading publisher, and he liked the picture. Perhaps this, too, was God's plan.)

"How much money would it take to start such a newspaper?" Father André asked quietly.

Riel did not have the faintest idea; but presently a figure popped into his head. "I think about $35,000 would do it," he said.

"And for this sum you will leave the country, regardless of what happens to your bill of rights?"

"That is correct, *mon père*. I will return to Montana and carry on the fight from there."

The priest promised to do what he could do advance Riel's claims.

When Louis had departed happily for Batoche, Father André joined the rest of the clergy in Father Fourmond's rectory. After telling them of the conversation that had just taken place, he took up again the question of Riel's sanity. These men all were aware that the métis chief had suffered a breakdown in the past, that he had spent some time in an asylum in the East. Knowing of his outburst in front of Father Vegreville, having witnessed his performance today, they concluded that he was unbalanced again now. At least so far as matters of religion and politics were concerned, he was, in their view, irresponsible; and because this was so he could not be considered sinful when he railed against the Church. Thus, to answer Father Moulin's question, they could not deny him the sacraments—but for the sake of the rest of their flock they must continue to do what they could to encourage his return to Montana.

All through Advent Louis heard Mass daily in the little church of St. Anthony of Padua. As he was now doing with everything else, no doubt he used his religious experiences to bend the reality around him so that it would fit the pattern that his brain told him should exist. If this was so, he must have taken heart from the second lesson chosen for the Ember Saturday of this season. It came from the book of Isaias and it began: "Thus saith the Lord: The land that was desolate and impassable shall be glad, and the wilderness shall rejoice, and shall flourish like the lily."

When he read it, how could it fail to seem to him an omen of success? So far as he and his people were concerned, this land *was* desolate, to be sure; but the Lord had promised that it would flourish like the lily—and the lily is a flower which signifies resurrection and hope. Word would come from Ottawa soon that his petition had been accepted; the lily of justice would flower in all its beauty, and the people would prosper.

Recently, Father Fourmond had been heard to say, with bitterness, that most of the métis already looked upon Riel as "a Joshua, a prophet and even a saint". If this were true, what would they think of him when his mission had finally born fruit? Surely he would have his glory, for they would be proud to confirm him as their permanent chief. As for his personal claims against the Government, Father André had sent word to him that he would bring D. H. MacDowall of the North West Council to see him soon.

In due course this meeting took place; but next to nothing was accomplished, for Louis' ideas about his own worth had passed the bounds of reality by this time. Coolly, he told MacDowall that he would settle for $100,000. He had been offered $35,000 long ago, he said, by an emissary of Sir John Macdonald, to leave Red River; the additional $65,000 would compensate him for the personal hardships he had suffered during his exile! For this sum he would arrange to make his followers well satisfied with whatever settlement the Government was willing to negotiate with them, and he would leave the country for good.

Father André was dumbfounded. He had become convinced that Riel had a claim against the Government, but the amount now demanded was patently ridiculous. And yet—even $100,000 was a small enough sum if it would put an end to the present unrest. "The granting of some indemnity to which he really has a right," he wrote to Lieutenant-Governor Dewdney, "will conciliate all the French half-breeds. I strongly advise you not to look to some paltry dollars when the peace of the country is at stake. The half-breeds sympathize with Riel, and feel sorely in seeing how poor and wretched their leader is, who was obliged to run and hide himself in a foreign country because the Government had not kept faith with him according to their pledged promises."

MacDowall was disgusted. "I believe myself about $3,000 to

$5,000 would cart the whole Riel family across the border," he wrote to the Prime Minister after his interview. "Riel made it distinctly understood that 'self' was his main objective, and he was willing to make the claims of his followers totally subservient to his own interests. He said: 'My name is Riel and I want material,' which I suppose was a pun."

As he waited on the banks of the Saskatchewan for his hopes to be crowned, perhaps reality glimmered for a brief instant, like a false dawn, on Louis' consciousness again. But if it did its light was too harsh to be endured. What would happen to the vision that had sustained him for so long, if he received no recognition soon? What would happen to *his* plans for the métis race? On January 27, 1885, he got word from Jackson that the Government had acknowledged receiving the petition, but had not even bothered to mention his name! Here was concrete evidence that his influence was waning in the Cabinet's eyes. Immediately, he refused to acknowledge this fact. He would show the world that he *could not* be ignored.

According to the evidence given later by Charles Nolin, he flew into a towering rage. "Some time ago you submitted a tender for the job of constructing a telegraph line from Duck Lake to Edmonton," he shouted. "I am here to ask you to wire the Government, withdrawing your tender and explaining that you do so in protest over their silence about my personal claims. I am sure they will listen to you."

Nolin laughed nervously. "Do you think I'm crazy, Louis?" he asked. "Business is business—I want that contract."

"If they continue to ignore me you'll get no contract, I promise you. I will go to Quebec—I will raise an army and return to this land with fire and sword."

Nolin had heard this all before, yet he was impressed. "I will wire the Government on your behalf," he agreed.

But the Government's mind was made up; at all costs, Louis

Riel must be ignored. On the 29th Nolin received a reply from Sir John Macdonald himself, stating simply that the Commons was occupying itself with the métis question.

When Louis heard this he could hardly believe it. So he, the lifelong leader of the métis nation, was to be by-passed?

"In forty days Ottawa will hear my answer!" he thundered. Then he added that the English had been robbing people long enough. Even if it meant risking a shooting war, he must fulfil his mission. No one could deny him his destiny; he *would* succeed, for God had promised him that all glory would be his!

During the first two weeks of February those in charge of government were beseiged with messages from the North-west. MacDowall telegraphed Lieutenant-Governor Dewdney, on the 2nd, that "Riel and leading half-breeds have been here to hear intentions of Government respecting Breeds matter . . . great discontent . . . I anticipate no immediate danger but urge Government to declare intention immediately." Major Crozier, of the North-West Mounted Police, followed this up next day. "I urge immediate action in the matter—and settlement if possible," he advised the Government's representative in the West. On the 6th, Father André telegraphed a message in much the same vein. In reply, Ottawa did nothing more than to repeat what it had said many times before: it "intended" to investigate the claims of those half-breeds who had not received scrip in Manitoba.

This was not good enough for Riel. He, as well as the métis people, was being ignored! The fact could not be hidden from public view much longer. There must be a meeting; the messages from Ottawa—at least the one that Jackson had received—must be disclosed. How humiliating that would be; and yet . . .

Riel himself subsequently maintained that he decided, at this time, to return to Montana and acknowledge that his mission had failed. Charles Nolin told a different tale. According to him, Louis sought him out, with a full-blown plan to save the day. A meeting would be called; after the Government's telegram to Jackson had been read, Louis would announce that he felt he must leave the country, that he would only be a hindrance to the métis cause if he remained any longer in Canada. Several friends, planted in the audience, would then shout, as loudly as they could, "No! No!"; and he would allow himself to be "persuaded" to remain. Nolin claimed that, because he thought such a course of action would demonstrate métis solidarity to the authorities, and thereby help the cause, he consented to become a party to the plan.

Regardless of which version of this episode is true, on February 24th a meeting was convened at Batoche. The message from the Government was read to the crowd. When Riel announced that he planned to leave, he was noisily prevailed upon to remain. Both Fathers Moulin and Fourmond were in attendance, and Captain Gagnon, of the N.W.M.P. detachment at Prince Albert, arrived just as the gathering broke up; so both the Bishop and the Government must soon have had reports of what occurred. If he really wished to impress Ottawa with his power, things could not have gone better as far as Louis was concerned.

It was shortly after this that Riel composed the following prayer and recorded it in his journal: "Lord . . . grant us . . . the grace to seize during this month of March, 1885, the position of '69, and to maintain it in the most glorious manner for Your Sovereign Domain." Whatever his intention had been when he spoke to Nolin, he was committed in his own mind now to the fulfillment of his "mission" in the Canadian West.

Six days later there was a similar meeting in Prince Albert. By this time Riel's thoughts were definitely floating free of all reality—and at least one lay person in Prince Albert was sure that he was mad. Before the meeting there Riel went to dine with his secretary Jackson's brother, a druggist who lived above his store. According to Thomas Jackson's version of the episode, Riel arrived taut as a violin string in anticipation of the meeting. After a painful few moments of small talk, Mrs. Jackson announced that dinner was ready. As soon as her guests were seated she excused herself and went downstairs to the store, in search of some pills to relieve a headache.

In her absence Thomas Jackson began to carve. First he cut the outside piece from the roast, laid it to one side; then he carved a second slice of meat, put it on a plate and passed it to Riel. Suddenly, as Jackson turned his attention back to the business of carving, Louis stood bolt upright. In a shrill voice he accused his host of plotting to poison him. Then, grabbing his hat, he rushed from the room. Such was the blindness of his flight that on the way down the stairs he almost knocked down his hostess, who was returning to the living quarters.

"What in heaven's name was *that* all about?" she asked, coming into the room.

Her husband told her what had occurred. "The man's mad," he concluded bluntly. Then he turned to his brother, who sat calmly in his place. "You must resign your position and come home, Willie." (The family called him by his first name, the métis called him by his second.) "You'll have nothing but trouble with a leader who is so unbalanced."

And there can be very little doubt that Riel *was* unbalanced by this time. Recounting the incident in a letter to his mother, he wrote: "I was invited to dinner . . . the meat on my plate was so covered with pepper and a spiced sauce that the first mouthful made me choke. I got up from the table . . . I acted as if nothing had happened . . . I turned around . . . but my impression was . . . they wished to poison me."

At the meeting after this dinner, Riel was again requested noisily to remain in Canada. When he consented to do so, he took care to reaffirm that the resistance he advocated must be passive

227

only, that English Canadians had nothing to fear. Many of those present were impressed by his modesty, his sanity; but after the meeting, when he went to the home of Father André with Napoleon Nault and another companion, the priest was not.

Bluntly, Louis asked Father André for the Church's approval of a meeting he planned to call, to which the métis would be invited to bring arms. "We do not plan to use them, of course, *mon père*," he added hastily when he saw the priest frown. "Our object will be simply to remind the Government that we *have* arms, if you know what I mean."

"Take care, Riel," Father André said sternly. "When people bring arms to a meeting they often develop an overpowering urge to use them. And if that should happen—"

"If it should happen, Father?"

"You know the Church's answer as well as I do, Riel. It has been explained to you many times. Anyone who bears arms against the Government of Canada will be put under sentence of excommunication."

"You priests were not so lily-livered at Red River fifteen years ago."

"Conditions were entirely different then. Now, there is no question of whether the Canadians have a right to be here. There is no danger of chaos, for the police are among us to maintain law and order. There is no doubt at all that adequate machinery exists through which men's grievances can be aired. The Church is not blind; she can see injustice and inequity in this land as well as you can. She knows the Government has been slow to act. But Canada is a young country. Its public servants are at least trying to set things right. That is why the Church does not consider that conditions here are bad enough to justify a resort to arms. This is the Church's answer, my son, and you would be wise to heed it."

Riel exploded. Who did this priest think he was, talking to

228

him like that? And what did he know of government—legal or illegal, for that matter? He was supposed to be a man of God, yet he spoke now as if he were an agent of Sir John Macdonald! "You have turned against the métis race," he thundered. "You have sold out to the invaders of my people's land. This cannot go unanswered. I will form a provisional government, as I did at Red River. If you refuse to acknowledge its authority, I will have you shot! Is that clear?"

Father André did not blanch. "Get out!" he ordered quietly. "Get out, go home and cool off. And don't dare ever to speak to me like that again."

For a moment Louis stood there, his head in such a turmoil that he could think of nothing to say. Then, followed by his two companions, he slunk out into the night. But when the "prophet" returned to his home, he sat down and wrote out a notice, summoning his followers—with their arms—to a gathering at Batoche.

When Nolin heard what was afoot he hurried to his cousin's side and told him that such a course of action would be madness —especially now, when the Government had already sent word that it was looking into the métis problems. But Louis felt too sure of himself in his dream world to heed such advice. It seemed to him that ice-water flowed in his veins instead of blood, that his plans and ambitions were the most sensible thoughts in the world. He would show these Canadian politicians, these priests, that he could not be ignored! Did Nolin expect him to sit back quietly while the Government ignored his rightful claims? No! They must take up arms, capture hostages while they could, in order to make their bargaining position strong. They must fight for the glory of God, for the honour of religion and the salvation of souls!

Momentarily, Charles Nolin was stunned by the impact of these words. He himself was essentially a schemer; the thought of rushing headlong towards total commitment appalled him. Then a possible means of causing delay suggested itself to him. St. Joseph was the patron saint of the *Union Métisse,* was he not? Then why not ask the priests to organize a novena to him? "Today is the 5th of March," he concluded. "St. Joseph's feast day falls on the 19th. If a novena were to begin on the 10th, it would end on the eve of St. Joseph's feast. Think of it—the whole métis nation united in prayer to its patron saint! Surely, after that, we could be confident that whatever decision we came to would be in accordance with God's will."

After some hesitation, Louis agreed to the plan. With his cousin, he rode over to St. Laurent, pursuaded Father Fourmond to conduct a novena between the dates which Nolin had suggested. Thus the call to arms was postponed and a summons to prayer substituted in its place.

XV

THE REBELLION HAS
COMMENCED

A NOVENA is a devotion requiring special prayer on nine successive days. This particular one began on March 10th, as scheduled, with a Mass and sermon in the church at St. Laurent. Father Vegreville, who came down from his own parish of St. Louis to assist Father Fourmond, was much encouraged by the numbers who attended from among the restless métis. "Riel, who had said that he would pull us in his wake," he wrote to Bishop Grandin on the 12th, "finding his load too heavy and seeing no advantage in separating himself from us, marches before us, or at least chooses to follow us in our way." But his optimism was premature. Riel was following no one.

Novena or no novena, the métis were now in a mood to demonstrate their strength. Persistent rumours began to be heard that they were about to be called to arms. Major Crozier, in charge of the N.W.M.P. detachment at Fort Carlton, telegraphed the Government as early as March 11th to say that the métis were greatly excited; on the 14th he wired Colonel Irvine, his superior officer in Regina, asking that reinforcements be sent forthwith. On the 15th Father Fourmond made one last attempt to discourage his flock from the path they seemed bent on taking.

The little church at St. Laurent was filled, as it had been during each day, for the religious exercises. When he came to the end of the first part of the Mass, the priest advanced to the altar rail to deliver his sermon. He spoke about St. Joseph, stressing the saint's humility, his faithfulness to the will of God under circumstances which must have been both bewildering and humiliating to him. He exhorted his flock to model their own conduct after that of their patron saint. He concluded his sermon by stating bluntly that he would deny the sacraments to all who, in the present circumstances, took up arms.

Riel was sitting at the back of the church, with Gabriel Dumont, Maxime Lépine and Damase Carrière. To him, the priest's statement must have seemed like a final declaration of war. He must defend himself, now, or submit with the people to the Church's will. Leaping to his feet, he walked quickly to the altar rail. Father Fourmond, who had been about to resume the Mass, saw him coming and remained where he was. For a moment Louis stood staring at the priest, as if uncertain what he should do next. The people, watching, dared not breathe. Then, deliberately, Riel raised his right hand and pointed at Father Fourmond. "You have turned the pulpit of truth into the pulpit of falsehood," he shouted. "You talk politics now; you foster discord. We are sick and tired of the things you say."

For an instant shocked silence hung heavy in the little church. Then the people began to cheer their leader's words. Gazing steadily at Father Fourmond, Louis drew himself up to his full height, smiled. He had done it! He had driven a wedge between the métis and their priests. From now on he would supply the only leadership that mattered here.

"You will continue with the Mass," he announced imperiously, as soon as the congregation had quietened down. "But there will be no more politics, Father. Do you understand?"

The priest inclined his head, but he did not answer Riel.

The novena went on according to plan, but it could have borne little spiritual fruit, for by now the métis were determined to ignore their consciences and to follow Riel blindly wherever he wished to lead.

That very evening the métis leader began touring the district, with Gabriel Dumont and Michel Dumas at his side; everywhere he went he exhorted the people to assemble on the 19th with their arms, so that they could celebrate the feast day of St. Joseph by firing a *feu-de-joie*. (It had long been a tradition of the race to express their joy in this manner.) He promised that, as an added attraction, his Protestant secretary would be baptized in the Catholic faith at that time.

This matter of the baptism of Henry Jackson had long been in the wind. After hearing of it from his brother's lips, at the time of the "poisoning" episode, Thomas Jackson had written to Riel as follows: "Will you as a true friend of Willie advise his immediate return. . . . He had been undergoing a severe mental strain for a long time and he must have a season of perfect quiet or his mind will give way. . . . If Willie carries out his program . . . it will kill the success of the movement completely amongst the Canadians and English. . . . It will furnish the additional argument to the opposition that there is a Proselyting [*sic*] Scheme connected with it." But his letter had had no effect. William Henry Jackson was determined to receive the sacrament of baptism from the hands of a Catholic priest—the same priest whom Louis, his leader, had just denounced before the world!

All the next day Louis rode about, in great excitement, stirring up his people. On the 18th, while pausing for dinner at the home of Baptiste Rocheleau, some seven miles south of Batoche, he and his party ran into Dr. John Willoughby, a medical practitioner from Saskatoon. It seemed like a wonderful opportunity to tell an "outsider" what was on his mind.

While sixty or seventy armed métis milled about outside, Riel announced to the doctor that he was about to stage a coup; with the aid of these métis "police", he would wipe the little government police off the face of the earth! His plans were mature; this rebellion would be far bigger than the one of 1870. He would divide the North-west into seven portions—for Bavarians, Poles, Italians, Germans, Irish, Hungarians, and others who helped his cause. He would exclude Orangemen, he added with vehemence.

When Dr. Willoughby asked him if this meant no Protestantism, Louis said no. Taking the doctor by the arm he escorted him outside, pointed towards a tree. The Church was like that tree, he said. As the branches left the trunk in ascending order, they became weaker. The branches were the various religions that had diverted from the true Church. And what was the true Church? the doctor asked. "The Roman Catholic Church," Riel replied. Whereupon he shook hands all around and rode off with his men.

That same day, a party of half-breeds met Lawrence Clarke, the Hudson's Bay Company factor at Prince Albert. He was a member of the North West Council, a man to be believed. When he told them that reinforcements of police had been ordered into the area to capture Riel and the leaders associated with him, they took at face value all that he said. In great haste they rode to Batoche, to inform their leader of what they had learned.

Now, the situation long feared by priests and police authorities was about to come to pass. Unless Louis capitulated, force would meet naked force—and soon! But Riel had no intention of capitulating, and his people had no intention of deserting him at this time. When he heard Clarke's news he publicly burned his final bridge. He announced: "We must capture Fort Carlton! We must take hostages! It is the only way in which we can bring the Cabinet to its knees."

Like a prairie fire, word spread that the moment for action had arrived. All over the settlement half-breeds who had not already done so sprang to arms; Indians on the reservations talked openly of doing the same. When they heard the news, lonely settlers from the Manitoba border to the Rockies grew fearful for their wives and families, and checked with care their supplies of food and ammunition.

John Lash, an Indian agent, and William Tompkins, his interpreter, were the first Canadians to run afoul of this new métis activity. On the afternoon of the 18th, while driving back to Carlton after a visit to One Arrow's reserve, they stopped at the Kerr Brothers store in Batoche to buy some potatoes. While inside, they were arrested by Gabriel Dumont and about sixty métis, who had come to requisition the merchant's guns and powder. Presently, Riel himself drove up, announced that he would detain them for only a few hours. "The rebellion has commenced," he said loftily. "And we intend fighting until the whole of the Saskatchewan Valley is in our hands." Then he ordered that everyone must come with him to the church.

Carrying the prisoners with them, the throng swept like a great wave up the hill to St. Anthony of Padua's. Riel, at the lead, seemed to be in top form. When Father Moulin came running from his rectory to protest against the profanation of his church, he brushed him aside with a pun. "Listen to him!" he quipped. "He protests—he is a Protestant!" Then, telling the priest that he could no longer hold services here, he led the people inside.

While Lash and Tompkins looked on, Riel quieted his followers and told them to sit down. As the first order of business, he despatched a party of men to cut telegraph lines to the west and north. Then, turning to Dumont, he announced that he was going to St. Laurent, to inform the priests of what had taken place. "While I am gone, I appoint you to elect a council," he said. Abruptly he left the building, with Henry Jackson, Michel Dumas, and Moise Ouellette at his heels.

When they arrived at St. Laurent, Riel and his followers burst in on Fathers Fourmond, Paquette and Vegreville. "The Provisional Government has been declared," Louis shouted, "and the old Roman woman has been broken! From now on you will be priests of the new religion—and you will obey me!"

"Never!" one of the fathers declared.

Riel laughed harshly. "Then your churches will be empty," he told them, "for your flock will follow my orders. You had better obey me, too; I am God's prophet and you know it."

When no one made further reply Louis frowned, passed one hand before his eyes, turned and went into the church. Quietly, Jackson followed him. There the two men prayed loudly for about two hours. While they were thus engaged Father Paquette slipped out a side door and made his way to Fort Carlton, to warn the police that the armed rebellion had at last begun.

But the armed rebellion had not in fact commenced; no irreversible steps had as yet been taken against the established Government of Canada; there would be shadow-boxing for a few more days. And while there was shadow-boxing, there would remain some hope that the métis leader was bluffing, that his sole objective was to put on a show, that he would back down when the moment of truth arrived. Yet it seems abundantly clear, in retrospect, that by now he had become a piece of flotsam swept up by the incoming tide.

Before leaving St. Laurent on the night of the 18th, he consented to have Henry Jackson baptized privately by Father Fourmond, rather than having it done publicly on the 19th as arranged. The first thing next morning he set up headquarters in Xavier Batoche's store, around which a great many métis had assembled with their arms, and began to hold a political meeting. This was to replace the closing novena exercises that had originally been planned.

After announcing "officially" that a large body of police was approaching and that the hour of decision had arrived, he called for nominations to the Council of the new Provisional Government. Though he refused office for himself, on the grounds that he was not a citizen of the country, he made it known that the people might acknowledge him formally as their inspired prophet; and he assumed publicly once again the name David, after the ancient Hebrew king.

Then the Council was elected. Pierre Parenteau was named President, Charles Nolin Commissaire, Gabriel Dumont Adjutant-General; there were twelve ordinary members, and W. H. Jackson acted as Secretary until he became ill on March 21st and Philip Garnot took his place. Louis guided all their organizational moves. Among other things, he caused the Ten Commandments to be adopted as the law of the land; then he caused it to be declared that the corporate name of the group in control should be *Exovedate*—which was supposed to mean, in Latin, "those picked from the flock".

How much of this business was inspired by the métis tradition of self-government on the plains? The holding of elections, the adoption of an agreed-upon code of law—these things were entirely in keeping with the métis' ancient practice. But Louis' insistence that the councillors whom he dominated were equal members, acting on behalf of a "flock", smacks either of cunning manipulation or wishful thinking carried to the height of lunacy.

Let us examine Riel's own words to see if we can discover what was going on in his mind. "Without assuming any authority other than that which exists by itself in the condition of our nature," he wrote after his surrender to Canadian authorities, "we recurred to the right of self-preservation; and those who agreed to act together in the protection of their existence, threatened in so many different ways, took the names *Exovede*, so that having their distinctive title for the time being and to be known by the men of the movement when the crisis would be over, the reaction would be as light as possible. . . . What would have been undertaken and accomplished under the sound authority of good sense, could have no other result than good ones, and consequently the movement proved to be less a disturbance than a remedy to some things that were previously going too far in the wrong. . . . Being composed of *Exovedes*, we have called it [the Council] the *Exovedate*."

The thought processes seem to be hopelessly mixed up here. But, whether one should construe Riel's tactics as being the result of clearly thought-out cunning, or as fantasies generated in a sick mind, the point is that, on the local scene at least, they worked. From the moment he undermined the civil power and weakened the influence of the Church, he required an instrument through which he could govern. Now, somehow, he had hit upon a most acceptable one. From the day of its inception the métis rank and file were impressed by the *Exovedate*; and being impressed, they were willing to accept each pronouncement that it made.

The organizational phase having been dealt with, the Council now turned to the task of drawing up plans. In order to appreciate the line of reasoning they followed, it is necessary to digress for a moment and examine, at least superficially, the state of affairs among the Indians of the West.

Between 1871 and 1877, seven treaties had been negotiated by the Government of Canada with the aboriginal inhabitants. Treaty No. 1 had been signed at Fort Garry between the white men, the Crees, and the Ojibways; Treaty No. 7 had been signed, in sight of the mountains, between the white men and the Blackfoot nation. In six short years almost all the arable land of the North-west had been taken over by Canada and the original Indian owners had been persuaded to retire to reservations.

That the Indians had no conception of what they were doing is illustrated with clarity by the following statement, made by the

Lac Seul chief in connection with the signing of Treaty No. 3: "We are the first that were planted here," he said. "We would ask you to assist us with every kind of implement to use for our benefit . . . a little of everything, and money. We would borrow your cattle; . . . the waters out of which you sometimes take food for yourselves, we will lend you in return. . . . The time may come when I will ask you to lend me one of your daughters and one of your sons to live with us; and in return I will lend you one of my daughters and one of my sons for you to teach what is good, and after they have learned, to teach us."

Treaty No. 6, embracing the Indians of the area in which the métis of the Saskatchewan lived, had been concluded in 1876. Incorporated in it was a "famine" clause. Thus, when the buffalo disappeared, between 1878 and 1880, the chiefs called upon Ottawa to feed them. Ottawa agreed to do so only if the aborigines retired, once and for all, to the reservations set aside for them. (Having no real appreciation of the concept of private property, they kept leaving the reserves whenever the spirit moved them, in search of game.) The long, painful process of trying to teach these nomadic people to farm had begun.

By 1883 a business recession held all Canada in its grip. The Government at Ottawa, desperate for funds, decided to embark on a policy of retrenchment. Naturally the Indians, being without votes, were among the first to feel the economic axe. As central authority began arbitrarily cutting back the "wasteful" expenditures of its Indian agents the whole atmosphere throughout the West began to change. As Major Crozier put it, in one of his reports, it seemed as if "there was a wish to see upon how little a man can work and exist". And: "My firm conviction is, if some such policy as I have outlined is not carried out, there is only one other—and that is to fight them."

Big Bear, a Cree chief of the area, had refused steadfastly to be a party to Treaty No. 6 when it was signed. He had refused to select a reserve for his band, had continued to roam across the plains whenever he felt so inclined. When told to retire to a reserve or lose his rations, he had retaliated by making efforts to unite all the Indians of the West, with a view to conducting further negotiations from a position of strength. From the beginning another Cree chief, Poundmaker, associated himself with this desire to unite, although he and his people remained on their reserve near the town of Battleford. Between them, these two chiefs managed to achieve a gathering of nearly two thousand Indians, in June of 1884, in the Saskatchewan area. When Crozier went with eighty-six Mounted Police to break it up, several nasty incidents occurred.

Throughout all these developments, Dumont had maintained a liaison with his Indian friends. When Riel arrived back in the district, he had arranged that he should meet several of the more prominent chiefs. Métis and Indians began to feel that they had much in common, for, as Big Bear himself put it, "We have all been deceived in the same way." During the summer, plans had been laid for a great and representative Indian council to be held in 1885.

Now, therefore, it seemed natural to Dumont—the man of action—to propose that they raise the Indians, engage the police in battle before reinforcements could arrive, overrun Fort Carlton, Prince Albert, and Battleford, and avail themselves of the stores and ammunition in these places. When one considers that this scheme was advocated by a man who had no appreciation of the strength of the forces that could ultimately be marshalled against him, it must be judged as sensible. Riel, who had breathed fire on occasion but more often advocated the mere capture of hostages, raised objections. Quietly he insisted that the métis, though armed, must remain passive unless they were attacked.

After much debate it "was moved by Boucher, seconded by

Carrière, that we desire to effect the capture of the fort [Carlton] without spilling any blood, and the greater our force the more certain of attaining our objective, but in case we are compelled to fight, justice compels that we should take up arms." Then, on further urging from the practical Dumont, it was decided that, in spite of this resolution, a list of trustworthy Indian chiefs must be prepared, and that these chiefs must be interviewed and informed of what the métis nation was about to do.

In effect the métis Council had endorsed, over Dumont's protestations, Riel's false dream of personal negotiation through strength. The fort was to be captured without bloodshed; then the Canadian Government was to be invited to parley! Surely, this was an egoist's dream, superimposed upon and distorting beyond recognition the cause of the ignorant people whom he led.

Riel knew the outside world—he had been taught, to his sorrow, how it functioned. If he was sane, how could he have believed that justice would result from the methods he now chose to employ? Even if he had managed to capture a sizeable number of hostages, how could he have hoped to bring Canada to terms, with a few hundred poorly armed men, in 1885? Well-organized passive resistance might have done the trick; political agitation had in fact already shown signs of resulting in success; but blackmail and half-hearted military manoeuvres could only invite retaliation—and weight of numbers must prevail in the end.

Where, in Riel's actions at this time, was the harmony or the proportion he had shown on occasion before, the harmony and proportion that distinguish reasonable ambition from the blind compulsion of a madman? Already, by his actions, Louis had *forced* the missionaries, who were the métis' staunchest friends, to turn against him; he had *forced* the police to call his bluff and ask for reinforcements. Now he was about to compel Sir John Macdonald to destroy him.

When plans had been decided upon, the Council adjourned for the night. Next day, at Riel's request, it addressed itself to a matter of discipline. Some time during the interval Charles Nolin had been arrested because he refused to support the métis call to arms; now he must be brought to trial. After hearing evidence for and against him, the Council decided that he must be shot. But by this time it was past noon; like judges of Her Majesty's courts, the Councillors rose gravely to take lunch. While they were gone from the room Riel talked privately with his cousin, came to some understanding with him. When the Council reassembled, Louis, the prosecutor, reversed his previous stand and announced that the prisoner must be pardoned for his crime. "We have the big wheel in the movement with us again," he explained inadequately. And happily for Nolin, the veteran politician, that was the end of that.

On the same day it was decided that contact must be established with the Mounted Police. Accordingly, Hilliard Mitchell, a storekeeper at Duck Lake, was prevailed upon to journey to Carlton on the métis' behalf to tell the police what the *Exovedate* had decided to do. Just as Mitchell arrived at his destination, some forty to fifty volunteers, summoned by Crozier from Prince Albert, marched in. Among them was a guide named Thomas Mackay. At Crozier's request, Mackay arranged to accompany Mitchell back to Batoche to ascertain what was really going on there and to gauge the temper of the people. They started out in the middle of the night, in an open sleigh. By about 8 A.M. on the 21st they had reached the west bank of the Saskatchewan, opposite Batoche. There they found twelve to fifteen men milling about Walter & Baker's store. When they had made themselves known, a sentry was delegated to accompany them across the river.

Presently they found themselves in a little building just south of the church, which the métis were now using as their council-house. A number of armed men were talking among themselves. Riel was sitting at a long table having breakfast. When Mitchell introduced Mackay to him, he made it perfectly clear that the guide had joined the Government side. "It makes no difference," Louis assured him grandly. "Because he came with you, he will receive the same protection as you do." Then: "What do you hope to accomplish by coming here like this?" he asked Mackay.

The new-comer shrugged. "I came over to see what the excitement was all about."

It was the wrong thing to say. Frowning, Louis set aside the plate that was before him. "There is no excitement at all," he replied carefully. "The people are merely trying to redress their grievances, that is all."

Mackay ignored the warning. He shrugged. "I hope you know how dangerous it is to take up arms."

This was not what Louis wanted to hear at all. "Dangerous!" he shouted, loudly enough to attract the attention of the whole room. "What do I care about danger? I have waited fifteen years for this moment."

"There are other ways of protesting to the Government, Riel."

Louis flushed scarlet. "The métis have been trying for ten years to get justice by 'other' means. You know that as well as I do. Why have you neglected to do anything on their behalf?"

"I haven't neglected to do anything on their behalf," Mackay replied with some heat. "And, even if I had, who are you to talk? You stayed away in the States long enough, didn't you?"

With that Riel began stamping his feet and shouting that there must be a war of extermination. The Canadian Government, the Hudson's Bay Company, the Mounted Police, must be driven from the land. If blood must be shed, the first should be Mackay's, for he was nothing but a speculator, a scoundrel and a thief!

Instantly, Mackay stepped forward, pounded the table with

a massive fist. As he did so, he overturned a cup. Its contents spilled over the table and onto the floor. The liquid was red and heavy-flowing; it appeared to be blood.

"Look! You have spilled the first blood!" Louis screamed, pointing at the mess. "My bullock's blood, which I take for my indigestion." Obviously he was pleased with his own quickness of wit. Laughing, he went on: "You came here to pick a quarrel and now you have spilled the first blood!"

Mackay was unimpressed. "I didn't come here to pick a quarrel, Riel, and I won't have you saying that I did. I came here merely to tell you—"

"To tell me lies, to try and separate me from my people, as others have tried in the past!"

"There's no need to put words in my mouth, Riel. If you wish to hear me speak for myself I will do so—and if not, I won't."

The Councillors had gathered close during this exchange. Now, by a spontaneous murmur of approval, they indicated that their sympathies lay with Mackay. He had a right to be heard, one of them suggested firmly.

Riel had enough presence of mind to swim with the current. He threw up his hands. "He has a right to be heard? Of course he has a right to be heard! Everyone has a right to be heard. I agree to that; but the Government of Canada won't agree to it." Then, glaring at Mackay: "Tell them truthfully why you have come here."

Mackay turned to face the Councillors. "I came here because Major Crozier asked me to. He told me to make it perfectly clear —the danger for yourselves and your families that will follow if you take up arms."

"We're not looking for a fight," a voice protested. "All we want is that the Government should listen to what we have to say."

There was a chorus of assent to this. When it had died down

Mackay made his reply. "What you want and what you may get if you continue on in this way are two distinct things. You ought to realize that."

While this exchange was taking place Riel seemed to cool down. "It has all been decided," he broke in presently. "Nothing can be altered now. But no harm will come from talking about it if you wish to do so." Then: "Unfortunately, I myself have a committee meeting awaiting me upstairs." He bowed low. "If you will excuse me?" With that he crossed the room and mounted the stairs to the second floor.

When he was gone Mackay reopened the discussion; for a long time he talked with the Councillors. Though Riel had left the room with a show of great confidence, he must have been worried still about how the talking would go, for whenever an exchange of ideas injected some heat into the conversation he came partially downstairs, complained about the noise, and hovered briefly in the room to catch the thread of the discussion.

Yet he had no cause for alarm. As he had said, it seemed that nothing could be changed now. Mackay soon began to realize this; to realize also that he was hungry, for he had not breakfasted today. Terminating the discussion, he asked for something to eat. When it had been brought to him and his belly filled, he began to feel heavy-eyed with sleep. Rubbing his eyes, he yawned. Seeing this, a Councillor suggested that he have a nap. Without argument, he retired to a corner of the room and lay down.

When he awakened it was afternoon; Mitchell was standing over him, with Riel hovering nearby. In the background the Councillors were still talking among themselves. "Come on," Mitchell told him. "It's time to head back towards Carlton. I've got another message to give Major Crozier."

Mackay was stiff from lying on the floor. Awkwardly he stood up, stretched, swaying slightly on his tingling feet. Riel took him by the arm. "I am sorry for what I said this morning," he told him. "If you would agree to join us I would be glad to have you in my force."

Mackay smiled. "Thanks, Riel. I know that's meant as a compliment. But I'm afraid I'll have to stay on the other side of the fence." Then: "Please don't do anything rash during the next few days. Maybe this thing can still be straightened out."

Louis tossed his head. He did not want things "straightened out". Neither did he want to fight if he could avoid it. "I'm giving Crozier his last chance," he said stiffly. "If he fails to surrender Carlton, we will attack at midnight. You must make this quite clear."

Mackay shrugged. "We'll give him your message."

The three men shook hands; Mitchell and Mackay departed for Fort Carlton. As soon as he had heard what they had to say, Major Crozier announced that he would not consider the idea of surrender. The honour of the police was at stake—and reinforcements from Regina were on their way. If Riel wanted Fort Carlton he would have to come and take it the hard way.

But instead of moving against the police, Riel settled for more delaying tactics. "If we are well united," he wrote to the English half-breeds on March 23rd, "our union will cause the police to come out of Carlton as the hen's heat causes the chicken to come out of the shell." Then he went on to explain that, if this should happen, they could take hostages and negotiate with Ottawa.

But the English half-breeds—while insisting that "every man is with you"—refused to take up arms. They would petition the Government once again to "do justice to the settlers, treat with them and save the effusion of blood"; but they would do no more. As Father André testified later, at Riel's trial, they swung over at the last moment to a policy of strict neutrality. Yet, by attending meetings, helping to frame the petition to Ottawa, and

246

contributing money, they had given Riel the impression that all of them were solidly behind him.

At Fort Carlton (which was merely a collection of log buildings dominated by a hill three hundred feet high, not a fort in the accepted meaning of the word) Major Crozier, too, was being buffeted by the emotions of the people. Ever since the new year he had been quietly moving police reinforcements into the area from other points in the West. On the 15th of the month he had received word that Colonel Irvine was on his way from Regina with more than one hundred men. He was a sensible officer. He knew that the wisest thing to do would be to ignore Riel until these reinforcements had arrived. But since the 18th, English-Canadian volunteers from Prince Albert had been coming to his side, and now, on the 25th, his whole force was itching for a fight. To ease the tension among his men, he announced that on the following day he would send out a reconnaissance patrol.

Early the next morning the métis Council decided to move its headquarters to Duck Lake. Hearing this, Hilliard Mitchell rushed to tell the police authorities that the goods in his store were in danger of being confiscated. Crozier ordered the small patrol that he had despatched—fifteen police and seven volunteers, under Sergeant Stewart—to investigate. Before it could do so, Dumont and a few scouts intercepted it and forced it to turn back. Boasting that he had rebuffed the police, Dumont rode back in high spirits to Duck Lake. The rank and file of the métis nation was filled with jubilation at the news.

But victory was not to be that cheaply won. By 10 A.M. Sergeant Stewart had made contact with Major Crozier. Quite understandably, the Major decided that the impression must never be allowed to get abroad that the side of law and order had suffered a serious blow. With fifty-three policemen and forty-one volunteers he marched out from Carlton, determined to secure the provisions and ammunition that were stored at Duck Lake.

From this point on events began to control themselves. At métis headquarters, a guide rushed in to say that the main police force was drawing near. Dumont was elated; there would be fighting at last. Riel, for all his previous reluctance, appeared to be elated, too. With the news all uncertainty seemed to vanish from his mind. While Dumont dashed off with his scouts to intercept the foe, he rushed into the settlement's tiny chapel, tore the crucifix from its place above the altar, and announced that now they would defend themselves in the name of the Holy Trinity. Then he waited at Duck Lake to lead the main force as soon as it could be assembled.

About two miles westward at a point where the trail broke, downhill, out of a poplar wood, Dumont saw the police ahead. With the skill of a veteran hunter he recognized that if he were to remain where he was he would possess every advantage of ground. After placing his men behind trees and folds in the hard, crusty snow, he waited for the enemy to draw near.

The police had been moving, some in sleighs, some on foot, in column of route along the trail. When Major Crozier saw what was happening ahead, he called a halt, then ordered that one of the sleighs be placed across the road as a barricade. After this had been done, he advanced with his guide to parley.

Dumont feared a trick. Remaining under cover with the men, he sent forward his older brother Isidore and an Indian named Assiyiwin to meet the police. Crozier demanded to know why the métis had so many men under arms; the Indian demanded to know why the police were there in such force. Crozier asked a second question; the Indian turned it back upon him in a similar manner. In an atmosphere of heightening tension the parley went on. Meanwhile, at the edge of the woods, the métis reinforcements for whom Riel had been waiting began to arrive and to take up positions to right and left of the police in the snow. Watching this development, Crozier's guide realized that they were being outflanked. Without ceremony, he broke into the conversation to point it out.

From this moment on things happened very quickly indeed. As Crozier turned to order his men to deploy, the Indian beside Isidore Dumont made a lunge for the guide's rifle. Drawing a revolver, the guide shot at his adversary. Though he missed the Indian, he wounded Isidore Dumont fatally in the head. The métis toppled from his horse; Major Crozier gave the order to fire. Instantly, Gabriel Dumont did the same. In spite of Riel's vague dreams of bloodless glory, the Battle of Duck Lake had begun.

XVI

WE COULD KEEP
THEM AS HOSTAGES

I T was a skirmish at Duck Lake rather than a battle; the
métis had won more difficult engagements many times
before, and here they began with every advantage of
ground. Sallying forth to "show the flag", Major Crozier
had blundered into a situation such as no commander, however
inexperienced, would have chosen of his own free will; having
done so, he had simply to make the best of it now. Ordering his
men to deploy through the deep snow to right and left, he commanded that his solitary cannon be brought up along the hard
trail and fired straight ahead. But the fates must have been set
against him that day, for almost with the first shot the cannon
became permanently jammed.

For their part the métis merely lay where they were and, with
sharpshooters' skill, picked off the Government men. As reinforcements arrived Dumont despatched them to positions opposite the enemy's flanks; when he himself was put out of action
with a superficial head wound, his brother Edouard carried on
in his place. While the battle raged about him, Riel rode up and
down in a frenzy of zeal, brandishing his stolen cross and exhorting his followers to keep up their fire in the name of the Father
and of the Son and of the Holy Ghost!

Soon Major Crozier realized that, even though his forces possessed a superiority of weapons, there was nothing he could do
to dislodge the métis. Inexorably, he was being outflanked.

Without hesitation, he ordered his men to begin the difficult manoeuvre of withdrawing westward parallel to the trail. They had just commenced obeying when, as if by a miracle, the métis firing ceased. Less than thirty minutes after the first shots were exchanged, the Battle of Duck Lake had come to an end.

Riel himself had ordered the cease-fire. Dumont, lying helpless in the snow, was furious over the decision, for he knew it had lost for him the opportunity to inflict a crushing defeat; but his chief could not be reasoned with. "There has been too much blood spilled already," Louis repeated, over and over again. Then he sent word to the police that they might come and collect their dead.

The police and volunteers had suffered ten dead and thirteen wounded; the métis had lost five dead and one prisoner. At the height of the battle Charles Nolin had seized a cutter and driven off towards Prince Albert—only to be arrested, when he got there, and put in prison by the police.

In the settlement of Duck Lake, the métis population went wild. Led by Riel himself, they cheered for St. Mary, St. Joseph and St. John the Baptist. Though Dumont had chosen the ground and directed the soldiers throughout the fight, Louis quite easily convinced his "flock" that it was thanks to no mere human skill that their victory had been won. And he took care to add, of course, that *he* was the medium through whom divine intervention had flowed.

On the following morning the *Exovedate* was called into session. "Moved by M. Boucher, seconded by M. Xavier Tourond", its members agreed that "the Canadian half-breed *Exovedate* acknowledges Louis 'David' Riel as a prophet in the service of Jesus Christ and Son of God and only Redeemer of the world; a prophet at the feet of Mary Immaculate, under the visible and most consoling safeguard of St. Joseph, the beloved patron of half-breeds—the patron of the universal Church; as a prophet, the humble imitator in many things of St. John the Baptist, the glorious patron of the French Canadians and the French-Canadian half-breeds. *Yeas 8, Nays none.* Ouellette did not vote, but said if after a time his views changed, he would record his vote."

At about this time, Riel wrote: "I saw myself in the mirror of justice, and wisdom shone forth from me. It illuminated my countenance." When commissioners were sent from Ottawa to bargain with him, surely he would get his way. But no commissioners were sent by the Government of Canada.

Sir John Macdonald was growing old—seventy years old that January—and the members of his Cabinet were growing old, too. Increasingly often it seemed to all of them, as they pondered Government problems in Ottawa, that the goal they had set themselves so long ago could not possibly be achieved. One strong, sure Canada, stretching from sea to sea! Could this vision be attained—or must it fade forever into the mists of time, disclosing itself to be nothing but a mirage?

Indeed, the questions at issue before the Cabinet seemed as formidable now as they had seemed more than twenty years earlier, when the Canadian dream of federation had been conceived at far-off Charlottetown. The country was wallowing in the mire of a financial depression; Nova Scotia was seething with dissatisfaction; Ontario was maintaining defiantly that the provinces were sovereign unto themselves; Manitoba, the teen-aged offspring of Confederation, was bucking against parental control and flirting outrageously with the idea of giving herself to the United States; British Columbia, impatient as a bridegroom, demanded in ever more strident tones to know when it might expect to unite with its betrothed, and receive thereby the dowry that it had been promised.

What was to be done? The solution to most of these questions could be found in the completion of the transcontinental railway line. But how was the line to be finished? Though it had been under construction since 1872, it was not yet four-fifths done. Perhaps it never would be completed; perhaps it was just too big an undertaking for a nation of four million people to have taken on in the first place; yet without it as an artery of trade and communication this new entity called Canada could not long survive. Both political parties had recognized this fact; both had tried without success to grapple with it.

After the "Pacific Scandal" of 1873 and Sir John Macdonald's disgrace, the Liberals had attempted to construct the line as a public enterprise. By 1880, when the Conservatives returned to power, they had proved beyond a doubt that this could not be done. Gladly, Macdonald had signed a contract with a new Canadian Pacific syndicate for the completion of the line. In return for a cash subsidy of $25,000,000, land grants totalling 25,000,000 acres, and protection against competition for twenty years, the group had undertaken to complete the railroad by May 1, 1891. This syndicate—headed by George Stephen and Richard B. Angus, with the vast fortune of Stephen's cousin, Donald A. Smith, in the background—had accomplished much during the past four years. Construction time-tables were well ahead of schedule; soon three-quarters of the system would be complete.

And yet the mighty project was now about to fail. The money raised for construction had all been spent; the financial markets of the world had all been exhausted; the private fortunes of the men involved had all been thrown into the enterprise. As a final gesture the Government itself had guaranteed, last year, a loan of some $30,000,000 at 4 per cent for four years in return for shares in the company. All this capital had been raised and set to work—yet all of it had been devoured by the fantastic costs of construction. Not another mile of track could be laid. Already workmen at Port Arthur had struck because of delay in delivery of their wages. Without further immediate Government assistance, the whole gigantic enterprise would be sucked forever into the muskeg of financial failure.

"What alarms me," Stephen had written to Macdonald recently, "is the apprehension that the patient will die while the doctors are deliberating." Fifteen million dollars' worth of 5 per cent bonds, secured by fifteen million acres of land, must be marketed at once; but they could be sold only if they carried with them a Government guarantee of both principal and interest. Thus, Parliament must be persuaded—and quickly—to come to the rescue of the C.P.R. But how could Parliament be persuaded when the Cabinet itself was unwilling to bring the distasteful matter before the House?

"We dare not ask for another loan," Macdonald had written to Tupper, who was the Canadian High Commissioner in London by this time. In fact, the Prime Minister had determined that, in spite of Stephen's quite genuine alarm, his only hope lay in playing a waiting game.

And now, on top of all these other worries, the métis of the North-west had decided to cause a commotion. Here was one more problem that must be faced and thought through at last. Ever since Riel's return from Montana, the news from Saskatchewan had given cause for worry; since Christmas time it had been downright disturbing. There had been Jackson's petition— the Cabinet had discussed it on January 9th and referred it to the Minister of the Interior for action. There had been reports from Father André and D. H. MacDowall about the métis chief. Before that there had been opinions from Amadée Forget and Bishop Grandin on the same subject. As a result of all the information he had received—in spite of some of it—Sir John had become convinced that Riel was nothing but a cold-blooded extortioner who must under no circumstances be appeased.

But the Cabinet must do *something* to remedy the métis grievances. In the matter of land, they must deal as quickly as possible with the half-breed claims. Though the issuance of scrip had been disastrous for most of those who received it in Manitoba —and one could predict with certainty that it would be equally disastrous for the métis on the Saskatchewan—if scrip was what they wanted now, scrip was what they would get! "They will drink it or waste it or sell it; but let us have peace," the Prime Minister had said when the question was discussed. And the Cabinet had agreed with him. No matter how it was to be done, the métis problem must be cleaned up once and for all so that the orderly settlement of the West could go on unhindered.

They would have their scrip, then—their pieces of paper representing allocations of land by the Government. So that their claims could be dealt with fairly, a commission of three men would be appointed to make an enumeration of the métis in the West. On February 4th the news of this decision had been telegraphed to Lieutenant-Governor Dewdney. For a while thereafter things had been relatively quiet; then, about the middle of March, conditions had rapidly begun to become more grave. And now, on the evening of the 27th, Sir John received word of the Battle of Duck Lake.

At once it seemed obvious to him that none of the steps agreed upon could be implemented until authority had been restored along the Saskatchewan. Not commissioners, but troops, must be despatched to the prairies. If a general Indian and métis rising was to be forestalled, the three hundred Mounted Police already in the West must be reinforced quickly with soldiers and Riel, the cause of the trouble, must be publicly brought to account.

Suddenly, while pondering these facts, Sir John's sharp old eyes spotted a ray of sunlight piercing the gloomy overcast. Perhaps Riel's threatening posture could be used to solve the railroad dilemma. Of course it could! The key word was "troops"; the key question: how were they to be moved? Fifteen years ago it had taken Wolseley all summer to get his troops to Fort Garry.

Now, thanks to the still incomplete C.P.R., a far larger force could be moved in a fraction of the time. There were gaps in the line of steel, to be sure; there were places where bridges must still be thrown up; but if the company's officers could be prevailed upon to attempt the task, troops might be carried west in spite of these details. And if they were transported successfully, the whole nation would see in a flash the value of the C.P.R. Then it would be a relatively simple chore to persuade Parliament that the railroad *must* be saved. Time and circumstance and his own fertile brain might yet save this Canada which he had done so much to sire.

Without wasting a moment he sent for the railroad's general manager and outlined his plan. He could not have asked for a more willing ally. This practical genius, this giant of a man, was William Van Horne, whose philosophy of life, publicly stated on many an occasion, was: "I eat all I can, I drink all I can, I smoke all I can, and I don't give a damn for anything." He understood Macdonald's idea instantly. Of course the C.P.R. would cooperate! They'd carry troops across the gaps in the line on horse-drawn sleighs; they'd march them across the still frozen rivers at places where bridges had yet to be built. Though rolling stock was in desperately short supply, with accurate planning they'd be able to make do with what they had. There was no money in the till—but that fact would just have to be ignored for the time being. "Lastly," Van Horne assured the Prime Minister solemnly, "you can be sure that every employee in our company will bust his guts trying to get this job done!"

That very night the Winnipeg Rifles entrained for Qu'Appelle, which was almost due south of the trouble spot. By March 30th more troops were on the move. In less than two weeks eight thousand men—more than four thousand of them from eastern Canada—stood poised on the prairie, ready to fight! From Ontario, from Quebec, from Manitoba, from the distant Maritimes, the youth of Canada had flocked to arms. Dreaded differences of race, of language, of religion, of history, had been forgotten in the face of the common task; and the C.P.R., Canada's own railroad, had become a byword in every home.

At Batoche, however, Riel's *Exovedate* kept their attention focused on the local picture. What they saw prompted them to feel encouraged. On March 26th, a few hours after the Battle of Duck Lake, Colonel Irvine had arrived at Fort Carlton with his police reinforcements. Two days later, on orders from Middleton, the General Officer Commanding the Canadian Militia, he had retired to Prince Albert to protect the civilian population there. Misreading the significance of this purely tactical move, the métis and Indians had become convinced that the police were now in full retreat. A few of the more hot-headed among them began to say that if everyone worked together, white rule might be finally overthrown.

In complete contrast to his avowed present policy and his moderate attitude in 1870, Riel promptly decided that in order to maintain his ascendency he must demonstrate his power over the Indian tribes. Despatching highly inflammatory notes of encouragement to several of the chiefs, he fanned their already smouldering feelings into flame. To Poundmaker he wrote: "Bless God with us for the success He has granted us. Rise. Face the police. . . . Take Battleford. Destroy it. . . . All that you do, do it for the love of God." Now was the time for the "New Nation" to declare itself, for the Indians of the West to seek with him the destiny they deserved! To bewildered and often half-starved aborigines, this was powerful medicine indeed.

Four days after the Battle of Duck Lake, Chief Poundmaker did as he was asked. Solemnly, he announced that he would take the warpath. When they heard this, settlers adjacent to Battleford abandoned their homesteads, fled to the safety of the fort. Immediately Poundmaker's braves began looting and burning their vacated farms. Further west along the river, young braves of Big Bear's tribe, under the spell of a white-hating medicine man named Wandering Spirit, embarked on a more grisly escapade. Sweeping down on the tiny settlement of Frog Lake, they cold-bloodedly murdered nine inhabitants, including two Oblate priests. Suddenly, it seemed as if every white person in the West might be massacred by the Indian tribes.

At Fort Pitt a disaster even bloodier than the one at Frog Lake was avoided by the narrowest of margins. When Trader W. H. McLean of the Hudson's Bay Company observed Big Bear's braves, fresh from their exploit at Frog Lake, gathering outside, he walked calmly out to meet them. The Company and the Indians had always been friends, he declared. What was this commotion all about?

Receiving him cordially, Big Bear insisted that his braves were hostile only to "Government people" within the fort, not to civilians or Hudson's Bay Company employees. But some of the younger tribesmen broke in at this point to declare bluntly that they were determined to drive *all* white men from this land. Whereupon Big Bear repeated what he had said before: he had come to fight only the police; he would do the civilians in Fort Pitt no harm. But how could his men attack the police, McLean countered, without endangering the lives of the civilians, too? Big Bear shrugged; that was none of his affair.

Here was a nice opportunity for exercising judgment—the sort of judgment that an experienced trader possesses in his bones. Without hesitation McLean decided to rely on Big Bear's goodwill. After extracting from the chief a promise of protection, he led the civilians—including his own wife and children—from Fort Pitt into the Indian camp. And his decision proved to be the wise one. Though they all suffered hardships during the next few weeks, as they wandered with their "protectors" across the northern parklands, none of the civilians was molested in any way; whereas the police detachment within the fort was immediately subjected to an attack. Later, while attempting to escape down-river on a scow, one of their number was killed by an Indian bullet, another wounded, and a third taken into captivity.

As the news of these incidents spread, as the implications connected with the police defeat at Duck Lake became understood across the land, the effect produced was the reverse of what Riel had anticipated. Everywhere, people reacted emotionally; angry Canadians from all parts of the country united righteously on the side of law and order. Few white men understood why the métis and Indians had sprung to arms; still fewer cared. That there might be mitigating circumstances was almost entirely overlooked. To the average person it all boiled down to whether or not one could stand idly by while honest subjects of the Queen were slaughtered in cold blood.

Major-General Frederick Middleton, the General Officer Commanding the Canadian Militia, was not so filled with enthusiasm as the rest of the nation over this chance to fight Riel. A professional soldier, an Englishman, he was nearing the end of a distinguished career; it was only natural that by this stage of life he should have become a cautious warrior. He mistrusted the very eagerness of his raw volunteers. According to his views, troops should approach their tasks mechanically, unsmilingly, as Britain's regular soldiers would have done. Even as he embarked on this campaign he was filled with doubts about the Canadians' ability to fulfil the assignment that had been given them. With infinite patience and much hesitation, he drew up a plan of attack, the complexity of which—even acknowledging the very real threat presented by the twenty thousand Indians in the West —seems out of all proportion to the size of the military problem he had been called upon to solve.

Before advancing one foot north of the railway line, he divided his force into three columns. The first, under his personal command, would march northward from Qu'Appelle. The second, under Lieutenant-Colonel W. D. Otter, would proceed simultaneously from Swift Current. The third, under Major-General T. B. Strange, a retired officer ranching in Alberta, would move very quickly from Calgary to Edmonton, then down the North Saskatchewan River to Battleford. With the timing and co-ordination of a trooping of the colour, his soldiers would show the flag everywhere on the plains. Having thus discouraged the Indians from rising, they would converge on the rebel chief with his few hundred armed métis.

While Middleton's trap closed slowly around him, Louis still clung to his dream of a negotiated peace. This fact is attested to by the following incident. Shortly before the clash at Duck Lake, Henry Jackson had become so ill that Philip Garnot, a native of St. Laurent, had been drafted to take his place. Hoping to ascertain at first hand the state of his brother's health, Thomas Jackson attached himself to the party that was sent to Duck Lake on March 29th to collect the Government supporters' dead. Though he was unable to see his brother, who lay abed at Batoche, he managed to gain an interview with the métis chief.

Riel said he had no quarrel with the settlers, but only with the police and the Canadian Government. Then, in a memorandum which he asked Thomas Jackson to carry away with him, he revealed what was still uppermost in his mind. "If the police could be isolated from the people of Prince Albert, we could make them [the police] surrender easily. I think we could keep them as hostages. . . . Send delegates to meet us. We will discuss conditions of our entering Confederation as a province."

But there were other, less Olympian, minds close at hand— simpler men who understood instinctively the true significance of the métis position now that the constitutional authority of Canada had been openly defied. Of these, Gabriel Dumont was both the heart and the mind. As soon as he learned of the

Canadian military activity he placed a spy, posing as a Government freighter, in Middleton's camp. Then he and several fellow-members of the *Exovedate* began proposing concrete tactics for disrupting the enemy's advance. Without Riel's approval they ordered Michel Dumas to go to Montana for assistance, another man to journey to Pembina, a force of métis to seize stores and ammunition in Prince Albert and Battleford.

When he heard of these plans, Louis resolved to put a stop to them. The whole métis force was needed at Batoche, he insisted, to guard the people against a possible attack from Prince Albert. As for help from the United States, he refused to consider it. "The invitation of American aid is dangerous," he told his Councillors emphatically (conveniently ignoring the fact that he himself had often threatened such a move). "Take care about the adventurers of the United States, for they are to be feared. They have neither manners, faith, nor heart. They are dirty dogs, foul jackals, ravening wolves and furious tigers. O God, preserve us from the misfortune of having anything to do with the United States!" Then: "Let the United States protect us indirectly by the arrangements of Holy Providence, but never by direct engagement or understanding on our part . . . it is an awful misfortune to seek refuge in it."

Several wavering members of the *Exovedate* were pulled back into line by Louis' plea. But Dumont, who was responsible for military affairs, could not be brought to heel by eloquence.

"All right, Louis," he challenged after a moment of thought. "We refrain from attacking the Canadian soldiers, we refuse to seek American help. Then how in the name of God can we hope to win this battle to which we are now committed?"

Riel looked at him hard, blinked several times. "O ye of little faith," he murmured, in a voice just loud enough for all to hear. "Can you doubt for a moment that to us will flow all the power and glory that is our due? I tell you that with God's and Christ's help we shall yet surround the Canadians and force them to come to terms. But until our moment of destiny arrives we must not shed needless blood. Cannot you understand? I know exactly how it must all come to pass."

Dumont shrugged, but said nothing. What could be gained by further argument at this time? Instead of engaging in fruitless public debate with Louis Riel, he must work quietly on the members of the Council in private and try to convert them to his view.

The métis would continue, then, to do nothing with their arms while the Canadian army advanced. They would continue, too, to take prisoners at every opportunity—and to store them, as it were, against the day when they might be useful pawns in the chess game of negotiation Riel still imagined he was playing.

One of the last victims of this aspect of Riel's policy was Thomas Jackson, the Prince Albert druggist. All during the week following his first visit to métis headquarters he heard persistent rumours that his brother's illness was, in fact, insanity. Resolving to find out the truth for himself, he set out in search of Henry. First he went to Fort Carlton, which was now nothing but a burned-out and abandoned shell; then he went to Duck Lake, which he found deserted. Finally, on April 7th, he arrived at Batoche, to which place all the métis force had by this time returned. As soon as he saw his brother he realized that the rumours were true; some time on the 20th or 21st, Henry had suffered a break-down of his mental powers.

Jackson sought out Riel, requested that he be allowed to take poor Henry home. Louis would not hear of such a thing. "Your brother will recover more quickly if he remains where he is," he insisted loftily. "And besides, he is sick only because God has made him so—it is a judgment against him for having quarrelled with me." (Though he refused to divulge what the quarrel had been about, Louis added at this point that the priests, too, had opposed him and they, too, were selfishly wrong.) When Thomas followed up his plea by going before the *Exovedate,* he was thrown into prison—on the ground that he had overheard discussions of the Council and could no longer be allowed to go free!

Since the rebellion began Riel had collected six other prisoners —not counting the Jackson brothers—on one pretext or another. All during this period he kept them more or less comfortably in the home of Baptiste Boyer, in Batoche. (Only when, during the course of some "excitement", they were forced into a cellar measuring sixteen feet square and nine feet deep, did they suffer real discomfort, according to their own admission later. And never during the entire span of their captivity did they feel themselves in danger from any métis ill will, though they feared the animosity of Riel's Indian allies from time to time.) When the right moment came, Louis would use them in his bargaining game.

Meanwhile, having been proclaimed a prophet, Louis must behave like one. The days of the week must be renamed in accordance with the new state of affairs. The Lord's day must be observed on Saturday, as of old; the other days must be renamed in a truly Christian manner. Starting with Monday, they must become *Christ Aurore, Vierge Aurore, Joseph Aube, Divine Aurore, Deuil Aurore, Calme Aurore, Vive Aurore*; and the pagan memories of their old names must be forgotten for the common good. These new names might be roughly translated as Christ's Morn, the Virgin's Morn, Joseph's Dawn, Divine Morn, Morn of Sorrow, Tranquil Morn, and Morn of Life. They were approved by the *Exovedate* by a vote of nine to one.

Priests who insisted on talking about excommunication must be committed to prison. (Father Vegreville actually was, for a short time.) Bishop Bourget must be invited to proclaim himself the Pope of the New World. Then, too, the mundane aspects of life must be attended to; approval must be given to the loan of a bull to J. Pivedan for the use of farmers in the neighbourhood. And last but not least, the growing opposition of factions within the Council must be born with patience and wisdom.

"O God," Riel wrote in his book of prayer during this period, "grant to guard the army and the entire Council against Maxime Lépine. Give me grace to treat him gently and with humility, but sincerely and frankly, so that he may change his conduct and cease to have a feeling of repugnance and hostility against us." And: "I have seen Gabriel Dumont. He was afflicted and ashamed. [For continuing to advocate more aggressive tactics, presumably.] He did not look at me. He looked at his table stripped of everything. But Gabriel Dumont is blessed. His faith will not fail. He is firm by the Grace of God."

Indeed, Dumont's faith would not fail. All the same, his nature would compel him to become more emphatic daily in his demands for action. His sight was not clouded with visions; his mind was not troubled by prophetic wishful thinking. By nature he was a fighter; he saw the situation from a military point of view and appraised it accurately. The die had been cast; armed combat was inevitable now. Realizing this, he understood that the métis' only chance of success lay in guerilla action; either inertia or a direct engagement with the invaders would spell disaster. Accordingly, he advocated that they attack the Canadian army as coyotes would attack a herd of buffalos—on its flanks, at its heels, relentlessly, but never in a frontal engagement. Only in that way could the invaders be whittled down to a size small enough to be handled. For many days he pleaded for these tactics without success. Then, suddenly, with unanimous support, he got his way.

Time was flowing against Louis now. Since April 6th General Middleton's column had been advancing across the prairie from Qu'Appelle. Though it had consumed only a week in marching to Clark's Crossing (the up-stream end of navigation on the

South Saskatchewan River, below Saskatoon), from that point on its progress had been infinitely slow. The distance between Clark's Crossing and Batoche is barely thirty-five miles, but there are several streams and ravines to be traversed along the way and, at this time of year, with melting snow and slushy mud lingering in the hollows everywhere, the terrain can provide rough going indeed. At last, on April 23rd, Dumont received positive advice that the enemy was drawing near. With more emphasis than ever before, he insisted openly that if Middleton was to be dealt with at all he must be ambushed before reaching Batoche.

Long and bitterly the Council argued over what should be done. When it became evident that Dumont's views could no longer be opposed successfully, Riel himself capitulated. Instantly, Dumont brought forth his plan. Leaving a small detachment under his brother Edouard at Batoche to guard the women and children against possible attack from the police at Prince Albert, the main métis force would ride southward; near Fish Creek, or Tourond's Crossing, they would lay a trap for General Middleton and his men.

That evening, led by Gabriel Dumont—with Riel and his stolen crucifix beside him—less than two hundred armed métis, reinforced by some Indian allies, set out towards the south. They were thoughtful men; as far as they knew from the advice their scouts had brought in, they might have to fight the entire Canadian army in the morning; but they did not flinch for an instant from what their conception of duty demanded of them. At every stop Riel ordered that a decade of the Rosary should be said. "Pray for us sinners, now and at the hour of our death," the men entreated Christ's Mother, with all the fervour they could command. They were as brave a little band as ever had gathered to defend what they believed to be the right.

Throwing an advance party ahead to camp on the south side

of Fish Creek, the métis force bedded down for the night near Tourond's farm. No sooner had they done so than a messenger arrived from Edouard Dumont: it was believed that a large detachment of police was about to attack Batoche. Riel was much alarmed; Dumont thought the rumour false. An argument ensued. When the matter was put to a vote, it was decided that Louis should return with fifty men to reinforce the defenders of Batoche.

Now, on his own, Gabriel Dumont could work freely at last. For better or for worse he could grasp reality in his hands, wrestle with it, force a decision. The métis nation must now discover the actuality of its fate, confront it with all the determination it possessed. The ordeal by fire must begin.

XVII

MAKE EVERY
BULLET COUNT

ALL during the night of April 23rd–24th, the opposing forces slept within four miles of each other—450 Canadian troops in their camp, ringed by transport vehicles and guarded by well-mounted sentries; less than two hundred métis and Indians beside their horses on the ground. Next morning both camps were astir at dawn. By 6:30 the Canadians were advancing towards Fish Creek. By eight o'clock the battle had been joined.

How was it that, of the eight thousand soldiers gathered in the West, such a tiny force was all that lay ready now to confront Riel's desperate "New Nation"? The answer is to be found in Middleton's strategic plan. After dividing his force at Qu'Appelle, he had done the same thing with his column at Clark's Crossing. He had sent the 10th (Toronto) Grenadiers to the west bank of the Saskatchewan River; also twenty of Major Boulton's Scouts (commanded by the same Boulton who had been Louis' prisoner in 1870), all of Captain French's Scouts, the Winnipeg Field Battery, and a portion of A Battery from Quebec. These detached troops he placed under the command of Colonel Montizambert of Quebec. On the east bank with himself he had retained the 90th (Winnipeg) Battalion, C School of Infantry from Toronto, B Battery from Kingston, and the remainder of Boulton's Scouts (about forty men). To each column he had allocated about two hundred teams of transport.

So that physical communication could be maintained at all times between the columns, he had commandeered a scow and ordered it to follow the advancing troops as they made their progress along either side of the river. As for the rest of the Canadian troops, they were either in Otter's or Strange's columns, hundreds of miles away, or holding themselves in readiness at strategic locations to the north of the railway line.

When scouts began coming in with estimates of the size of the enemy's force, Dumont could hardly believe his ears. His heart leapt with hope. General Middleton had set up a situation in which it became distinctly possible for the poorly equipped and pitifully small métis band to win at least a battle in their own defence. The Canadians would move toward them along the trail. Just before arriving at Fish Creek, they would cross about a mile of level plain. Then, entering a wood, they would be compelled to make an S-turn as they descended sharply to the bridge that spanned the creek. Just before reaching this bridge they would pass an exceptionally thick clump of bush on their left. Métis sharpshooters would be lying in rifle pits in the heart of this thicket; other métis warriors would be concealed at the edges of the coulee on either side. At a prearranged signal, everyone would open fire and the Canadians would be caught in a trap from which there would be no escape.

Quietly, efficiently, Dumont deployed his force. Moving 130 men into the thicket at the bottom of the coulee, he allocated the remainder to the edges of the ravine. Hardly a twig was broken, hardly a rotting leaf was disturbed in the process. Just as he finished placing his men, word came to him that the Canadians were on the move. Hastily, he rode to a position in a clump of bush, near the south side of the ravine, that he had selected for himself.

While Dumont, with some twenty-five to thirty men, watched from his hiding-place, the Canadians came marching along the trail. In the lead, fifty yards apart, advancing on a half-mile front, rode sixteen of Boulton's Scouts. About two hundred and fifty yards to the rear, on the trail itself, came the other twenty-four Scouts in column of route; then the General and his headquarters staff, followed at a distance of about three hundred yards by the 90th Battalion. Further again to the rear were more troops and the lumbering transport. Dumont could not see them from where he stood, but already he had seen quite enough to dismay him. It would be impossible to trap these troops effectively, on account of the marching order in which they advanced. The forthcoming battle would be a slugging match, pure and simple; and, even though they fought from prepared positions, the métis would be outnumbered by at least two and a half to one.

Dumont could not know it, but Middleton's column had been forewarned of danger. Soon after the day's march began, scouts had discovered an abandoned farm, with grain lying about in patches on the ground nearby. From this they had concluded that horses had been fed recently here. Almost immediately thereafter they had come upon no less than thirteen still warm campfires—the fires of Dumont's advance party. These twin discoveries would have set even a novice commander on edge—and Middleton was both experienced and filled with caution. Immediately, he had ordered his scouts to reconnoitre on a broad front and well in advance of the main column.

The Canadian troops were drawing near. Silently, Dumont watched as the left wing of the advancing cavalry passed behind him. Now Boulton's twenty-four other Scouts were directly in front of him.

He gave the order to fire. Wheeling hard left, Boulton led a charge towards the bush in which Dumont and his sharpshooters stood.

"Ride for the coulee," Gabriel commanded quietly. "When you get there, let your horses go."

Like the wind his men covered the 150 yards of prairie to the ravine. Then, springing from their mounts, they spread themselves in a line behind the coulee's edge.

Now the Canadian column was alive with bugle calls; on the plain directly in front of Dumont, all forty of Boulton's Scouts were firing from the prone position, and their horses, like the métis' mounts, were galloping loose on their own. "Make every bullet count, *mes amis*," Gabriel shouted above the din; and, standing up momentarily, he shot with deadly accuracy at one of the scouts. In the time it took the clumsier scouts to aim, he had disappeared. With harsh laughter the rest of the métis joined in. This was a game which buffalo hunters could understand and enjoy. The battle had indeed begun!

For expert marksmen the stationary, exposed scouts made easy targets. While answering bullets whizzed harmlessly above their heads, Dumont's men picked off the enemy with precision and skill. Within minutes, Captain Gardner of the Scouts and Troopers Lanford, Bruce and Baker were hit. Baker was the first Canadian militiaman to die.

But presently the métis got an inkling of what they would soon have to face; a company of the 90th Battalion, under Captain Clark, arrived and opened fire. Then Major Smith, with C School of Infantry, joined in the fray, followed by Captain Drury, with an artillery piece.

Fifteen minutes after the first shot had been fired, the entire Canadian force was in action, while as yet only a portion of the métis defenders were engaged—and the Canadian troops were all bunched together, grouped around Boulton's Scouts, to the left of the trail. Then, methodically, the General began sorting out his men, moving them to positions from which they could do more good. Withdrawing Boulton's Scouts and three companies of the 90th, he deployed them to the right where, thanks to a curve in the course of the ravine, they could fire on the main body of the métis force. Instantly, the battle began to take on an entirely new aspect. By one simple manoeuvre Middleton had extended his front for a quarter of a mile along the coulee's edge and outflanked his enemy on either side.

There could be no doubt now that Dumont had failed to trap the Canadians; but there could be no doubt, either, that his men were inflicting serious casualties on the attackers while suffering insignificant losses themselves. The Canadians were raw volunteers fighting from exposed positions; the métis were experienced frontiersmen skilfully concealed. But, as the Canadians cooled down under fire, slowly, surely, their superior numbers began to tell. Seeing the exposed position he occupied on the coulee's face, Dumont ordered his immediate party to retire into the protection of the trees.

The enemy was firing from three sides now, yet the métis shot with such accuracy that they were in no immediate danger of being overwhelmed. The artillery pieces had been rolled into position. From the edge of the ravine the guns were firing at the métis in the bush below. But they failed to inflict real harm, for the crews who manned them could not depress their muzzles sufficiently to reach the bottom of the coulee's face. Like a host of angry gophers, métis kept popping from behind cover, firing their weapons, and disappearing again as they grimly returned the gunners' shot.

Now, in spite of heavy losses, the Canadian infantry was working its way down the ravine's south side. If both flanks could complete the manoeuvre they would trap the métis force within twin jaws of spitting lead. But presently General Middleton ordered his men to retire. The casualty rate was too high to be endured, he said. Such sacrifice was not necessary for the success of the campaign. Numbers and fire-power must ultimately do the trick; there was no need for more heroics to win the day. Sooner or later the enemy, caught in their own trap, would run out of ammunition; then, regardless of how effectively they had checked the Canadian advance, the battle would be as good as won. The troops were furious, but they did as they were told.

Dumont had lost the initiative and he knew it. Unless something could be done soon to alter this state of affairs, his men might lose the day. He was a frontier fighter; he decided now to employ one of the tricks of his trade. With a few picked horsemen he rode unseen up the ravine towards the east; circling around behind the Canadians, he set fire to the prairie at their flanks and rear. If the wind had blown from the right direction, perhaps he might have trapped the enemy between his own men and the flames. But it did *not* blow from the right direction; just as the grass began to burn, the wind shifted to the north-west, carrying the flames harmlessly away. And so there was nothing to be done but sweat it out, man to man, in the depths of Tourond's Crossing. Only with the coming of darkness could they safely begin to retire.

By early afternoon near-silence had descended upon the battle-field. Except for an occasional random shot, the fighting had utterly ceased. Middleton was content to have it so; he had successfully contained the métis force on its front and at either side. (Almost out of ammunition, Gabriel Dumont must have been content too; when reinforcements arrived from Batoche, he sent them home again.) When Colonel Grasett arrived with a portion of the Grenadiers and the Winnipeg Field Battery from the left bank of the Saskatchewan, the General refused permission to charge against the entrenched métis. "Their capture will in no way affect the work of the day," Middleton pronounced, with sensible restraint. Just after four o'clock he sounded the cease-fire. Leaving the Grenadiers and other fresh troops to keep the enemy pinned down, he retired with the rest of his force to a spot of open ground half a mile away beside the river. As dusk descended Gabriel Dumont, too, withdrew with his métis from the field.

The heroics were over, the day's work was done. Men on both sides had fought honourably and well. Of the Canadians, one officer and nine men had been killed; four officers and thirty-eight men had been wounded, and Middleton himself had received a bullet through his cap. Of the métis, eleven had been wounded, another eight killed. Indeed, they had given better than they had received, but in the long run they would surely fail, for they had undertaken an impossible task.

All through the night, as he rode at the head of his weary men towards Batoche, Dumont was sustained by a conviction that the day's engagement had been well worth while. His fighters had met the Canadian troops; man for man, they had proved their superiority beyond a shadow of a doubt. If only the Indian tribes could be persuaded, now, to wage guerilla war while the métis defended Batoche, the Canadians might yet be bled white and sent home to the East where they belonged!

Dumont, the superb tactician, was too ignorant of the outside world to possess a reliable sense of strategy. He did not understand, as Middleton did, that in a sustained trial of strength the "New Nation" must inevitably go down to defeat. He could judge things only as he saw them; from his point of view the métis force had inflicted a crushing defeat upon the advancing Canadian army.

But for all his confidence in himself and his men, Gabriel Dumont was still willing to occupy a subordinate role in the métis government. A humble, devout personality, to him Riel remained the heart and soul of his people's hope. When he heard on his arrival home that Louis had spent the whole of the previous day leading the women and old men of Batoche in prayer, he was deeply moved. "Then I attribute our success to the prayers of Riel," he said simply; and he meant it from the bottom of his heart.

The following afternoon, when Louis assembled the people

to harangue them, after the manner of the ancient Hebrew holy men, for their moral sloth, Gabriel felt no sense of annoyance or distress. It was true that the métis had suffered few human casualties; but, as Riel now pointed out, it was equally true that they had lost a great many horses during the fight. And perhaps —Louis insisted that this was so—this loss of animals *had* been caused by a vengeful Providence, whose wrath the métis people well deserved.

"You have offended Me," Riel shouted, as if possessed by the voice of God. "By your horse racing, by your bets on the detestable horse races, by your stubbornness and by your hateful contention over those bad horse races." Then, without pausing, he chastized the throng for their indolence and recommended that they change their ways. Presently, interceding as high priest for the nation whom he led, he asked God, quite humbly, to consider "in all kindness that the people give themselves to fasting and prayers in order to gain Thy good graces". He concluded by referring in true hell-fire-and-damnation style to the dead. "Always remember"—he was thundering again now—"that the road of the métis, which they follow to glory here below, is also the heavenly road which conducts to paradise the souls which the Saviour has chosen on the field of battle."

Dismissing the suitably chastened gathering, he entered the church to pray long and loudly for ability and power to make good a treaty with Canada. "Please God, cause that Canada may consent to pay me the indemnity which is due me," he entreated with emotion. "Not a little indemnity, but one just and equitable before time and before me."

The next morning, still dreaming of the glory that he considered to be his due, still clinging to a conviction that somehow he could effect a reliable alliance with all the Indians of the West, that he could bring the stubborn Government of Canada to its knees and make it acknowledge the baseness of its treatment of him, he called Dumont to his side and ordered him to prepare for the defence of Batoche.

By now Riel had withdrawn further than ever from the reality of the facts that hemmed him in. While Gabriel Dumont, with every available man and boy, began digging rifle pits in the woods and along the steep river banks that protected the approaches to Batoche, Louis rode about solemnly assuring his people that they had nothing to fear from either the priests or the Canadian army. Even if they were excommunicated by ecclesiastical decree for bearing arms, even if they were consigned to the awful fires of the nether world by invaders' bullets, God would not leave them to roast in hell. Eternity might be a million years or a day—but assuredly, it would not last forever. He, Louis "David" Riel, the High Priest of the Living Catholic Apostolic and Vital Church of the New World, could say this with authority, for God had revealed it to him in a dream!

Some of the métis believed him; others, less gullible, were afraid to admit that they did not. Still others, realizing that their fat was well and truly in the fire, made up their minds stoically to see this ordeal through. Almost all of them clung to a wild hope born of near-despair: if by chance Louis really was what he claimed to be—if, truly, he was their Anointed One—perhaps he might yet produce a miracle to save them.

While Middleton and his troops still lingered in their camp by the river and Louis became more and more convinced of the sanctity of his mission, the span of time since the battle at Fish Creek lengthened into ten days. Among the Canadians, arrangements had to be made for sending the wounded back to civilization; oats had to be procured for the horses; expected reinforcements had to be given sufficient opportunity to arrive. Then events began marching again. On May 4th, a proclamation was issued over the General's signature assuring the Indians and half-breeds that they would be protected if they chose to cease following Riel.

On May 5th, the steamer *Northcote* arrived from Clarks' Crossing with supplies and two companies of the Midland Battalion under Colonel Williams. On May 7th, the Canadian camp was struck and the entire force advanced as far as Gabriel's Crossing. On May 8th, it marched off in a north-easterly direction—obviously swinging wide of the river to avoid the thick wood just south of Batoche.

Each of these happenings had been reported by Dumont's spies as it occurred. And now, on the morning of the 9th, a last unexpected piece of intelligence was brought to the métis headquarters: the big stern-wheeler *Northcote* had been sighted, coming down-river towards the fortified village. But what of Middleton's army? Where was it today? According to Dumont's scouts, the soldiers had broken camp at 6 A.M.; they were marching now towards Batoche. It could logically be anticipated that they would attack this very morning.

Dumont nodded. He had expected as much. This boat, then, must be intended to provide nothing but a diversion at the métis' rear. It would be prudent to restrain any excitement on account of it. "To the rifle pits, as planned," he ordered curtly. "I will retain with me here thirty men, just to keep an eye on the approaching vessel."

In a matter of moments more than two hundred sharpshooters had gone quietly to their assigned positions, and Dumont, with his thirty men, had descended to the muddy river-bank. This was the spring of the year. The South Saskatchewan River, choked with ice until a few days ago, was flowing with the velocity of a mountain stream. The *Northcote*, hurtling around a curve that lay just up-stream from the village, was almost out of control. What its captain could hope to accomplish as he swept past the defenders of Batoche was hard to gauge. Why not let him go by unmolested and concentrate instead on the more serious military threat?

276

Louis, who was riding at Dumont's side, would not hear of such a thing. "Capture the vessel," he ordered wildly. "Think of the prisoners it will yield us!" Dumont considered what he should do. He had no boats in which to transport a boarding party; yet it was his duty to obey Riel's every demand. Suddenly, he got an idea. Perhaps he could snag the *Northcote* on the ferry cable that spanned the river just below. "You five men come with me," he said, like a small boy who had just conceived a piece of mischief. "The rest of you spread yourselves out along the river-bank —open fire the moment she comes within range. That'll keep the Canadians from shooting back."

Presently the métis were pouring forth a deadly fire—so deadly that hardly a Canadian dared show himself above the barricades erected on the vessel's deck. A moment later Dumont and his men had succeeded in hoisting the ferry cable high enough to ensure that it would foul the *Northcote* as she swept by.

This was all great fun—and hardly to be confused with war; but the manoeuvre would fail to accomplish the objective Louis had in mind, for the cable was too high to snag the vessel permanently. First it caught the wheel-house, which shifted with a jar; then it fouled the smoke-stack, causing it to collapse overboard. Briefly, the ship itself turned broadside and appeared to be enmeshed. But the current was too strong. Its sides pockmarked with lead, its whistle screaming in despair, the ill-starred vessel tore itself free and passed down-stream out of range. The encounter had ended in a draw. If the army had counted on the *Northcote* for support, it would be disappointed now; but Riel would be disappointed too, for his dream of more prisoners and protracted negotiations over their fate had likewise came to naught.

Even as the river boat disappeared out of sight, artillery shots could be heard along the southern front. The Canadian land force was approaching. Ordering his men to follow, Dumont galloped through the village; up a steep hill he spurred, to the bush that lay in a crescent shape two hundred yards behind the church. Dismounting, he moved on foot through the woods. With satisfaction he noted that of perhaps seventy-five men near at hand he could see only five, so well were their positions concealed. But there, almost half a mile distant down the trail, was the entire Canadian column. They were approaching from exactly the direction he had anticipated that they would. At their head were two artillery pieces, followed by the General and his staff. "We will remain here quietly until they close the distance," Gabriel murmured.

Presently he saw a puff of smoke belch forth from one of the guns, followed by another puff of smoke from the other. With a thud the first projectile ploughed the ground between the church and the tiny rectory; the second registered a near-miss on the other side. Great sport this—shelling the church and the priest's white house! But what could the General hope to accomplish by doing such a barbarous thing? Was he trying to announce to the world that he was a militant Protestant? Evidently not, for when Father Moulin and another priest emerged, with three nuns and a small cluster of civilians, General Middleton ordered his guns to cease fire. Then he rode out himself to meet them. In fact, he suspended all operations while he escorted them personally to the rear.

Now Gabriel could see the mounted scouts, spread out in a line as at Fish Creek, riding towards the church. Ringed by well-placed métis arms, they advanced at a steady walk—on past the white-towered building to the very edge of the bush in which Dumont and his concealed men lay. "When I fire, the rest of you do the same," Gabriel had said earlier in the day. Now, with casual deliberation, he raised his rifle and took aim. As he squeezed his trigger, the other sharpshooters opened fire.

Instantly the scouts recoiled. With disciplined haste they retired to the protection of the church's south side. The métis ceased their fire. For a moment utter silence dominated the scene. Then, back among the main Canadian force, a bugle called for an attack and two companies of the Grenadiers, extended in skirmish order, began moving forward. Dumont watched the infantry, all scarlet and blue and gold in the morning sun, as they advanced to the cemetery, passed through it, came on towards the brooding woods. But he held his fire. The job of the scouts had been merely to probe the village's defences, but these Grenadiers must sustain an attack if they could. Behind them, but well within range of the métis rifle pits, Dumont could see the silent pair of guns. They, too, were advancing now. When they reached the first slight rise of ground they were unlimbered and began bombarding the village below. Not until the troops had approached very close to the edge of the bush did he again give the order to shoot.

Now, flopping to the ground, these bank clerks and butcher's boys and farmer's sons of Canada commenced shooting indiscriminately at an enemy they could not see. For perhaps half an hour they played the soldier as well as they knew how. But it was no use. From directly in front they were subjected to a merciless hail of lead. Then, as Dumont had anticipated he would do, Middleton ordered his guns and his infantry to retire.

The Canadians had been checked—and, obviously, they knew it. While the métis continued to harass them, the Grenadiers fell back slowly to a line that passed through the centre of the churchyard. Then the 90th, standing by at their rear, were thrown along the edge of the river-bank behind the cemetery, and Boulton's and French's Scouts, dismounted, were placed on either side of a gully that threatened the Grenadier's right flank. "We're doing fine, *mes amis*," Dumont called as he circulated among his sweating men. "Keep up your fire. Pick off as many of them as you can. Make every bullet count."

Now the Midlanders were attempting to charge down the gully and force their way into Batoche. At first it seemed as if they might succeed, but they could not sustain their advance in face of the casualties they incurred. And the gunners could no longer work their guns. By noon, with the métis safely hidden in the bush, the Canadians unable to move a foot ahead, the battle had disintegrated into a stalemate. And so passed the remainder of the day.

With the coming of evening Middleton and his force retired to a ploughed field about a quarter of a mile south-east of the church. There, out of range of the métis rifle pits, the soldiers made their camp. Using wagons as a barricade, eight hundred troops and six hundred horses settled down for the night. They did not get much sleep. Though the Midlanders and one company of the 90th remained on duty throughout the hours of darkness—with orders to fire sporadically into the bush, to keep the enemy pinned down—Dumont's men succeeded in killing several horses and wounding several men, and keeping things stirred up generally until dawn.

XVIII

SURRENDER MUST BE UNCONDITIONAL

A T eight o'clock in the morning, while a working party dug graves in the cemetery to receive the métis dead, Dumont watched the Canadians prepare for another day. With much bugle calling and parade-square manoeuvring the Grenadiers formed up along the front. Boulton's Scouts were sent to cover the right flank, the Midlanders the left. But it was Sunday—even though most of the métis remained exposed on the open ground between the church and the woods, the Canadians did not attack. Instead, they occupied themselves with digging trenches—as if *they* were the defenders in this grim duel!

In the afternoon one of the batteries went briefly into action, firing a few shots indiscriminately in a line to the right of the church, and a party of French's Scouts rode off to make a reconnaissance towards the north. Truly, the Canadians seemed reluctant to resume the attack. Riel, with his ever-present crucifix held high, spent the day riding among his men. Things appeared to be going well. From what he could see, General Middleton had lost ground. "I tell you, Gabriel," he cried when he came upon his military chief, "our people are the best fighters in the world! Ottawa will soon be forced to sit up and pay attention to our just demands."

Dumont shrugged. "The only thing that worries me," he replied, "is our lack of ammunition. I've set the women and children to collecting all the old bullets they can find and melting 'em down. But sooner or later, if the enemy goes back to the attack, we will run out of lead."

"If only we could make them negotiate with us!" Louis said dreamily.

"If only we had enough bullets to kill every last one of them, you mean," Gabriel countered fiercely. "First, they try skinning you alive; then, when you protest about it, they send an army out after you. I tell you, the only good Canadians are dead Canadians, as far as I'm concerned."

"The only useful Canadians are captured Canadians," Louis replied. "Perhaps, after all, we shall find some way to make them negotiate."

Dumont spat, wiped his mouth with the back of his hand. "I'm a fighter, Louis. The rest is up to you."

Riel looked startled. "You mean the rest is up to God."

"Whatever you say. All I know is that we'll fight like the devil as long as our ammunition holds out."

The next day, while the scouts and an artillery piece made a feint to the north of the village, the Canadian infantry managed to regain the positions they had occupied initially. During the process much rifle fire was exchanged. That evening, when the Canadians retired to their camp, Dumont gave orders that they were not to be pursued. By now he knew that his ammunition would last but one more day; but before his men were finally overrun they must delay the enemy long enough for the women and children to get away. After that—well, Batoche would have to be abandoned and the fight carried on, Indian fashion, in the open country as opportunities occurred. When he informed Riel of his appreciation of the situation, Louis seemed appalled. "If what you say is true, it means we are overthrown," he said incredulously.

"You should have known when we took up arms that we might

go down," Dumont replied harshly. "Both sides cannot win."

"But what are we to do?"

"I've told you what *I'm* going to do, Louis. When it's all over here I'm going to take to the woods with as many cartridges as I can find." He chuckled. "I'll keep old Middleton dancing for the rest of the summer, at least."

"By doing that you will accomplish nothing," Riel told him. "In fact, you may cause positive harm to the rest of our people. I know these Canadians. They must punish someone before they will be willing to forgive and forget. Look what they did in Manitoba. They put a price on my head—yet they passed the Manitoba Act almost word for word as I had written it! If the worst comes to the worst, I must allow them to punish me again, in order that they may purge their souls and deal justly with the rest of the people. If I follow your suggestion, if I allow them to chase me like an animal across the land, I will make a mockery of my entire mission."

"And if you surrender, you'll hang."

Louis shook his head. "You do not understand the Canadians. It is far more likely that I will be imprisoned, or exiled as I was before." His eyes gleaming brightly, he drew himself up. "In all probability they will stage a trial," he explained. "And if they do, I will use it as a platform from which to speak of the métis' rights. After they have heard what I have to say, there will be an investigation in Parliament—all the grievances of our people will be exposed, and my mission will be fulfilled."

Dumont grunted. "When the moment arrives you can do what you like, Louis. It'll be every man for himself then. In the meantime, I'd suggest that you order the women and children to hide along the river-bank to the north of the village—tell 'em it's to protect them from the Canadian artillery—so that they'll have a chance to escape. Now I must go and look to our defences once again."

In the morning the Canadians appeared to be mounting an attack along the same lines as on the previous day. While Dumont watched, the main body of the army drew itself up before the rifle-pits guarding the village's southern approaches, and the mounted men, with two pieces of artillery, swung out once again on to the north-east plain. Though the foot soldiers made no move to advance, the artillery, under Middleton's personal direction, soon opened fire on the houses at Batoche.

"Is this a true attack, or merely another feint?" Dumont asked himself out loud. "Why shell the village—full of women and children as far as the Canadians know—yet leave our fighters undisturbed? Doesn't the General realize that there are Canadian prisoners in the cellar of one of the buildings he is doing his best to demolish?"

Riel, standing beside his second in command, suddenly became filled with animation. "What was that you said about the prisoners, *mon ami?*" he asked excitedly.

Dumont repeated his observation.

Riel's eyes lit up. "But of course! That is the answer to our problem, Gabriel! The prisoners! Why did I not think of it before?"

"Think of what, Louis?"

"This key that will open the door to negotiations at last."

Dumont shrugged. "If you've found a key you'd better use it fast. Should the enemy mount a real attack we have nothing to stop them with today."

"I will, *mon ami.* I will. At last God has shown me how victory shall be achieved!" And without another word, Louis turned his horse around and galloped down the hill to Batoche.

Going directly to the house in the village in which the prisoners were incarcerated, he commanded that John Astley be brought to him. This man was a Government surveyor who had joined the volunteers; he had been caught nailing up a proclamation issued by Major Crozier just before the engagement at Duck Lake. Because he had approached Louis several times during his captivity, demanding that an exchange of prisoners be arranged, his name had been the first to come to Louis' mind.

"I have told you many times that you would be useful to me for purposes of negotiation," Riel began. "Now the moment has arrived to prove that I was right. You are to take this note to General Middleton—I think you will find him with the artillery, to the north-east of us here. When you see him, tell him that if he harms any of our women and children with his guns, I will massacre the prisoners. Then return to me here with his reply. Do you understand?"

When Astley had said that he did, Louis gave orders for him to be provided with a horse.

The man departed, waving a white flag. Riel watched him go. "I think it would be prudent to send a second envoy," he murmured after a moment. "Just in case this Astley should be killed on the way. Bring me Thomas Jackson," he commanded of the guard.

Presently Jackson, too, had been despatched towards the Canadian lines, and now there was nothing to do but wait until one of them returned. Louis felt peacefully expectant—not at all on edge. "I have found the key," he muttered over and over again. "And in a little while I will have the opportunity of fulfilling my mission. I will tell the General face to face what is on my mind."

But when, towards noon, Astley brought Middleton's reply, Louis began to realize that things were not as easily to be resolved as he had hoped. "Tell M. Riel," the General had said, "that if he places his women and children together in one spot and lets me know where they are, I can guarantee they won't be shot at. Tell him further that, if he chooses to surrender, I will protect him until I have handed him over to the Government— but his surrender must be unconditional."

"That's all he told you to say?" Riel asked, not wanting to believe his ears.

"He told me to make it very clear—especially the part about surrendering unconditionally," Astley replied.

This was not what the métis chief had hoped for. But perhaps it was better than no negotiation at all. And—remarkable fact—the artillery bombardment had stopped! Why had he not noticed it before? "I hear no sound of fighting," Louis said. "Do you suppose the General has ordered a cease-fire?"

"They've probably stopped for lunch," Astley told him in a matter-of-fact manner. "I've noticed that they do, every day."

Riel shrugged, as if it were a small matter; but in fact he was very disappointed indeed. "So he suggests that I surrender, eh? That is out of the question, of course. I will send a message telling him so as soon as I have composed one."

"Why don't you go see him yourself?" Astley suggested. "He seems like a kind enough gentleman. I don't think he'd do you any harm."

Riel shook his head. "At a time like this, such a thing would be impossible. Please wait outside while I compose my reply."

The prisoner-messenger departed from the room.

Now Louis was alone. His wife and children were hiding with the other non-combatants in caves along the river-bank. Dumont was up at the front. Suddenly, the métis chief realized how utterly lonely he felt. It was like that morning, so long ago, when he had started it all by challenging the surveyors on André Nault's farm. But it wasn't like that, really—in those days he had been able to think more clearly than he could right now; and he had been too full of young life's confidence really to doubt that he would triumph in the end. He buried his head in his hands. "War is a terrible thing," he sobbed. "Why has this one been forced upon me? I have only been trying to help."

For perhaps half an hour he sat there, immersed in self-pity and gloom. Then the sound of artillery and rifle fire roused him. He was still the métis' leader! He must deal with these things, regardless of how he felt personally about them. Reaching for his pen, he wrote:

General Middleton:

I do not like war, and if you do not retreat, and refuse an interview, the question will remain the same as to the prisoners.

Louis David Riel

Before sending for Astley and despatching the message to Middleton, he reread several times the words he had written.

Presently Louis became conscious that the cannon fire was all about him. They were shelling the village in earnest now. If only Astley would return with a reply! Now the whole south-east front seemed to have burst into life. The racket of small-arms fire was rolling down the hill like an advancing fog. "I must go there and lead my men," Louis announced to himself. Seizing his crucifix, he quit the house, mounted his horse, and rode like fury towards the church and the sound of battle.

But even as he approached the high bank on which the church stood, he saw métis fighters streaming towards him, down and around the river-bank, as fast as their legs could carry them. "Our lines have been breached," a young man shouted shrilly. "All is lost! Run for your life!"

Just then Louis spied one of the métis captains among the mob. "Where is Gabriel Dumont?" he demanded.

"He stayed up there with a handful of men. The rest of us ran out of ammunition. He told us to get away while we could."

So this was the moment that Gabriel had feared! This was the moment of defeat. And yet—was it the moment to surrender? Perhaps, after all, Gabriel was right. Perhaps one should escape while one could and continue the fight, Indian style, as long as one could. "I must find my wife and family," Louis said, half aloud. "Then I must have time to think." Now was not the moment to make irrevocable decisions. Without another word he turned his mount around and rode back through the village to the protection of the river's bank. Then, with the other vanquished defenders of Batoche, he made his way northwards to the safety of the woods.

The defence of Batoche had ended on May 12, 1885. On the 15th Riel gave himself up. During the interval, he and Dumont became convinced that further resistance was hopeless. Because they had brought no provisions with them and possessed no ammunition with which to hunt for game, the people were half starved. Having fled from their homes without sufficient clothing, they were nearly frozen each night, for spring had barely arrived in these high latitudes. To add to the general despair, soldiers were everywhere, patrolling the trails and beating the bush each day, so that communication between the tiny clusters of métis became almost impossible.

After leaving his wife with his aged father, Dumont set out on the 14th for Montana. That same evening Riel received a message from General Middleton—brought to him by Moise Ouellette, who had been captured during the final charge—calling upon him to surrender. "Mr. Riel," it said with Anglo-Saxon bluntness, "I am ready to receive you and your Council and to protect you until your case has been decided by the Dominion Government."

It seems that when he read this Louis felt a slight resurgence of the hope that had sustained him for so long. "Note that he makes no mention of putting me under arrest, or turning me over to the police," he said to his wife Marguerite, to Ouellette and Napoleon Nault, who stood by. "Perhaps this means that my case will be handled by the Dominion Government. Perhaps they will treat me as a prisoner of state and will give me a chance to plead my nation's case before Parliament. For the sake of everyone, I should accept the General's offer."

"Don't do it, Louis," Napoleon Nault advised. "I have two good horses. Come with me to the United States. I hear that Gabriel Dumont has started for there already."

Riel shook his head. Once before he had escaped to the safety of the republic. He would not choose to do so again. "Cousin," he said affectionately, "you must go and try to cross into the United States, but I must surrender. It is me they are after. When my enemies get me they will be satisfied; and then my people will be safe and get justice."

Marguerite clutched at his arm. "Go away, Louis. Please go away," she pleaded. "The woods are full of soldiers. They will shoot you on sight. You have often told me what they did to Elzéar Goulet in the old days. How can you be sure that they will treat you any better now?"

Riel gave his wife a tender look. Poor Marguerite! This ordeal could not be easy for her—especially as she was pregnant again. "Do not fear, my love," he told her gently. "I will evade the soldiers and find my way to Middleton's side. Once I am there, no one will dare to harm me."

On the following morning, while walking with some other métis towards St. Laurent, where the General had set up his headquarters, Riel came upon three of Middleton's scouts and gave himself up. Armstrong, their leader, had been engaged by the General as his personal courier and scout after the fighting at Fish Creek. He was an accomplished buffalo hunter and plainsman; Louis had known him in Montana. "God has sent you here to arrest me," he said, smiling. "Had some of these Canadians arrested me, they might have shot me; but you are an American and without prejudice against me." With that, he handed over the message Middleton had sent him.

"I've seen that bit of paper before," the scout told him after he had read it. "In fact, I was at the General's side when he wrote it." He glanced behind him, then straightened in his saddle. "I'll take you to him, but we'd best get a move on. I don't *think* there'll be any trouble; but you never can tell—some of the boys got a bit out of hand a couple of days ago, though they've quieted down now." He grinned. "For that matter, hardly any of 'em would recognize you if they saw you—and there's no reason for me to let on that I know your name."

"You are very kind," Louis murmured. Then: "Oh! I'd better give you this." Groping inside his shirt, he drew forth a revolver and handed it to the scout.

Armstrong took the weapon, reached down, gave Louis a hand and pulled him up behind him on his horse. "Let's be on our way," he said shortly and kicked his mount into a walk.

Presently, when they came upon a loose horse, Armstrong rounded it up, gave it to his prisoner to ride. Jogging towards St. Laurent, the pair struck up an easy conversation; before long they were discussing the recent happenings in a friendly, dispassionate way. Casually, Armstrong asked Louis why he had left Montana in the first place.

Riel shrugged. "I thought I could do something for my friends up here. Believe me, I didn't expect any trouble like this when I came."

"How come you got involved in all this shooting and fighting then?" the scout asked.

"One thing led to another. I can't explain how it happened. We just drifted into it, I guess."

And so they talked on. Not until they had reached the camp was there any formality between them.

As they came inside the Canadian lines some soldiers called out: "Is that Riel you've got there?" Louis stiffened, but Armstrong took the question in his stride. "No," he shouted back easily. "It's only his cook." This seemed to satisfy the soldiers, for there were no further questions asked.

A few minutes later, at headquarters, the scout handed over his charge. "General, this is Mr. Riel," he said without elaboration; then he hovered quietly by while Middleton set aside his paper work, stood up, shook hands with Louis and invited him to sit down.

So ended Riel's last day of freedom. That evening he was placed in the custody of Captain George Young of the Winnipeg Field Battery. This officer was a son of the Rev. Mr. Young who had known him during the Red River trouble. Two mornings later, with his jailer and the Rev. Mr. Charles Pitblado, a Presbyterian padre, he went aboard the steamer *Northcote* and was taken up-stream to the head of navigation. Three days after that he rode overland to Regina, where he was to remain, with the eyes of all Canada upon him, as a prisoner for the last six months of his life.

XIX

BEFORE THE
BAR OF JUSTICE

WHILE Riel settled into the routine of prison life in Regina, Gabriel Dumont and Michel Dumas made their way furtively to the safety of the United States. On about June 1st they gave themselves up to the federal authorities at Fort Assiniboine in Montana. As soon as it could be arranged President Cleveland declared them to be refugees and ordered them released. For the rest of the summer they spent their time trying unsuccessfully to organize a plan for the rescue of their imprisoned chief.

Meanwhile, at Regina, Riel became a model prisoner. While Middleton's forces mopped up Poundmaker's and Big Bear's unruly Indians, Louis behaved charmingly to all whom he met. Perhaps the peacefulness of captivity soothed his overwrought brain. Perhaps the inevitability of his trial brought relief to his sorely taxed mind. Perhaps the expectancy of a platform from which to speak gave him hope that he would find his glory at last.

With Captain Young he discussed at great length the military aspects of his campaign. He was not so foolish as to imagine that he could wage war successfully against Canada and Britain, he said. But he had hoped, by his trouble-making tactics, to compel the Canadian Government to accede to his just demands. At Duck Lake he had attempted to surround the police force, but fighting had commenced and the police had retired. During

Middleton's advance from Qu'Appelle he had hoped that, by remaining quiet, he would induce the General to send a small force ahead which he could capture and use as a bargaining instrument against the Government. For the same reason, he had tried to capture the *Northcote*. Because he hoped to use the telegraph to negotiate with Macdonald, he had made sure that the communication lines to the East were not destroyed. Everything that he did, he concluded quietly, was designed to achieve practical results. To ensure that he had made this point perfectly clear, he wrote in Young's notebook: "I have a mission, so has everyone else; for me I understand my mission in this way: to bring about practical results."

With equal charm but much more fervour he explained to Mr. Pitblado his religious beliefs. He wrote by way of summary in a Greek Testament which he gave the minister before they parted:

I have a passion. I love truth, justice, righteousness above all other things. I pray to God that my knowledge of truth, of justice, of righteousness be certain and without error. The consciousness of reading the Scripture is full of life and consolation. The word of Christ purifies our souls. Let us live and die in perfect harmony with the Redeemer and we will be saved. A preacher who preaches humbly for the benefit of Paradise is a precious existence before God. I am an unprofitable servant of Our Lord Jesus Christ.

Louis David Riel

But if he really believed that he would be given an opportunity to defend himself at the bar of the House of Commons, he was soon to be disillusioned. On May 23rd he was delivered into the custody of Captain Dean of the North-West Mounted Police and informed that he would be dealt with as an ordinary criminal. Though this seemed to him yet another breach of faith on the part of the Government, he made no protest. Instead, he called for pen and ink and began composing his own defence; he would present the case of the métis people and show that the Canadian Cabinet, not himself, was responsible for the present state of affairs. With much zeal and much time off for silent meditation, he covered page after page with a torrent of words.

Though denied access to his personal papers, which had been captured at Batoche, and intercourse with other prisoners in the jail, he seemed quietly confident during this time. Then, in the middle of June, he received word that Dr. Eugène Fiset, a friend from his days in the East, had engaged expert counsel to plead his defence. With great calmness he said that he appreciated the gesture and approved of it—so long as he would still be allowed to address the court himself.

A few days before the trial was due to open, the defending lawyers—Charles Fitzpatrick, F. X. Lemieux, J. S. Greenshields, and T. C. Johnson—arrived from the East. After talking with Louis and listening to the tactics he proposed, they informed him that they had decided to enter a plea of insanity as their basis for defence. For the first time since his captivity, he flew into a rage, protesting that his reputation would be destroyed and his usefulness ruined if they did this; that he would a thousand times rather die than admit for one instant that his actions had been irrational. Calming down after a while, he finally agreed that for the sake of the friends who had rallied to his support he would not refuse these lawyers' services.

On July 20th he was brought before the bar of justice. He was placed in a railed dock, two North-West Mounted Police constables on each side of him. Dressed in a black frock coat, a freshly laundered white shirt, a black cravat, he gave dignity— an aura of elegance almost—to the overcrowded office that had been rented from a land company for the occasion. Regina, the new capital of the Territories, was only three years old. Hitherto it had been known as "Pile-o'-Bones"; now suddenly it was the focus of a growing nation's gaze.

Before this court, presided over by Magistrate Hugh Richardson and consisting of a six-man English-Canadian jury, which was normal for the Territories at that time, a charge of high treason was read out to Louis Riel. It ran to more than two thousand words and covered each of the battles of Duck Lake, Fish Creek, and Batoche—making due note of the fact that the accused was an American citizen who, "living under the protection of our said Lady the Queen", had failed to regard his duty of allegiance.

Although the defence questioned the jurisdiction of the court and requested that the prisoner be tried in Ontario or British Columbia, rather than in the aroused Territories, their plea was rejected. As soon as Louis had pleaded not guilty, they asked for a month's delay to bring witnesses to Regina, and were granted an adjournment of one week. When they asked that the Deputy Minister of the Interior be brought into court with official documents, and that Riel's own papers be made available to them, their requests were denied.

During the interval that followed, Riel's secretary, Henry Jackson, stood trial. Though he insisted that he shared his leader's responsibility for everything that had occurred, he was found insane in half an hour and taken to an asylum. Almost immediately he escaped and fled, unimpeded, to the United States. Inevitably, people began saying that he had been allowed to go free because he was an English Canadian.

On July 27th Louis wrote to his old patron, Archbishop Taché, to thank him for having sent a priest to minister to the métis prisoners. Briefly, he reviewed his own career, insisting that in all he had done he had received the clergy's blessing; now, if the Archbishop would acknowledge the fact that he was a prophet, he could get on with his career. Rome was a city of workshops, he said; furthermore it was held captive by the spirit of revolution. (Presumably this is a reference to the overthrow of the Papal States.) It was reasonable, therefore, to assume that the Spirit of God had chosen another vicar. Ignace Bourget was the man.

If the clergy came to his assistance now, they would open up a future for the Catholic nations of Europe; for Riel's influence would grow, and he would treat with the Government and arrange for a New Italy, a New Bavaria, a New Ireland, a New Poland. Lieutenant-Governor Dewdney had excellent qualities; such a man would bring success to these ideas if he only knew about them. Colonel Irvine would make a capable Governor of British Columbia. . . .

On and on it went—page after page of it. And off it went that very night to the unsuspecting Archbishop. But the next day Riel was confronted by reality again; for it was then that the lawyers for the prosecution began their task. They were an imposing team: Christopher Robinson and B. B. Osler from Toronto, T. C. Casgrain from Quebec, D. L. Scott, who later became the Chief Justice of Alberta, and T. C. Burbidge, the Deputy Minister of Justice for Canada. Skilfully they set out to prove that the prisoner had planned, organized and directed every move leading up to and embracing the rebellion. The defending lawyers countered by trying to show that throughout it all Riel had been insane.

The Government's evidence was damning. On March 23rd Riel had said at a public meeting, while pointing to sixty or seventy of his followers: "But these are the real police." Two days later he had told Charles Nolin that he was determined to take up arms. On March 17th he had informed another witness, in the presence of his métis guards: "You see, now I have *my* police. In one week the Government police will be wiped out of existence." On March 18th he had told Mr. Lash that the rebellion had commenced, that he had been waiting fifteen years and at last his opportunity had come. On March 21st he had sent a written demand to Major Crozier, calling for the immediate surrender of Fort Carlton and the police force there—and threatening a war of extermination if he was ignored. At Duck Lake and at Batoche, he had been seen exhorting the fighting men.

Furthermore, the Crown claimed—submitting evidence of the negotiations that had taken place between the prisoner, Father André, and MacDowall—that he had done all these things solely for personal gain; and, as his motives had been personal, he was not entitled to the clemency that a political prisoner might receive. To prove that he had tried deliberately to cause an Indian uprising, the letter that Louis had written to Poundmaker was read into the record. How could anyone contend, the prosecution asked, that he was filled with an unselfish desire to help mankind?

For the defence, Father André, when called to the witness stand, attempted to make the point that there had been justifiable dissastisfaction among the métis and Indians before Louis arrived in their midst, that the trouble had been at least partially the Government's fault; but B. B. Osler protested, with success, that they were not assembled to try the Government. When the priest revealed that he and his colleagues had decided long ago to treat Riel as if he was not responsible where questions of religion and politics were concerned, he was asked if he believed that all who differed with the views of his Church were insane. To this Father André said no; it depended on the way a man explained his ideas and on his conduct in expressing them. Riel had no fixed principles; he changed them as he wished. "Today he believed this and tomorrow denied it," he remarked. The only fixed principle he possessed was that he himself was the ultimate law.

Called to the witness stand, Father Fourmond tried to back up the opinions of his superior. "When he was quietly talked to about affairs of politics and government," the priest stated, "and he was not contradicted, he was quite rational. But as soon as he was contradicted on those subjects, then he became a different man and would be carried away by his feelings."

This evidence was quickly discounted. According to General Middleton, while it was true that the prisoner "talked a good deal about religion", the sum and substance of it all was that "Rome was all wrong and the priests were narrow-minded people; there was nothing, particularly, except the ideas of an enthusiast on some religious point." The impression was wide-spread that Riel thought himself a prophet. Well, he had not mentioned any such thing to him. But he had said, quite humbly, on the day of his capture: "General, I have been thinking whether if the Lord had granted me as decided a victory as He has you, I should have been able to put it to good use."

Garnot, Riel's last secretary, testified that he had heard Louis say the spirit of Elias was in him and that he was representing St. Peter. For two nights the prisoner had been his guest and had kept everyone awake by his loud and long prayers. Had Riel been acting? Garnot had not thought so at the time. In fact it was only out of fear of Louis, and under protest, that he had enlisted in the movement. Riel could make the métis do anything he desired.

Dr. François Roy now took the stand on the prisoner's behalf. He had been the superintendent of the asylum at Beauport during the time Louis was confined there. While under his care Riel had been suffering from megalomania. In this disease, "they sometimes give you reasons which would be reasonable if they were not starting from a false idea. They are under a strong impression that they are right and they consider it to be an insult when you try to bring them to reason again. On ordinary questions they may be reasonable and sometimes very clever. In fact, without careful watching, they would lead one to think that they were well." In his opinion, Louis had suffered a return of the disease. "From what I have heard . . . I am ready to say that I believe . . . his mind was unsound [during the time of the rebellion]." He concluded by stating that he did not believe Riel was in a condition to be the master of his acts. "And I positively swear it, I have people of the same character under my supervision right now. The same character of the disease is shown as when he was with us."

Dr. Daniel Clarke, the superintendent of the Toronto Lunatic Asylum, was called to give an opinion of the soundness of the prisoner's mind. "Assuming that the witnesses have told the truth . . . that the prisoner is not a malingerer . . . there is no other conclusion that any reasonable man could come to . . . than that the man who held these views and did these things must certainly be of insane mind." And yet, "He was quite capable of distinguishing right from wrong, legally speaking"; and his actions might be consistent with a skilful sham. It would take months of examination to be sure. On one point he agreed with Father André. His attitude towards religion was not consistent with "such leading spirits" as Brigham Young and Joseph Smith. These two, like other enthusiasts, had carried out their system. Riel had no system and was certainly not consistent.

Dr. James Wallace, from the Asylum for the Insane at Hamilton, was called upon for an opinion. As far as he was concerned, Riel seemed to be of sound mind and quite capable of distinguishing right from wrong. If a man suffered from megalomania, he contended, he would not take steps to arrive at his ends (as Riel had done), because he would already believe that he had arrived there. Instead, he would be utterly self-contained and self-possessed.

Dr. Jukes, the senior surgeon of the Mounted Police, who admitted that he knew very little about mental illness, rather thought that Riel had deliberately pretended to believe more than he really believed in order to influence the métis.

And so it went on. Louis himself, of course, made it perfectly clear by interrupting whenever he could that he thought himself to be eminently sane. Several times he went so far as to try to cross-examine the Crown's witnesses; but on each occasion he was told that he must either repudiate his counsel or keep silent. An opportunity would be given him to speak for himself before the case went to the jury. In the meantime, he must be quiet.

But how could he be quiet when his own lawyers were making light of his political policy and his religious views? How could he sit idly by while everything for which he had striven all his life was being dismissed as sheer lunacy? "I cannot abandon my dignity," he shouted when the magistrate tried once again to tell him that he must not speak out. "Here I have to defend myself against the accusation of high treason, or I have to consent to an animal life in an asylum. Well, I don't care much for animal life, if I am not allowed to carry with it the moral existence of an intellectual being." If it could be proved that he had acted irresponsibly, then he would not be condemned; but his whole life's work would be judged meaningless, nevertheless. Then there would be no glory for him, no redress of grievances for the métis whom he had led. Under such circumstances it seemed preferable by far to die accused of high treason than to live, branded a lunatic, for a few more years.

Charles Fitzpatrick was summing up for the defence, now, insisting that the prisoner had been insane during the whole course of the rebellion. And the jury seemed, by their attentiveness, quite willing to be convinced. "Had Riel been sane," the lawyer concluded, "and had he exercised the ordinary dictates of prudence, caution and common sense, all he had to do was to stay with the métis and remain in possession of their confidence and some day he would have arrived at the highest pinnacle of his ambition, whatever his ambition might have been."

Riel was on his feet. "No!" he shouted at the top of his voice. "No!"

The magistrate looked up. Realizing that Fitzpatrick had finished his address, he told Louis quietly that the time had arrived for him to have his say.

Riel set aside the notes he had prepared so carefully during the course of his trial, sank to his knees for a moment of prayer; then he launched into an impassioned address, the one objective of which was to discount the evidence of his own defence counsel and to prove to these people that, in spite of all they had heard, he was sane and responsible for everything he had done.

"Oh my God!" the prisoner entreated in a low voice. "Help me through Thy grace and the divine influence of Jesus Christ. Oh my God! Bless me, bless this honourable court, bless this honourable jury, bless my good lawyers who have come seven hundred leagues to try to save my life; bless also the lawyers for the Crown, because they have done, I am sure, what they thought their duty. Oh my God! Bless all those who are around me, through the grace and influence of Jesus Christ Our Saviour; change the curiosity of those who are paying attention to me; change that curiosity into sympathy with me."

Now Louis had the attention he so burningly desired. Silence reigned everywhere. If only he could take these people in his hands and mould them as he had moulded others before! If only he could prove to them that he was sane! He stood up, drew a deep breath, and began.

"Today, although a man, I am as helpless before this court as I was on my mother's knees. But nevertheless I will try to tell you what I have done." He cleared his throat. "When I came into the North-west, in July 1884, I found the Indians suffering. I found the half-breeds eating rotten Hudson's Bay Company pork and getting sick and weary every day. Although a half-breed myself, I could see that the whites, too, were suffering; for they were deprived of responsible government like the rest. I remembered that half-breed meant white-and-Indian, that the greatest part of my heart and blood was white, and I directed my attention to help the Indians, to help the half-breeds, and to help the whites."

All eyes were upon him—but they were hostile eyes, for the most part. He stared them down, then went on: "Those who have been in close communication with me know that I have suffered, that I have waited months to bring some of the people of the Saskatchewan to an understanding of certain important points in our petition to the Canadian Government. But they also know that I have done my duty." He sighed. "Yes, I have done my duty.

"Some people have said that I am an egotist. Perhaps this is true. A man cannot be an individual and do his duty without paying attention to himself. During my life I have aimed at practical results. I hope that after my death my spirit will bring practical results. I have written many things. All that I have done and risked, and to which I have exposed myself, rested certainly on the conviction that I was called upon to do something for my country.

"It is true that I believed for years I had a mission—I believe that I have a mission at this very moment. After I had obtained with the help of others a constitution for Manitoba, when the Government at Ottawa was not willing to inaugurate it at the proper time, I worked till the inauguration should take place—and that is why I was banished for five years. I had to rest five years. I was unwilling to do it. I protested. I said: 'Oh my God! I offer you all my existence for that cause, and please make of my weakness an instrument to help men in my country.' And seeing my intentions, the late Archbishop Bourget said: 'Riel has no narrow views; he is a man to accomplish great things!' And he wrote that letter of which I hope the Crown has at least a copy.

And in another letter, when I became what doctors believe to be insane, Bishop Bourget wrote again and said: 'Be blessed by God and man and take patience in your evil.'

"I ask you: am I not taking patience? Will I not be blessed by man, as I have been by God? I believe with conviction that I will." Louis paused, stared about him defiantly, then went on. "Today when I saw the glorious Middleton bearing testimony that he thought I was not insane—and Captain Young prove that I am not insane—I felt that God was blessing me and blotting away from my name the blot resting upon my reputation on account of having been in the lunatic asylum of my good friend Dr. Roy. Now, if I die, I will not be reputed by all men as insane."

With that he asked for a glass of water, waited for it, drank its contents slowly down. "A good deal has been said by the two Reverend Fathers," he went on. "I know that a long time ago they believed me more or less insane. But—Father Fourmond has said that I would pass from a great passion to great calmness. Does that not show great control under contradiction? According to my opinion, and with the help of God, I am demonstrating to you now that I have that control.

"Mr. Charles Nolin has spoken of my ambition; and others also. Yet there are men among the prisoners who know that last year Mr. Forget came to the Saskatchewan and said I could have a place in the North West Council if I wanted it. If I had been so anxious for position, would I not have grasped at this place? But I did not; and Mr. Nolin has some knowledge of that."

He frowned; it was almost a scowl. "The agitation in the North West Territories would have remained constitutional if we had not been attacked. When we sent petitions to the Government they answered us by sending police. And that is the truth of the matter.

"The truth is good to say—and I say it, not without presumption: through the grace of God I am the founder of Manitoba! Thus, I believe that my words are worth something. Now, listen to me—if I give offence, I do not speak to insult. You, the whites, are the pioneers of civilization. But you bring among the Indians demoralization. If at times I have been strong against my true friends and Fathers, the reverend priests of the Saskatchewan, it is because on this point my convictions are strong.

"As to religion"—he took care to speak very reasonably now— "what is my belief? What is my insanity about that? I wish to leave Rome aside, inasmuch as it is the cause of division between the Catholics and Protestants. I believe that, even if its takes two hundred years to become practical, after my death my children will shake hands with the Protestants of the New World in a friendly manner.

"If I am insane, of course I do not know it—it is a property of insanity to be unable to know it. But what is the kind of mission that I have? To achieve practical results. The half-breeds have some intelligence. It is not to be supposed that they would acknowledge me as a prophet if they did not think that I could see something into the future. We all see into the future, more or less. I have known half-breeds who say: 'My hand is shaking, this part of my hand is shaking. You will see such and such a thing today.' And it happens! I have tried to bring Sir John to my feet. What is unreasonable about that? Mr. Blake, the leader of the Opposition, is trying to bring Sir John to *his* feet, is he not? He never had as much at stake as I had; for, although the Province of Ontario is great, it is not as great as the North-west.

"I do not wish merely for my own sake the satisfaction of being named a prophet. Did I try to set myself up as Pope? No! No! What I said was that I believed Bishop Bourget had succeeded the Pope in spirit and in truth. Why? Because, while

Rome did not pay attention to us, he as bishop paid attention to us."

He paused to take up his notes and consult them. "I have only a few more words to say, your Honour. As I am aiming at practical results I will stop right here, master of myself through the help of God. The only things I would like to call your attention to are:

1st: That the House of Commons, Senate and ministers of the Dominion, who make laws for this land and govern it, are no representation whatever of the people of the North-west.

2nd: That the North West Council generated by the federal Government has the great defect of its parents.

3rd: That the number of members elected for the Council by the people make it only a sham representative legislature and no representative government at all.

"British civilization has defined such government as irresponsible government. Which plainly means that there is no responsibility." He giggled, in spite of an attempt to control himself, as the possibility of making a pun flashed to his mind. "Now, you are compelled to admit it, where there is no responsibility it is insane!" He paused for effect, but no one in the court-room laughed. Lamely, he went on: "This federal Government has been so irresponsible to the North-west that it has indicated absolute lack of responsibility; therefore, it has indicated irresponsibility, complicated by paralysis.

"Well," he went on, flushed and angry now, "the ministers of this insane and irresponsible Government made up their minds to answer my petition by attempting to jump upon me suddenly and upon my people. But when they showed their teeth to devour us, I was ready. That is what is called my crime of high treason!"

The magistrate was beginning to fidget; the eyes of several of the jurymen were beginning to glaze. He must stop talking soon, or he would spoil the effect he had created. "If you take the plea of the defence that I am not responsible for my acts," he said slowly, "acquit me completely. If you pronounce in favour of the Crown, which contends that I am responsible, acquit me all the same. You would be perfectly justified in declaring that, having my reason and sound mind, I have acted reasonably and in self-defence; while the Government, my accuser—being irresponsible and consequently insane—cannot but have acted wrong. If high treason there is, it must be on its side and not on my own!

"I put my speech under the protection of my God, my Saviour."

He had had his moment; he had used it to the full. Truly, he had delivered the performance of his life! He had spoken in English throughout, and his accent, slight though it was, had served to heighten the dramatic effect for which he had strived. Exhausted from the effort, Louis Riel sat down.

In the silence that followed, Christopher Robinson rose to sum up for the prosecution. With thoroughness he reviewed the evidence, striving to prove that the prisoner was legally sane. He might well have saved his breath. Riel himself had convinced the jury that he was responsible for his actions. After the presiding magistrate had delivered his charge, it took them only half an hour to return a verdict: the prisoner was guilty of high treason; but mercy should be shown him, for he had had good cause to do what he had done.

On August 1, 1885, Magistrate Richardson, ignoring the recommendation of mercy, sentenced Riel to be hanged on September 18th at the Regina jail.

XX

WITH THE DIGNITY
OF A KING

BUT Louis Riel was not to be hanged on September 18th.
Immediately after the conclusion of the trial, his
lawyers launched an appeal to higher judicial authority;
simultaneously, his friends instigated a popular clamour
designed to force the Cabinet to show him mercy. On August
3, 1885, A. G. B. Bannatyne wrote to J. W. Taylor, the United
States Consul at Winnipeg: "I see they have sentenced my poor
friend Riel. . . . By Heavens, they ought to string up a number
of the Government officials if they hang him!"

Generally speaking, people inclined to be well disposed towards
the métis—although determined to teach them a lesson—but
firmly set against their leader. To be sure, a tiny minority in Quebec had been from the outset against the idea of using military
force, and felt that a commission "composed of men who knew
the half-breeds" should be established to mediate instead. After
all, these people argued, the métis were only doing what men
should do; they were merely standing up for their rights.

But in the main, Canadians agreed with the verdict, as they
had agreed with the Government's call to arms more than four
months before. The young Dominion was a country in which the
rule of law prevailed; Riel had attempted to ignore this fact and
should not be allowed to get away with it. Whether or not the
trouble had been caused by Government mismanagement of the
West (and the Liberals had certainly been as blameworthy as the

Conservatives in this regard) was beside the point during this phase.

With the pronouncement of sentence, however, the country began to split wide open. Ontario could not understand why the jury should have recommended mercy. Quebec took it for granted that the sentence would be commuted to one of life imprisonment.

Privately, Macdonald's ministers were of the same opinion as the people of Ontario. From the first they had distrusted Riel and had been unwilling to admit that they themselves could be blamed in any way for conditions in the West. Now, having been bitten twice by the results of his agitation, they were disposed to have him hanged. Convinced of his guilt, but faced already with petitions for leniency from Quebec, they hoped that French Canada would not be unduly disturbed if the recommendation for mercy was ignored. They reasoned that the majority of *Canadiens* would follow the lead of their clergy—and they knew that the Church had claimed from the start of the Saskatchewan troubles that Riel alone was the chief instigator of the calamity that had occurred.

From the Government's point of view it would be best if the execution could be proceeded with as quickly as possible, before Quebec's vague sentiment had time to solidify into something politically effective. But this could not be achieved. Immediately after the trial Riel's lawyers appealed the verdict, as they had a right to do, causing the date of execution to be postponed. And with every passing day the divergent views of the country became further and further apart. There was nothing the Government could do; they were not willing to consider being merciful to a sane prisoner, for this would have been interpreted by the Opposition as an admission of their own maladministration. Whether they liked to or not, they must sit tight and await the results of the appeal.

At the outset Riel's defence counsel had questioned the jurisdiction of Magistrate Richardson's court, and had objected to the use of a six-man jury. Magna Carta, they contended, was part of Canadian law. It provided for trial by a jury of twelve. It should not be ignored. To counter this, the prosecution had argued that the Canadian Parliament had, for valid reasons, quite legally amended the law to provide for trial by six-man juries in the North West Territories.

After sentence had been passed, Louis' lawyers took their argument to the Manitoba Court of Appeal, without success. They then appealed to the Judicial Committee of the Privy Council in London—again without success. On October 22nd, more than two and a half months after sentence had been passed, a cable arrived in Ottawa from London. "Judgment delivered this morning Riel's case. Privy Council refused petition for leave to appeal." The whole disagreeable mess was thrown back in the Cabinet's lap!

At this point feeling in the country became rapidly more intense. Whipped into a high fever by those of their politicians who opposed Macdonald's régime, French Canadians began demanding that Riel be reprieved, began insisting that he was the irresponsible victim of the Government's ineptitude. He was guilty, yes, they said—but mercy must be shown him. What had ever been gained by vengeance? To counter this, English Canadians became firmer than ever in their resolve that the execution must take place.

"With respect to the fate of Riel a very strong feeling exists among our friends," one Conservative supporter wrote to Macdonald in late October, ". . . and I believe it is general all over the Province of Ontario. I have heard a large number state most positively that if Riel is not hanged they will never poll another Conservative vote. . . . The murder of poor Scott is not forgotten."

Another asked: "Has the Conservative party come to such a state that the leaders, in order to keep themselves in power, have to grovel to the dictates of the Roman Catholics of Quebec in their wishes in regard to Riel? . . . Should the Government sell themselves to the Romans, by making a loop-hole for the rebel Riel to crawl through, they will find at the next general election that things will be different."

Yet a third wrote: "I can furnish you with the names of five thousand straightforward, honest, fearless Conservatives. . . . If he is not hanged . . . in a few months there will be the greatest rebellion, one of the mightiest struggles for freedom and liberty from French domination by the loyal, intelligent, Protestant people of Ontario that this our beloved Dominion has ever witnessed."

Strong stuff indeed—and it poured into Ottawa in alarming quantities. Terrifying, almost irresistible stuff, to a politician! Before making a final decision, Macdonald, pressed by several of his Cabinet colleagues and by other influential men of moderate disposition, decided to take another look at the question of insanity.

There was no doubt in the Prime Minister's mind, as there had been none in the jury's, that Riel had been legally sane at the time of his trial. According to judicial precedent, "to establish a defence on the grounds of insanity it must be clearly proved that, *at the time of committing the act*, the accused was labouring under such a defect of reason, from disease of the mind, as not to know the nature and quality of the act he was doing; or, if he did know it, that he did not know he was doing what was wrong." Clearly, in Macdonald's opinion, Louis had known what he was doing during the rebellion, and, as clearly, had been capable of understanding that it was wrong.

But legally, the carrying out of sentence was quite another matter. It could be postponed indefinitely if a medical enquiry revealed that a prisoner had, since his trial, become insane; and postponement on such grounds might allow feelings to cool down and solve everything after all. Not without justification was the Prime Minister known as "Old Tomorrow". On October 31st, to give himself a little more time, Sir John made arrangements for three medical men—Dr. Jukes, the police surgeon at Regina; Dr. F. X. Valade, of Ottawa; Dr. M. Lavell, of the Kingston Penitentiary—to examine Riel. He gave them instructions to ascertain whether or not Louis was *presently* "so bereft of reason as not to know right from wrong and as not to be an accountable being".

If he hoped these doctors would solve his problem by declaring Riel insane, Sir John was to be disappointed. Having journeyed to Regina, they found their patient in his cell, busily at work on an essay entitled "A Metaphysical Disquisition of the Nature of God". Although Louis had a prison pallor by this time, he seemed in fairly good health, and his spirits were excellent. When they informed him that his sentence had been temporarily suspended, he smiled and observed that it was more pleasant to have the sentence suspended than the man.

By November 9th Macdonald had heard from his investigators. Drs. Jukes and Lavell had found Louis "perfectly accountable for his actions" and "a reasonable being". Dr. Valade had come to his conclusion "that he is not an accountable being; that he is unable to distinguish between wrong and right on political and religious subjects, which I consider well-marked typical forms of the insanity under which he undoubtedly suffers; but on other points I believe him to be sensible and able to distinguish right from wrong."

Two were for hanging, then, and one, with professional reservations, was against. For the last time the ball had been returned to the politicians' court.

By now it was abundantly clear that, if the Conservative Party was to survive in Ontario, Riel must hang. And it seemed almost equally clear that, in view of the hands-off attitude of the Catholic hierarchy, Quebec feeling on the question would sooner or later calm down. For the sake of unanimity, Dr. Valade's findings were made to appear as if they agreed substantially with the majority report. (This was simply done by omitting from the published version the four words "not an accountable being".) Then the final decision was taken that Riel must hang. He must hang to vindicate the Cabinet's policies towards the West. He must hang to provide an example to others who might be tempted to tamper with law and order in the Territories.

On November 12th a courier, bearing the Governor-General's warrant for the execution, left Ottawa by rail for Regina.

Most of the time during his last few days, Riel occupied himself with letter-writing. In a final message to his wife, who had gone to the old family home in St. Vital and there given birth to (and buried) his third child, he thanked her for the part she had taken so patiently in his difficult enterprises. He composed a written pardon for all who had done him harm and persecuted him; who, "without any reason", had made war on him; who had given him the "semblance" of a trial. He wrote to his mother. He told Dr. Jukes, who visited him, that he would arise from the dead on the third day after his execution. He said to Father André: "I love my family, my wife, my children, my compatriots . . . and to be able to live and be with them would fill me with joy. But the thought of spending the rest of my life in an asylum or penitentiary, away from society, obliged to submit to indignities, fills me with horror. I thank God for sparing me this experience and I accept death with joy and gratitude."

His body was to be buried in the St. Boniface graveyard, which was consecrated ground. After all that he had said and done against the Catholic Church, this was to be allowed because Father André's ruling of the previous year was adjudged by his superiors to be doctrinally sound. "Although his opinions upon religion are greatly erroneous," the priest had written on the last day of August to explain his point of view, "I do not hold him responsible and do admit him to receive the sacraments. And for all that, he often renews the errors which he has retracted and which he again retracts when I point out to him his heresies. . . . On the day following such a retraction he talks more ardently than ever about his revelations and his communications with some angel who honours him with a nocturnal visit."

One night he had a "vision" which he recorded in his book of "prophecies":

I have seen the first minister. He addressed me saying, "Mr. Riel," and pronouncing my name as if written "Reel". And he said: "Is your name Reel or Riel?" I told him that it was Riel. "But you may pronounce it in English as the languish [*sic*] wants you to do." And when I pronounced my name, as it is pronounced in French, it struck the attention of those who were present, that it was a brilliant name. I did, even Iself [*sic*], realize that it was a glorious name to tell. My name rang somewhat as a silver bell. The first minister was affable and gentle to me. He said: "What you want is a lawyer that will take interest in your case. Whatever may be the issue of the appeal, that is what you need. I will throw you over in Montana. (The manner in which the first minister expressed himself here is: "I will overthrow you Montana.") And continuing to speak, he added: "You may find there a good lawyer. I will give you Pounds." And when he said Pounds, I saw that he was used to carry the weight of his words with money. The first minister was in the wrong. I was not. The door is wide open towards the south.

The next day he recorded in his notebook that, when he told his lawyers of this "revealed" interview with the Prime Minister, they appeared unable to answer him!

They appeared unable to help him, too. Nothing they said or did had the slightest effect on the verdict. Summer passed, autumn slid quickly by; winter was about to begin. Death lurked very near now—and yet Louis still thought of the mission it was his destiny to fulfill.

"I have heard by chance some of my guards speaking . . . about a reporter of the *Globe* . . . wishing to have an interview with me," he wrote to Judge Richardson two days before he was to die. "I ask your Honour to allow me to see that gentleman. . . . I am the Prophet of the New World. I have revelations which coming from God are glorious to publish. . . . And if you . . . give me the permission of an interview . . . I will try that it be not only useful to the New World but that it be agreeable to those whom God has appointed to take care of me."

But at last even he had to admit that time was running out. According to Father André, who passed the last night with him, Louis accepted his fate like a hero. "All night long he had not a word of complaint against his death sentence, or against his conspirators. . . . He embraced me with enthusiasm and thanked me warmly for having remained with him to the end. He said to me emphatically: 'Do not fear. I shall not shame my friends or rejoice my enemies by dying a coward.' "

And in the morning—it was the 16th of November, 1885—they led him from his cell to the hangman's noose. As he stepped outside, the sun came up over the horizon and a billion hoar-frost crystals caught its rays. Perhaps nature was bestowing some form of benediction on this man as, flanked by two priests, followed by a cluster of pinch-faced officials, he approached the awful scaffold. With the dignity of a king he submitted his neck to the rope. Then slowly and with fervour he began to recite the Lord's Prayer. As he came to the words "deliver us from evil", the executioner sprang the trap. Moments later, his earthly life had reached its end.

And so he went to the gallows at the age of forty-one, and died gallantly, and was buried beside the Red River where his public career had begun. And his wife died at St. Vital before six more months had passed, and his children followed her without leaving heirs; but the West, about which he had dreamed such impossible dreams, lives on.

BIBLIOGRAPHY

Anderson, F. W., *Louis Riel, Patriot and Rebel* (unpublished manuscript);
Legislative Library of Manitoba.
Begg, Alexander, *Alexander Begg's Red River Journal and Other Papers*,
with an Introduction by W. L. Morton; Toronto, Champlain Society, 1956.
Begg, Alexander, *The Creation of Manitoba, or a History of the Red River
Troubles*; Toronto, Hunter Rose, 1871.
Benoit, Dom, *Vie de Mgr. Taché, Archevêque de St. Boniface*, 2 vols.;
Montreal, Libraire Beauchemin, 1904.
Boulton, C. A., *Reminiscences of the North-West Rebellions*; Toronto, Grip
Printing & Publishing Co., 1886.
Canada, Parliament, *Sessional Papers, 1870*, Vol. 5, No. 12. (Contains,
among other things, instructions to surveyors, Orders in Council, D. A.
Smith's report, Thibault's report.)
Canada, Parliament, *Sessional Papers, 1886*, Vol. 19, Nos. 12 & 13. (Con-
tain numerous official documents, medical reports on Riel, records of Riel's
trial and others, métis petitions from 1874 to 1883, documents regarding
land in Prince Albert and St. Laurent areas.)
Canadian Illustrated News, Toronto, 1869-70; Legislative Library of
Manitoba.
Cochin, Louis, "Reminiscences of Father Louis Cochin, O.M.I. (a veteran
missionary to Cree Indians)"; *North West Historical Society Publications*,
Vol. 1, No. 2.
Collard, E. A., *Canadian Yesterdays*; Toronto, Longmans, 1955.
*Correspondence Relative to the Recent Disturbances in the Red River
Settlement* (English Blue Book); London, Colonial Office of Great Britain,
1870.
Creighton, Donald, *John A. Macdonald—The Old Chieftain*; Toronto,
Macmillan, 1955.
Davidson, W. M., *Louis Riel*; Calgary, The Albertan Publishing Co. Ltd.,
1955.
de Tremandau, Auguste-Henri, *Histoire de la nation Métisse dans l'ouest
Canadien;* Montreal, Editions Albert Levesque, 1935.
Frémont, Donatien, *Les Secrétaires de Louis Riel* (Louis Schmidt, Henry
Jackson, Philip Garnot); Montreal, Les Editions Chantecler Ltée., 1953.
Galbraith, John S., *The Hudson's Bay Company as an Imperial Factor,
1821-69*; Toronto, University of Toronto Press, 1957.
Gunn, Donald, and Tuttle, C. R., *History of Manitoba*; Ottawa, Maclean,
1880.
Healy, W. J., *Women of the Red River*; Winnipeg, Women's Canadian
Club, 1923.
Hind, Henry Youle, *Narrative of the Canadian Red River Exploring Ex-
pedition of 1857 and the Assiniboine and Saskatchewan Exploring Expedi-
tion of 1858*; London, Longmans, 1860.
Historical Sketch of the Parish of St. Vital (pamphlet); St. Boniface,
d'Eschambault Collection.
Howard, Joseph Kinsey, *Strange Empire*; New York, Morrow, 1952.
Knox, Olive, "The Question of Louis Riel's Insanity", *Transactions and
Proceedings*, Ser. 111, No. 6, Historical and Scientific Society of Manitoba;
Winnipeg, 1951.

Lamb, R. E., *Thunder in the North* (conflict over the Riel Risings, 1870-85); New York, Pageant Press, 1957.

Le Chevallier, Jules, *Batoche, les missionaires du nord-ouest pendant les troubles de 1885*; Montreal, Presse Dominicaine, 1941.

McKay, Douglas, *The Honourable Company* (a history of the Hudson's Bay Company); Toronto, McClelland & Stewart, 1936.

Minutes of Exovedate (Photostat); Public Archives of Canada.

Morice, Adrien Gabriel, *A Critical History of the Red River Insurrection*; Winnipeg, Canadian Publishers, 1935.

Morice, Adrien Gabriel, *Dictionnaire historique des Canadiens et des Métis Français de l'ouest*; Quebec, J. P. Garneau, 1908.

Morton, A. S., *A History of the Canadian West to 1870-71*; Toronto, Thomas Nelson, 1939.

Morton, W. L., *Manitoba: A History*; Toronto, University of Toronto Press, 1957.

New Nation; Winnipeg, Legislative Library of Manitoba, 1870.

Oliver, E. H. (ed.), *The Canadian Northwest*: its early development and legislative records, minutes of the councils of the Red River colony and the northern department of Rupert's Land; Public Archives of Canada, 1914.

Ouimet, Adolphe, *La Vérité sur la Question Métisse au nord-ouest, biographie et récit de Gabriel Dumont, sur les evenements de 1885*; Montreal, B.A.T. Montigny, 1889.

Pope, Joseph (ed.), *Selections from the Correspondence of Sir John Macdonald*; Toronto, Oxford University Press, 1921.

Red River Insurrection: Hon. Wm. McDougall's Conduct Reviewed; Montreal, John Lovell, 1870.

"Report of the Select Committee on the Causes of the Difficulties in the North-West Territory in 1869-70"; Ottawa, *Journals of the House of Commons, 1874*, Vol. 8, Appendix 6.

Riel, Louis "David", *Poésies religeuses et politique*; Montreal, Imprimerie de L'Etandard, 1886.

Riel Papers; Archives of Manitoba.

Saunders, E. M., *The Life and Letters of Sir Charles Tupper*; London, Cassell & Co., 1916.

Stanley, George F., *The Birth of Western Canada, a History of the Riel Rebellions*; London, Longmans, 1936.

Stanley, George F., "Gabriel Dumont's Account of the North-West Rebellion"; *Canadian Historical Review*, September, 1949, Vol. 30, No. 3, pp. 249-69.

Taché, Alexandre Antonin, *The Amnesty Again, or Charges Returned*; Winnipeg, *The Standard* office, 1875.

Taché, Alexandre Antonin, *Amnesty Question with regard to the North-West difficulty* (communicated to *The Times* on April 6, 7 and 8, 1874); St. Boniface, Canadian Publishing Co., 1893.

Taché, Alexandre Antonin, *Fenian Raid: an open letter from Archbishop Taché to Hon. Gilbert McMicken*; Winnipeg, 1871.

Thomas, L. H., *The Struggle for Responsible Government in the North-West Territories, 1870-97*; Toronto, University of Toronto Press, 1956.

Le Véritable Riel (pamphlet); Montreal, Imprimerie Générale, 1887. (Letters and court testimony of Father André; also letters of Father Fourmond, Brother Piquet, Father Leduc, a Batoche missionary sister, Father McWilliams, Father Touze; Riel's condemnation of Archbishop Taché; brief condemnation of Riel by various bishops.)

Wade, Mason, *The French Canadians, 1760-1945*; Toronto, Macmillan, 1956.

INDEX

1795
5112K